TREES IN BRITAIN

SILVER BIRCHES

TREES IN BRITAIN

WILD, ORNAMENTAL AND ECONOMIC

AND SOME RELATIVES IN OTHER LANDS

BY

L. J. F. BRIMBLE

B.Sc. (London and Reading), F.L.S.

Joint Editor of *Nature*.   Formerly Lecturer in the Universities
of Glasgow and Manchester

MACMILLAN AND CO. LIMITED
ST. MARTIN'S STREET, LONDON
1948

TO MY SISTER
CAROLINE

PRINTED IN GREAT BRITAIN

PREFACE

Nor less attractive is the woodland scene,
Diversified with trees of every growth,
Alike yet various. Here the gray smooth trunks
Of ash, of lime, or beech, distinctly shine,
Within the twilight of their distant shades ;
There lost behind a rising ground, the wood
Seems sunk, and shorten'd to its topmost boughs.
No tree in all the grove but has its charms,
Though each its hue peculiar : paler some,
And of a wannish gray ; the willow such,
And poplar that with silver lines his leaf,
And ash far stretching his umbrageous arm ;
Of deeper green the elm ; and deeper still,
Lord of the woods, the long-surviving oak.
Some glossy-leav'd, and shining in the sun,
The maple, and the beech of oily nuts
Prolific, and the lime at dewy eve
Diffusing odours : nor unnoted pass
The sycamore, capricious in attire,
Now green, now tawny, and ere autumn yet
Have chang'd the woods, in scarlet honours bright.

The Task : WILLIAM COWPER

Flowers in Britain was introduced last year "for anyone who is interested in or wants to know something about flowering plants." It was not intended solely for the professional botanist, and therefore no previous knowledge of botany was assumed. The encouraging reception of that book has convinced me—if, indeed, conviction were necessary—that there are many people, apart from botanists, who want to know something about flowering plants. But *Flowers in Britain* contains only passing references to trees, because, though from the botanist's point of view trees cannot be looked upon as a separate entity, to the ordinary enquirer 'trees' are something different from 'flowers.'

But most trees are flowering plants, and since, as Cowper wrote: "Nor less attractive is the woodland scene," it is clear that a mere allusion to trees is not enough for the reader who wants a comprehensive view

v

of flowering plants. So here now is *Trees in Britain*, which, for all intents and purposes, may be looked upon as Volume 2 of *Flowers in Britain*. Indeed, both books could be read simultaneously, for both are arranged according to their botanical families. Furthermore, similar points of view are adopted, similar diagnostic features stressed, and similar methods adopted in choosing and describing examples. The structure of trees, their classification, habits and habitats are considered; and here again special stress is laid on the parts played by trees in folk-lore and on their role in literature.

But there is one outstanding difference between the two volumes. 'Flowers' (even common ones) vastly outnumber 'trees.' Therefore, in *Flowers in Britain*, though about two thousand species are mentioned, some of these receive only cursory attention in order to allow more space for the most important. On the other hand, in *Trees in Britain*, a higher percentage of species receives comparatively detailed treatment. Also, a very high percentage of trees in Britain to-day are exotics, so we are really dealing with trees *in* Britain and not necessarily with British trees.

As in the companion volume, the coloured plates have been prepared by artists who have specialised in this field. All the photographs (of which there are about eighty), too, have been taken by experts not only in photography but also in natural history. Again I am responsible for the line drawings, of which there are about sixty. In this connexion, I must take the opportunity of thanking my sister Caroline, my niece Ann, my friends and colleagues Miss M. L. Cox, Mr. H. Cowdell and Mr. E. Taylor and others for assistance in collecting material from which the drawings were made. My mother also helped me in my enquiries concerning certain trees mentioned in the book.

But the illustrations which, I am sure, will appeal most to the reader are the reproductions of the beautiful pencil drawings by the late the Venerable Lonsdale Ragg, D.D., whose co-operation in this connexion was a continued source of encouragement to me. Archdeacon Lonsdale Ragg was not only one of our leading artists in arboreal subjects—the late Director of the Royal Botanic Gardens, Kew (Sir Arthur Hill) described his drawings as 'where botanist and artist are agreed'—but he was also an authority on trees, having written several books about them. He was also editor of *The Tree Lover*. I am sorry that lack of space has precluded my reproducing more of the many beautiful drawings he placed at my disposal.

My friends and colleagues, Mr. H. A. Evans and Mr. H. Cowdell, have not only given me the benefit of their knowledge of book production and book illustration respectively but have also in other ways helped me with commendable sincerity and patience.

Finally, three other friends have come forward again. Major T. H. Hawkins, who was good enough to make valuable suggestions during the preparation of a new impression of my *Flowers in Britain*, has read all the proofs of this book; Mr. Thomas Mark, who aided me in making a representative choice of prose and verse for *Flowers in Britain*, has done so again; and Miss M. L. Cox has once more assisted in preparing the manuscript for press. My sincere thanks are due to all these friends.

L. J. F. BRIMBLE

LONDON, *August*, 1945

Note to the Second Impression. During the preparation of the second impression I have been able to incorporate several changes, some of which were suggested by friends. I am especially indebted to Mr. W. A. Dayton, chief of the Division of Dendrology and Range Forage Investigations of the United States Department of Agriculture, and to Dr. N. B. Drury, director of the National Park Service of the United States Department of the Interior.

ACKNOWLEDGEMENTS

I am indebted to the following, among others, for permission to quote certain lines : Mrs. Laurence Binyon, for lines from the following poems by the late Laurence Binyon : 'The Birch Tree,' from *London Visions* ; 'The Death of Adam,' from *Collected Poems* ; 'The Junipers,' from *The North Star and Other Poems* ; 'The Orchard' and 'The Burning of the Leaves,' from *The Burning of the Leaves* ; Messrs. Jonathan Cape, Ltd., for 'O Dreamy, Gloomy, Friendly Trees,' from *Selected Poems*, by Herbert Trench ; Mr. Wilfrid Gibson, for lines from *Collected Poems*, 1905–1925 ; Lady Margaret Sackville and Messrs. Williams and Norgate for lines from 'Magnolia,' from *Return to Song and Other Poems* ; the Hon. V. Sackville-West ; Mr. Edward Shanks, for lines from *Poems*, 1912-1932, and *The Night Watch for England*, and Mr. Edward Thompson.

CONTENTS

PART I

INTRODUCTORY:

A GENERAL REVIEW OF FLOWERING PLANTS

PART II

CONIFERS AND OTHER GYMNOSPERMS

PART III

BROAD-LEAVED TREES (ANGIOSPERMS)

COLOURED PLATES

INTRODUCTORY: A GENERAL REVIEW OF
FLOWERING PLANTS

I

THE PLANT KINGDOM

> Distant! The wizard air has breathed away
> The heaviness from earth. The sombre trees
> To cloud change unimaginably ; nay ;
> To fire, to mind. Ancestral images,
> Ere that unfallen Eden had its day
> Of yet undimmed forest and flower, these
> Living and lustrous and ethereal shapes
> I see with sight unblind,
> In heavenly valleys or on glittering capes
> Glowed in the Magian's mind.
>
> *Wood Magic* : A. E.

It is obvious that plants vary considerably in size and form. But though it is clear that many plants differ from each other, it is equally as clear that others resemble each other. On these grounds, therefore, it is possible to place plants in divisions and sub-divisions according to their structural affinities and differences, and when this has been done it is seen that classification generally follows evolutionary sequence.

SEED PLANTS AND NON-SEED PLANTS

Many plants bear seeds ; on the other hand many other plants do not. The total number of *different* kinds of seed-bearing plants on the earth is between one hundred and two hundred thousand.

Plants may therefore be classified first into two groups, namely, those which bear seeds (called Phanerogams or Spermophyta) and those which do not (Cryptogams). This classification, however, like most

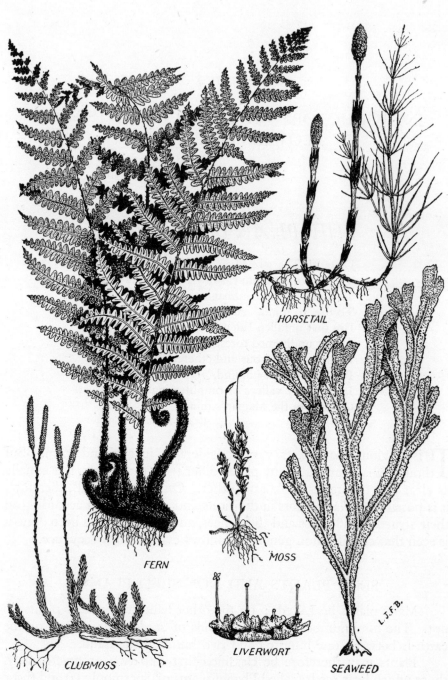

HORSETAIL

FERN

MOSS

CLUBMOSS

LIVERWORT

SEAWEED

L.J.F.B.

Non-seed Plants.

other classifications of living things, cannot be absolutely rigid, for intermediate types are known, especially from past ages.

The plant kingdom can be sub-classified into five divisions, three of which contain non-seed plants and two, seed plants. The five divisions can then be arranged roughly in order of complexity, beginning with the Thallophyta.

The three non-seed plant divisions are : (1) *Thallophyta* (algae, such as seaweeds ; fungi and bacteria) ; (2) *Bryophyta* (mosses and liverworts) ; (3) *Pteridophyta* (ferns, horsetails and club-mosses). None of the members of these three divisions achieves the dimensions of trees in Great Britain, though many handsome tree-ferns flourish in the tropical forests. Examples of these may be seen in the tropical houses of botanical gardens in Britain ; those at the Royal Botanic Gardens, Kew, are particularly good. In the Coal Age there were horsetails the size of trees.

It is significant that many members of division (1) live in fresh or salt water or in damp situations ; the majority of divisions (2) and (3) favour aquatic or damp habitats ; whereas by far the majority of seed plants thrive best under terrestrial conditions.

Dr. K. Biswas

Indian Tree-Ferns.

Harold Bastin

Cones of the Common Spruce (*Picea abies*).

SEED PLANTS

The first of the two seed plant divisions is the *Gymnosperms*. Nearly all of these are trees. They bear flowers from which seeds develop; but, unlike the next group of flowering plants such as rose, buttercup, pea, ash and elm, the seeds are naked and exposed instead of being enclosed in a protective case. By far the most important examples of Gymnosperms in this country are the conifers, such as pine, fir and larch. They are so called because their seeds are borne collectively in cones. Most of these plants, too, bear leaves which are needle-like in shape. Nearly all Gymnosperms are large plants; in fact, the group contains some of the largest and chronologically the oldest of plants existing to-day.

For example, the redwood (*Sequoia*), or big tree of California, is so large that in one case a carriage drive has been cut through the base of the trunk without impairing the life of the tree itself. One of the largest of these redwood trees is still growing on the south side of San Francisco Bay. It must be of very great age, although the exact date of its birth is not known. In 1931 its history was traced, and it was then

WAWONA
26' THROUGH THE OPENING
CUT IN 1880

E.N.A.

A Roadway cut through the Trunk of a living Big Tree or Giant Redwood
(*Sequoia*) at Wawona, California.
The tunnel is 10 feet high and 9½ feet across at the bottom.

learned that the earliest records go back to the first Spanish explorers of that region. In 1769 Gaspar da Pabola camped beneath it, and in 1777 it was already a large tree, 135½ feet in height and with a trunk 15 feet in diameter. Now the diameter is 23 feet.

The second division of seed plants is the *Angiosperms*, and this contains most of our familiar flowering plants—herbs, shrubs and trees. All these plants differ from the coniferous plants and other Gymnosperms in that their seeds are enclosed in some kind of case. All British broad-leaved trees, such as oak, ash and elm, belong to this division.

2

TYPES OF SEED PLANTS

The average seed plant is composed of roots, stems, leaves and flowers ; but it is very clear that these structures vary considerably in dimensions, shape, colour and so forth. These superficial characteristics are frequently so definite that they are sufficient to enable a person to identify the plant. Nevertheless, so many of the plants in question have features in common that they can be placed into rather plastic groups according to their vegetative structure.

Some plants grow to a considerable size. Their stems become thick and woody, thus forming trunks. These are the trees.

At the other end of the size-scale is the very large number of plants which vary in height from a few inches to several feet, for example, buttercup, primrose, stitchwort (p. 8), potato (p. 9), grasses, foxgloves, etc. ; the creepers, such as moneywort and ivy ; the climbers, such as runner bean. Although most of these plants contain a certain amount of wood which varies, there is never very much compared with the wood in trees. Their stems are usually soft and flexible, sometimes even juicy. All these plants are herbs, and from the point of view of evolution they have been more successful on the earth than trees have been, despite their size and strength.

Intermediate between the trees and the herbs are the shrubs. These are bushy plants with many branches, all of which are woody. But, unlike trees, there is no pronounced trunk. Examples of shrubs are privet, bramble, and gorse (p. 10).

R. St. Barbe Baker

A Turkey Oak (*Quercus cerris*) growing in the Cotswolds.

B

LENGTH OF LIFE

The length of life of organisms, plant and animal, varies within very wide limits. The shortest-lived creatures are usually the microscopic ones. For example, some bacteria can reproduce themselves within half an hour of birth. In the animal kingdom there is also great diversity. Many houseflies complete their life-history within ten days, whereas elephants have been known to live for more than a hundred years. Among the oldest living animals are the Galapagos turtles, some of which have been known to achieve an age of two hundred years.

But the oldest living things on the earth to-day are certain plants, and they are all trees.

> Generations pass while some trees stand, and old families last not three oaks.　　　　　　　*Hydriotaphia* : SIR THOMAS BROWNE

Harold Bastin

Greater Stitchwort : **a** delicate Herb.

Harold Bastin

Potato : a sturdy Herb.

As a general rule, herbs carry out their life-history in one season. That is, they are born, they develop and they reproduce themselves all within the space of a year. Such plants are therefore called annuals. Wheat, barley and the poppy are common examples.

Some plants can complete their life-history so quickly that the off-spring they produce through their seeds can also complete their life-history and produce seeds during the same year. Such plants are therefore called ephemerals. The groundsel is an example, and for this reason it is an objectionable weed.

Certain plants take two years to complete their life-history. The foxglove and the beet are two examples. They develop vegetatively in the first year and produce seeds in the second. Therefore they are called biennials.

Many plants go on living year after year, sometimes producing seeds every season and sometimes only once every few seasons. These are the perennials, and our best examples are trees and shrubs.

In some cases, such plants have been known to live for a long time. such as the redwood tree mentioned in Chapter I. Then there is the bald cypress still growing in Mexico, the well-known Big Tree of Tule. It is the biggest and one of the oldest trees in the world to-day. Its trunk is 50 feet in diameter where it begins branching. It must have been a big tree when the pyramids of Egypt were being built. The General Sherman Tree in the Sequoia National Park, California, is another world-renowned veteran—probably 3,500 years old. The Fortingall Yew in Perthshire is considered to be one of the veterans of European vegetation.

Harold Bastin

Gorse : a Shrub.

E.N.A.

One of the oldest living Trees in the World.
The Great Bald Cypress (*Taxodium mucronatum*) at Tule, Mexico. It stands within the walls of the old Spanish Church. This tree is 154 feet in circumference at its base.

EVERGREEN AND DECIDUOUS PLANTS

Perennials in temperate regions seldom maintain the same appearance throughout the year. The majority of British trees, for example, shed their leaves in the autumn. They are said to be deciduous. Good examples among the angiosperms are oak, elm, and beech, though the last-named often retains its leaves during the winter in spite of the fact that they are dead ; they are shed in the following spring when the new ones are sprouting.

Those plants which do not shed their leaves for the winter months are said to be evergreen. Holly, laurel and most conifers are evergreen ; but it must be realised that though these plants are evergreen they do shed their leaves, but it is a continuous process. Never are all the leaves shed at the same time, and each individual leaf usually remains on the tree for a varying number of years.

Leaf-fall is closely related to seasonal climate. The leaves of deciduous trees are shed just before winter sets in, and that is why plants growing in the humid, warm tropics, where there is little seasonal variation in climate, are nearly all evergreen. Some plants may be said to be partially evergreen, that is, although they are never leafless, they bear more leaves during the summer than during the winter. Privet is an example of this. During the summer, this plant is so thick with foliage that it is difficult to see through a hedge of it ; whereas although the same hedge still bears leaves in the winter, the number has been so reduced that it is possible to see through it.

MECHANISM OF LEAF-FALL

I have done all I could
For that lady I knew! Through the heats I have shaded her,
Drawn to her songsters when summer has jaded her,
Home from the heath or the wood.

At the mirth-time of May,
When my shadow first lured her, I'd donned my new bravery
Of greenth : 'twas my all. Now I shiver in slavery,
Icicles grièving me gray.

The Tree and the Lady : THOMAS HARDY

Winter is not conducive to good growth in any plant, since low temperature, high winds and lack of sunshine, adversely affect living

Winter Scene.
Evergreen conifers are seen in the foreground ; deciduous broad-leaved trees
in the background.

processes. Therefore, during the winter months the plant needs the minimum supply of food. In fact, most perennials manage to store enough food to tide them over the winter so that food manufacture, even were it possible, is not necessary during winter. Now the food factories of the green plant are the leaves, which are green by virtue of the green colouring matter called chlorophyll (see Chapter 3); so, since during winter the food factories are not required, the familiar falling of the leaves takes place in autumn.

> Leaves have their time to fall,
> And flowers to wither at the north-wind's breath,
> And stars to set.
> *The Hour of Death*: FELICIA HEMANS

Gradually, while the leaves are falling, the ascent of sap through the food channels in the stems and trunks, that is, the rise of water and dissolved substances absorbed by the roots from the soil, slows up and is eventually abandoned during the hard winter months. For one thing, the water is no longer required, since the food factories are falling. Furthermore it could not rise, for this movement is made possible by the suction of the leaves, among other agencies. It is only when the new leaves begin to burst forth again in the following spring that the vitalising sap can rise again through the stems.

As is well known, leaf-fall is usually preceded by a change of colour in the leaf itself. During the autumn, the leaf often loses its characteristic green colour and changes into many beautiful shades.

> Though summer goes, remember
> The harvest fields;
> The colour-work of autumn
> And what it yields.
> *To One Who Fears Old Age*: F. H. ADLER

The changes into autumnal coloration are connected with the chlorophyll (p. 27), for during this intermediate season it disintegrates. What exactly occurs chemically is not clearly understood; but it is known that the chemical substances which go to make up chlorophyll and perhaps other chemical substances in the leaf become converted into other chemical substances which produce the autumnal colours.

With the disappearance of chlorophyll, the manufacture of new food materials naturally ceases, what foods are present in the leaf pass out from it into the plant's system, and thus the food factory becomes useless. Then leaf-fall sets in.

But leaf-fall is not a sudden process, for Mother Nature has to make several provisions not only for it but also against it. Across the whole of the leaf-base there is a layer of cells which begin to change their shape and gradually become spherical. This layer is called the absciss layer.

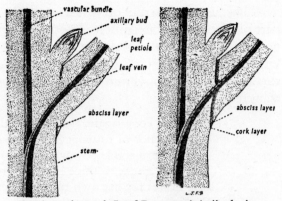

Sections through Leaf-Bases and Axils during the formation of the Cork and Absciss Layers. Left, early stage ; right, late stage.

It stretches across the whole of the leaf-base, and is several layers of cells thick. The rounding-off process begins in the outer tissues of the leaf-base and gradually passes inwards. Naturally by the time all the cells in a complete cross-section of a leaf-base are rounded off, this area is no longer firmly knit together, and there is nothing on which the leaf may hold. Then, by virtue of its own weight, sometimes hastened by high winds and heavy frosts, it falls off.

In that way Nature prepares for leaf-fall. But she also prepares against the evil consequences of leaf-fall. If the absciss layer were the only one formed, then after the leaf had fallen, an open wound of thin living cells would be left, and it can well be imagined how a tree with many thousands of wounds might suffer by exposure to rain and bacterial and fungal infection. But this is prevented by a process which takes place simultaneously with the formation of the absciss layer. The layers of cells immediately beneath the absciss layer (on the plant side and not the leaf side) begin to form cork on their surrounding cell-walls. This goes on at such a rate that by the time these cells become exposed, they are no longer living but form a layer of cork. Thus the wound is protected with a cork layer as soon as the leaf has fallen. This makes a scar on the twig which is called the leaf-scar, and on it may often be seen also the marks left by the veins which originally passed up through the leaf-base into the living leaf (see Chapter 3).

... what a beautiful thing God has made winter to be, by stripping the trees, and letting us see their shapes and forms. What a freedom does it seem to give to the storms! DOROTHY WORDSWORTH

The annual destruction of leaves might seem uneconomical on the part of Nature, but actually it is not, for very little is wasted—certainly not the fallen leaves, for while fresh leaves appear next spring to re-vitalise the plant the old leaves return to the earth where they eventually rot and become converted into humus, one of the best of natural manures.

> They will come again, the leaf and the flower, to arise
> From squalor of rottenness into the old splendour,
> And magical scents to a wondering memory bring ;
> The same glory, to shine upon different eyes.
> Earth cares for her own ruins, naught for ours.
> Nothing is certain, only the certain spring.
> *The Burning of the Leaves* : LAURENCE BINYON

3

GENERAL STRUCTURE OF BROAD-LEAVED TREES

(*Angiosperms*)

> Almond, apple, and peach,
> Walnut, cherry, plum,
> Ash, chestnut and beech,
> And lime and sycamore
> We have planted for days to come ;
> No stony monument
> But growing, changing things,
> Leaf, fruit, and honied scent,
> Bloom that the bees explore,
> Sprays where the bird sings.
> *The Orchard* : LAURENCE BINYON

A typical tree, like any other flowering plant, is clearly composed of various organs. These may be divided into two main groups, namely, those which grow above the soil (collectively called the shoot) and those which grow beneath the soil-surface (collectively called the root). Here we will examine the general plan of angiospermous plants, with special reference to trees, and then consider the gymnospermous plants in the next chapter.

ROOTS

If a wallflower plant be dug up carefully from the soil and thoroughly washed, it will be seen that the root system is composed of a main or tap root which grows vertically downwards. The tap roots of most plants are much longer than we usually imagine, for they are frequently broken off when the plant is roughly pulled from the soil. This is well exemplified in the beet and the dandelion. The tap root gives off branch roots, and these branch roots are still further branched, and so forth, thus giving an extensive root system.

Root of beet shown growing *in situ*.

Differing from the tap root system is that system, equally as common, where the first root, instead of persisting and thus remaining the main root, withers away, and a series of roots, more or less of equal size, takes its place. This can be seen in grasses, and is called a fibrous root system. The majority of the roots in a fibrous root system are given off from the lower parts of the stem which are in or near the soil. Therefore these roots are not the products of the first root or radicle. A root which is not originally produced from the root system but which arises from some other part of the plant is said to be adventitious, and such roots are to be seen in a fibrous root system and sometimes elsewhere.

Rothamsted Experimental Station

Harold Bastin
Root System of Sapling Oak.

The root systems of trees are very complicated since they have usually been developing for many years. Most, however, begin as tap roots, but often adventitious roots also arise.

SHOOTS

The shoot is normally composed of stems which bear leaves and flowers. In the case of most trees, the shoot is composed of a central axis or main stem with many branch stems.

BUDS

On the side of the stem, the leaves are borne. That part of the stem to which a leaf is attached is called the node. The angle which the leaf makes with the stem is called the axil, and frequently borne in the axil is a bud which is called the axillary bud. This is a lateral bud in contradistinction to the terminal bud which is to be found at the end of any stem or twig. That part of the stem passing between two consecutive nodes is called the internode. Appendages such as leaves are seldom given off from an internode. Buds are young, undeveloped shoots. If they are leaf-buds only they finally grow out to produce either single leaves or branch stems bearing other leaves. On the other hand, if they are flower-buds, they finally produce the flower or flowers and then their growth ceases. The production of a flower anywhere almost invariably results in the cessation of development in that direction. Axillary buds produce branch shoots, or single leaves or flowers. But not all axillary buds develop in normal conditions.

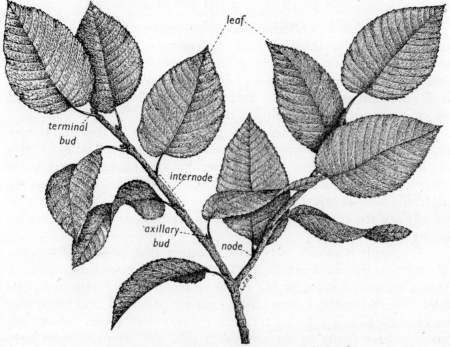

Twig of Common Elm (*Ulmus procera*) in Leaf.

In the case of trees especially, considering the enormous number of leaves on one tree, if all their axillary buds developed to produce branches, the tree would soon become a tangled mass. Such sleeping buds are called dormant buds. In exceptional circumstances, however, dormant buds will awaken and actively develop new branches. This awakening is frequently stimulated by the cutting off of a terminal bud. If the terminal bud is severed or injured so that it cannot itself develop, then some of the dormant axillary buds develop. However, this does not often occur in Nature, though in horticultural practice it is common.

If the main trunk of a tree, such as the oak or the elm, be cut down, a dense outgrowth of branches develops from the base of the trunk. These branches are produced from dormant and other buds which arise adventitiously. The phenomenon is known as tillering. This sometimes occurs in certain kinds of trees, even if the main trunk is still flourishing. Tillering is very common in the elm, though it also frequently occurs in trees, such as the beech, especially when growing in woodlands or under other conditions where they are crowded together.

POLLARDING AND COPPICING

Closely related to tillering are the processes known as pollarding and coppicing ; but these are not connected with dormant buds. Dormant buds are there all the time whether they develop or not. On the other hand, there are adventitious buds which develop in unusual places, as do adventitious roots. They are not axillary and when they do appear, which is not often, it is usually on trees.

The process of pollarding is quite common in Britain. It consists in lopping off the top of a tree and leaving just the bole. This is sometimes done to willow trees growing along the banks of rivers and to ornamental trees lining city streets. When the top has been lopped off, adventitious buds arise, where there were no buds before, usually near the edge of the cut end of the trunk. They then develop into branch shoots.

Coppicing is similar to pollarding except that, instead of lopping off the tree at the top of its bole, it is lopped off at the base near the ground. This is done to a considerable extent in Great Britain with hazel and alder. By this method, very bushy trees are produced, and when they are growing closely together they make a very thick copse. Most trees can regenerate parts of themselves in this way, as those who have wanted to get rid of a tree must know. Frequently it is essential to eradicate most of the rooting system as well, otherwise, either fresh shoots arise from any part of the trunk that has been left in the ground, or suckers appear from the roots.

> I cut it down, because it blocked the light :
> And now the sunshine streams into the room
> At noonday ; but, at closing in of night,
> I hear a ghostly murmur in the gloom—
>
> A ghostly wind that stirs a spectral tree
> To scornful whispering of phantasmal boughs—
> *O foolish man, who thought to murder me ;*
> *My live roots still run under your frail house.*
>   *The Tree* : WILFRID GIBSON

GROWTH IN THICKNESS

Many plants, especially perennials (including trees), could not continue to grow in length indefinitely unless there were also some growth in thickness, otherwise the plant would become so long and slender as to

Lonsdale Ragg

A Pollarded Willow at West Mark, Somerset.

be unable to remain upright. Such growth in thickness takes place, of course, in the stems and the roots.

Nearly all stems and roots contain a certain amount of wood, and when such stems and roots begin to thicken, they do so chiefly by the formation of new wood. This growth in thickness is known as secondary thickening. Trunks of trees, which are nothing but secondarily thickened stems, are therefore composed chiefly of wood.

TREE TRUNKS

The thickened main stem of a tree is the trunk ; that part of the trunk below the lowest branches is called the bole. If the trunk or thick branch of a tree be severed, the cut surface will reveal to what extent the deposition of wood has taken place in the stem. The wood forms the chief part of the thickened stem, and it can be seen to be composed of two parts : that in the centre which is darker in colour (heart-wood) and the lighter part surrounding it (sap-wood). The heart-wood is darker because it is dry and contains no sap. The sap, which is water containing dissolved substances passing up through the tree from the soil, travels through the sap-wood. This explains why so many trees are seen to flourish year after year though their main trunks are hollow and rotten inside.

> Hast thou so much withstood,
> Dumb and unmoving tree,
> That now thy hollow wood
> Stiffens disdainfully
> Against the soft spring airs and soft spring rain,
> Knowing too well that winter comes again?
> *A Hollow Elm* : EDWARD SHANKS

Every year during the growing season, which is spring to early autumn in Great Britain, the tree develops a fresh layer of wood in its trunk and branches. This new layer is deposited on the outside of the already existing cylinder of wood. No new wood is formed during the winter when growth has more or less ceased. Wood is composed chiefly of a series of minute tubes, used for water conduction, and long, woody fibres for strength. Therefore, when we examine the cut trans-verse surface of a trunk with a hand lens, these tubes will look like thousands of minute circles. The tubes which are produced during the spring period of growth are much larger than those produced during the autumn. Then during winter the formation of new tubes ceases alto-

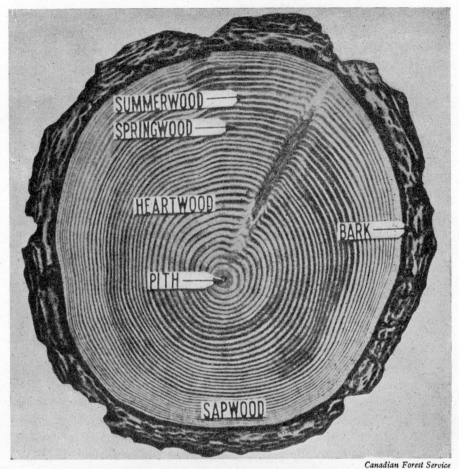

Canadian Forest Service

Transverse Section of a Soft-wood Log.

gether. Eventually, when the spring approaches new formation of larger tubes begins. Thus, between each season's growth there is a distinct line of demarcation which can be clearly seen even with the naked eye. So the complete cross-section of a trunk presents the appearance of a series of roughly concentric rings. Because each ring represents one year's growth, they are called annual rings. Furthermore, some annual rings are wider than others, thus showing that during the year in question better growing conditions prevailed. By counting the number of annual rings in the bole it is possible to tell the age of a tree.

Annual rings are useful in forestry practice and even in other respects. To be able to tell the age of a tree is often desirable, and in some

c

cases gives surprising results. For example, there is a trunk (in section) of a Californian redwood tree in the British Museum (Natural History) which shows 1,335 annual rings. On p. 129 is reproduced a photograph of a transverse section of what is claimed to be the oldest known redwood. It will be seen that the size of this tree at various important dates in the Christian era has been estimated by counting the annual rings.

By examining comparatively the growth of the annual rings of a single trunk, it is possible to deduce what kind of weather that tree experienced during its years of existence. This idea has been carried still further by an American, Dr. A. E. Douglas, who examined the trunks of some fossilised trees which must have been alive several millions of years ago. From his results he was able to deduce certain facts of meteorological and geological interest about those times when the trees were growing. Dr. Douglas has also made some interesting discoveries concerning climates of more recent times by adopting the same methods. For example, he has been able to show that in the United States there was a great drought which commenced in 1276 and lasted for twenty-three years.

CORK AND BARK

Surrounding the woody cylinder of the thickened stem are other important layers of tissue. Some are not clearly visible to the naked eye. Immediately surrounding the wood, however, is one which may sometimes be thus identified. This is called the bast or phloem. Down this layer of cells pass to the rest of the plant those foods which have been manufactured by the plant's green leaves. Outside the phloem is another layer which varies in thickness according to the species of tree. This is the cork, and in some cases, especially the cork oak, it is so thick as to form a source of commercial cork. Finally, outside the cork layer is the bark. This layer also displays considerable variation in thickness and texture. That of the elm, for example, is thick and broken up, giving a wart-like appearance, whereas that of the beech is much thinner and smoother. That of the London plane is so thin that it frequently peels off in patches leaving the underlying yellowish tissues exposed. As will be seen in Chapter 25, this character helps to explain why this tree can withstand sooty atmospheres.

Bark is in any event shrivelled because it is a dead tissue, since neither water nor food supplies can get to it across the underlying layer of impervious cork.

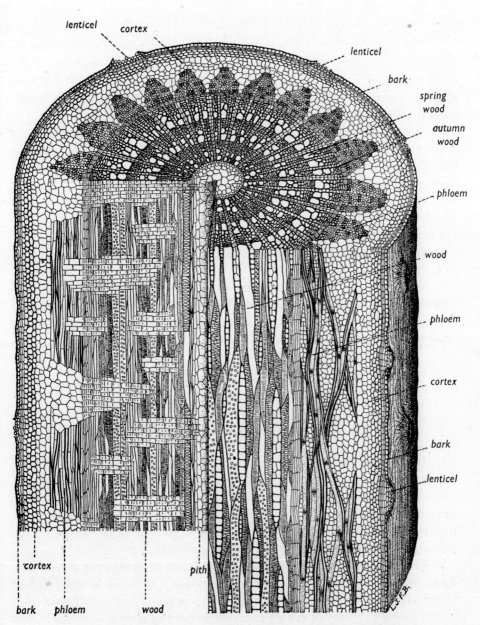

Diagrammatic Representation of a Woody Stem in its third year.
At the top is represented the stem as seen in transverse section under the microscope. To the left, the stem is viewed in a plane passing downwards through
the centre (radial longitudinal); to the right, in a plane downwards but not
passing through the centre (tangential longitudinal).

THE TWIG IN WINTER

The examination of a twig during the winter reveals other interesting characters of a tree. For example, the scars of the leaves which have
been shed are clearly visible. They are either crescent- or horseshoe-
shaped or circular, and on them even the small scars of the veins which
passed up into the leaves may sometimes be seen.

A twig in winter also affords a splendid opportunity of examining
winter buds, for example, that of the horse-chestnut. This bud is
usually covered with a glutinous material as a protection against excessive moisture which might get into the heart of the bud and cause
it to rot. The outermost scales of the bud are boat-shaped, and are used
for the protection of the tender tissues inside. If all the scales and leaves
are dissected from such a bud, it will be seen that there is no line of demarcation between the bud-scales and the young foliage leaves, but that
one gradually merges into the other.

When spring comes and the sap again rises in the trunk and
branches, the buds develop. The bud-scales gradually open out and
eventually fall. Then the leaf or leaves and, if present, flowers begin to
emerge.

> In all a pushing, a thrusting,
> An irregular twisting, a breaking-out at corners,
> Lopsidedness. Daggers on a twig
> Burst and there is a leaf.
> *Ferns in the Waste* : R. C. ORMEROD

Bud-scales, like foliage leaves, leave their scars after they have
fallen. These small scale-scars, as they are called, left after the bud has
grown out, collectively form a ring round the stem. At the end of the
next year, a fresh ring of scale-scars is formed, and so on. Therefore,
the distance between one ring of scale-scars and the next represents the
amount of growth in length of that twig for one year.

Other marks of the young twig are small dots all over its surface.
Each one is scarcely bigger than a pin's point. They are usually lighter
in colour than the rest of the surface of the twig. They are composed of
microscopic particles of cork very loosely packed so that the whole area
is porous. Now trees, like all other living plants and animals, take in
oxygen and give off carbon dioxide during the process of respiration.
Such gases cannot pass through solid cork quickly enough, and we have
already seen that a solid layer of cork surrounds the living tissues of the

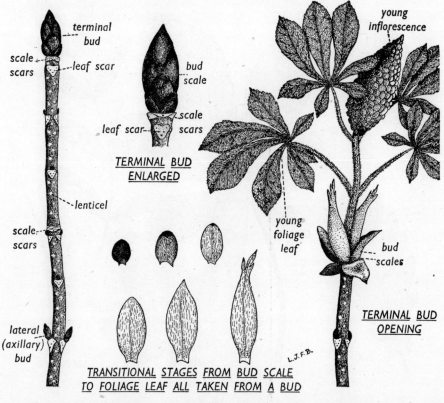

terminal bud

scale scars

leaf scar

bud scale

leaf scar

scale scars

TERMINAL BUD ENLARGED

young inflorescence

lenticel

scale scars

young foliage leaf

bud scales

TERMINAL BUD OPENING

lateral (axillary) bud

L.J.F.B.

TRANSITIONAL STAGES FROM BUD SCALE TO FOLIAGE LEAF ALL TAKEN FROM A BUD

Horse-chestnut twig in Winter (left) and Spring (right).

thickened stem; hence the spongy areas in the form of dots on the twig's surface. They are called lenticels and form a passage for gaseous interchange. This gaseous interchange also takes place through pores in the leaves of nearly all terrestrial plants.

LEAVES

The green leaf is the food factory of the plant. Water and dissolved substances pass up to it from the roots which have absorbed the solution from the soil. Carbon dioxide is absorbed from the atmosphere through the pores called stomata in the leaf. From these raw materials, under the influence of sunlight, and with the agency of the essential green colouring matter called chlorophyll, the leaf is able to manufacture the complicated foods which the plant requires.

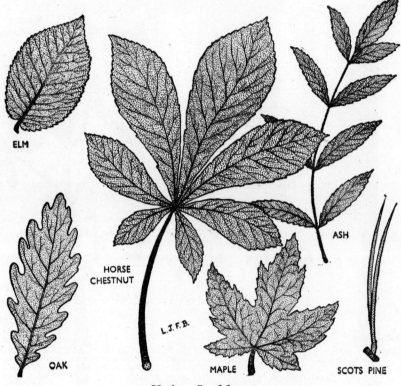

ELM

HORSE
CHESTNUT

ASH

OAK

L.J.F.B.

MAPLE

SCOTS PINE

Various Leaf-forms

Leaves are diverse in size and form. Thus we have the comparatively small and simple leaf of the privet, and, in contradistinction to this, the leaf of the banana plant which, though roughly similar in shape, is anything from one to three yards long. Though leaves vary in shape, they do conform roughly to certain types. One should be able to recognise the simple elm leaf with its serrated edge, the common oak leaf with its deeply indented margin, the palmate leaf of the maple and the compound leaf of the horse-chestnut and of the ash. Then there are many leaves having entire or smooth margins.

A typical leaf is composed of a leaf-stalk or petiole which usually widens at its base where it joins the stem at the node. The main flattened expansion of the leaf is called the leaf-blade or lamina. In some cases, the leaf-blade is borne direct on to the stem, that is, there is no leaf-stalk, in which case the leaf is said to be sessile. Where there is a leaf-stalk, it may be thick or thin, long or short.

Sometimes wing-like outgrowths arise at the leaf-base. They are very prominent in the rose. These outgrowths also vary considerably in size and form and are called stipules. In the leaves of trees, however, stipules are frequently absent. In some cases, a pair of the outer scales of the axillary bud act as stipules when it opens ; but they are soon shed.

On the leaf-blade thicker lines are visible. These are the veins, and are the channels for conducting water with its dissolved substances into the leaf and for transporting manufactured food substances away from the leaf. The main veins give off branch veins, thus presenting a complete net-work of veins. The whole arrangement of veins in a leaf is called venation. In some leaves there is one main vein which branches. The branches give off secondary branches, and so on, thus producing a reticulate or net venation. This is seen in such leaves as elm, oak and all broad-leaved trees. In other leaves, especially the blade-like leaves of grasses, though in very few trees except palms and conifers, instead of one main vein with branches there are several veins of equal size running parallel to each other. This is therefore called parallel venation.

In many leaves, despite diversity of shape, the whole leaf-blade is a single structure, as is the case in the elm, oak, maple and pine. Such leaves are simple. In other cases, each leaf is composed of several leaflets arranged in a definite order, for example, horse-chestnut, ash and acacia. Such leaves are compound. It is most likely that compound leaves have become derived from simple leaves during evolution ; deep serrations have appeared and these have gradually become deeper and deeper until they practically meet.

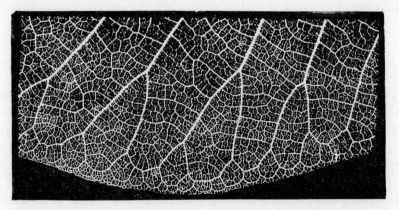

Part of a Leaf Skeleton showing Net Venation.

FLOWERS AND FRUIT

Many a tree is found in the wood,
And every tree for its use is good;
Some for the strength of the gnarled root,
Some for the sweetness of flower or fruit.

Salute the Trees : H. VAN DYKE

There is no other part of a plant which presents such diversity of form, size, colour and beauty as the flower itself, though in most trees the flowers are inconspicuous compared with those of herbs and certain shrubs.

The flower is really that mechanism whereby a plant reproduces itself, for it is so constituted as to produce seeds, and inside each seed is a young, embryonic plant.

SEXUAL REPRODUCTION

Seeds are produced by a process of sex, and therefore plant reproduction by means of seeds is called sexual reproduction. This process involves two important cells, both microscopic in size. These special cells are called gametes, and there are two kinds, namely, male and female. The female gamete is not as a general rule capable of developing to produce a new plant like the parent in which it is formed until it has received some form of impetus. This is given by the male gamete. The female gamete is called the egg or ovum; the male gamete is the sperm.

Fusion between a male gamete and a female gamete is the basis of sexual reproduction, and such fusion is called fertilisation. In flowering plants, the organs which produce eggs and sperms are the flowers.

HERMAPHRODITE AND UNISEXUAL FLOWERS

Many species of angiospermous flowers are capable of producing both eggs and sperms : this is so in the case of the horse-chestnut (p. 303) and the tulip-tree (p. 135). Such flowers are therefore said to be hermaphrodite. In some other trees, however, the sperms are produced in one kind of flower and the eggs in another. Those flowers which can produce one sex of gamete only are said to be unisexual. In other words, there are separate male and female flowers. Here there are two possibilities : either a tree can produce both male and female flowers or it can produce only male or female flowers but not both. Examples of those trees which bear both sexes of unisexual flowers are oak, hazel and sycamore; those which bear the two sexes of flowers on different plants are willow and poplar.

THE INFLORESCENCE

In some trees, the flowers are all borne singly, for example, the tulip-tree (p. 135). But this is not common among trees, for most of them bear their flowers in clusters called inflorescences. There are several types of inflorescence, each following a definite form, such as the complicated raceme of the horse-chestnut (p. 303) and the catkin (a pendulous spike) of the hazel (p. 242) and walnut (p. 316).

THE FLOWER

A comparatively simple hermaphrodite flower bears four kinds of different organs on a swollen part of the stem called the receptacle. Passing from the outside of the flower to the inside, the four sets of organs can be clearly distinguished. All the organs are arranged around the receptacle in definite groups called whorls.

The outermost whorl is composed of structures, frequently boat-shaped and green, called sepals. The whole collection of sepals is called the calyx. The function of sepals is not a very important one; in fact, some flowers have no sepals. The main function is to protect the other floral organs while in bud and sometimes to support them when the flower is open.

Next come the petals, collectively called the corolla. The petals are frequently large and highly coloured, for in such cases their function is to attract insects which pollinate the flowers. If insects are not utilised in pollination the petals are often absent or, if present, then very insignificant. In some cases, the sepals are similar to the petals (they are said to be petalloid), and the similarity is frequently so close that it is not possible to tell the difference between the two kinds of organs. Then calyx and corolla are grouped together and collectively referred to as the perianth.

Next to the corolla, passing inwards, are the stamens, and the innermost organs of all are the carpels. The number of stamens and of carpels varies considerably, but when small, the number usually remains constant for the species.

Neither the sepals nor the petals are directly concerned with the production of eggs and sperms; they are therefore looked upon as being of secondary importance. It is the stamens and the carpels which are the main organs of reproduction, for it is they which produce the male and female gametes. The stamens are responsible for the production of sperms, and the carpels for the eggs. Therefore, in hermaphrodite flowers, stamens and carpels are both present in each flower; whereas in unisexual flowers there are either stamens or carpels, but not both. Frequently, especially among trees, flowers may occur with both stamens and carpels; but they are really unisexual because either all the stamens or all the carpels are sterile.

If a single stamen be examined under a hand lens it will be seen to be composed of a stalk or filament which supports a swollen head called the anther. The anther is not a solid mass of tissue when ripe, but contains cavities (usually four in number) running along its length. In each cavity there are hundreds of microscopically small spherical bodies called pollen grains. The ripe pollen grain is usually

Harold Bastin

Buttercup Flower
Top left, flower in section; top right, complete flower viewed from above; bottom, sepals, petals, stamens and carpel dissected away.

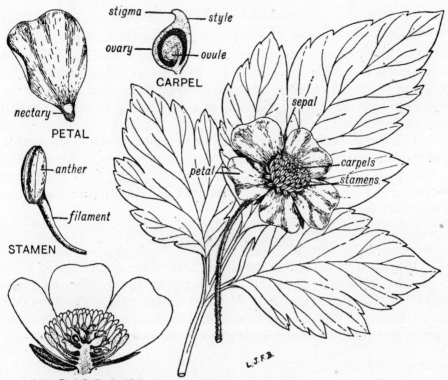

Details of a Buttercup Flower.

beautifully marked on its surface, and these markings are so diagnostic for each species that frequently a species can be identified by them. The pollen grains are not the male sperms, but once they have germinated they produce the sperms.

The main bulk of a carpel is called the ovary. Frequently at the top of this there is a projection of varying length called the style, which terminates in a sticky surface called the stigma. The ovary encloses a cavity, and into this, from the ovary wall, projects an ovoid structure called the ovule. The ovule contains the egg or ovum. In some flowers there is only one ovule in each ovary, whereas in others there are several or even many. Very often in flowers several carpels (usually a definite but small number) fuse, thus producing a common ovary with a common style. In other cases, though there is a common ovary, the styles are separate.

Flowers display considerable diversity in number, size and form in their various parts.

POLLINATION

Pollination is the process whereby the pollen (which produces the male gametes) can be brought into such a position that those gametes can approach the eggs present in the ovules and fertilise them. The position which the pollen grains take up in order to effect this is on the stigma of the carpel. The stigma is by nature sticky so that the pollen easily adheres to it.

Pollination can take place in one of two general ways. Either the pollen from the stamen of a flower passes to the stigma of the same flower or the pollen of one flower is transferred to the stigma of a different flower of the same species. The former is self-pollination; the latter, cross-pollination.

SELF-POLLINATION

When the pollen within the anther head of the stamen is ripe it becomes dry and loose. Then the anther becomes ruptured longitudinally and thus the pollen is exposed. In self-pollination the pollen then falls on to the stigma of the same flower or sometimes the stamen bends so that its ripe head comes into contact with the stigma.

CROSS-POLLINATION

Some plants have developed the most wonderful methods for ensuring cross-pollination, and indeed they frequently go still further and, by varying means, ensure that self-pollination is impossible.

Wind-Pollination.—The simplest method of cross-pollination is by means of wind. This is very common among unisexual flowers, such as those of sycamore and hazel. Wind-pollination is indeed common among most British trees and grasses. For this reason the flowers of such species are usually inconspicuous, for they do not need to attract insects.

Of course the chances of a pollen grain reaching a stigma (possibly a considerable distance away) through the agency of wind are very remote, so many thousands of times more pollen is produced than is actually required for fertilisation. The method is therefore a very wasteful one, and explains why one sometimes sees clouds of pollen being blown away from such trees as the catkin-bearing hazels.

Insect-Pollination.—A more efficient method of cross-pollination involves insects—chiefly bees, wasps, butterflies, moths, flies and beetles

—as the agents of pollen distribution. These animals can easily collect pollen on their hairy bodies and legs, when visiting the flower for nectar. So, as the insect passes from flower to flower, the pollen picked up from the stamens of one flower is passed on to the stigma of another. In its simplest form this is what happens in the case of the apple and the rose.

But some flowers are prepared more precisely for the insect's visit, and in such cases various devices adopted by the structure of the flower make pollination certain.

First of all, the flowers must attract the insects. This is done in several ways. One is by the bright, attractive colours of the petals. Another is by the production of the delicate perfume so familiar to us in certain flowers. Insects are attracted by perfume; in fact, perfumes attract insects more certainly than do bright colours. It is clear from this that such trees as the horse-chestnut and apple which have bright and conspicuous flowers are insect-pollinated.

FERTILISATION

Having got the pollen on the stigma of the carpel, the next problem is to see how the male gametes (sperms) from the pollen get to the female gametes (eggs) present inside the ovules. The egg is passive and does not move; it is the male gamete that makes the move to bring male and female gamete together. This is made possible by the pollen grain itself. Once it has become attached to the stigma, it grows and sends out a tube, called the pollen tube, which pushes its way down the style. Growth of the pollen tube continues until it reaches the cavity of the ovary containing the ovule or ovules. Then it passes across the cavity and pierces the ovule itself. Meanwhile the male gamete in the pollen tube has been developing, and eventually this comes in contact with the egg of the ovule. Then sexual fusion takes place. After this the fertilised egg is able to develop to produce an embryonic plant.

SEED AND FRUIT

The new young plant developing within the carpel is now the seed. All the time that the young seed is developing, the carpellary or ovary wall is getting stronger and stronger, so that when the seeds are ripe it is strong enough to contain them. The wall develops into a thick and hard or thick and fleshy tissue according to the species of tree.

Reproduction in the Oak

Above, acorns (fruit) of the common oak (*Quercus sessiliflora*); middle left, acorn in section showing embryonic plant; below left, acorn germinating; below right, seedling at end of second year's growth.

The whole ovary, with its developed wall enclosing the seed or seeds inside, now forms what is called the fruit. Within the fruit, therefore, we have the most important part of the plant, namely the seed, for it is the seed which is responsible for carrying on that species into its next generation. The fruit is really only a means of protection and distribution of the seed or seeds which it contains. The number of seeds corresponds, of course, with the number of ovules which have been fertilised. Given the necessary conditions these germinate to produce new plants.

VEGETATIVE REPRODUCTION

Many trees can reproduce themselves without the help of seeds. New plants sometimes arise direct from the tissues of the parent plant. This is called vegetative reproduction.

In Nature, for example, there are the suckers which grow up from the roots of such trees as plums. Then, if a branch of such a tree as the willow be placed in the soil, given suitable conditions it will develop adventitious roots on that part of the stem below the soil-surface and eventually grow to form a new willow tree.

Then there are the artificial methods of vegetative reproduction, namely, budding and grafting. The latter is frequently adopted in the case of fruit trees.

4

GENERAL STRUCTURE OF CONIFEROUS TREES

(Gymnosperms)

Cedar, and pine, and fir, and branching palm,*
A sylvan scene, and as the ranks ascend
Shade above shade, a woody theatre
Of stateliest view.

Paradise Lost : MILTON

As has already been seen, the seed plants are subdivided into Gymnosperms and Angiosperms. The latter have already been reviewed

* Palms are not Gymnosperms.

Young seedlings.   Older stages.

Harold Bastin

Scots Pine.

in general in Chapter 3. The Gymnosperms are lower in the scale of evolution than the Angiosperms. In fact, the latter are relatively young from the point of view of geologic time. They date from the Cretaceous period. The Gymnosperms, on the other hand, date back to the Devonian period.

All Gymnosperms, both present-day and extinct, are characterised by the free exposure of their seeds, thus differing markedly from the Angiosperms, the seeds of which are entirely enclosed by their fruit walls.

Actually the present-day Gymnosperms are survivors of a much larger class of plants. They comprise four main groups, namely, *Cycadales*, *Ginkgoales*, *Gnetales* and *Coniferales*. The last-named is by far the largest group, comprising several families, and it is the most highly evolved of the four. It contains the conifers. The Ginkgoales contains one plant only, the maidenhair tree, which is sometimes cultivated in Britain (p. 51). The Gnetales comprise a few curious shrubs distributed chiefly in tropical and sub-tropical regions. The Cycadales contain some woody plants which sometimes achieve the proportions of small trees. They also are tropical and sub-tropical, though some examples may be seen under cultivation in botanical greenhouses in this country.

Among the best-known examples of Coniferales in Britain are the pines, yew, spruces, larches and junipers. Then there are the exotic redwoods and the peculiar monkey puzzle sometimes grown in this country. All these trees have soft woods compared with the hard-wood trees such as oak.

The familiar Scots pine is a typical conifer. On germination (p. 38) this plant produces a dominant upright axis which maintains a radial shape with branches of flattened form. The main shoot grows more strongly than the lateral branches, thus giving the familiar pyramidal effect ; but, unlike many other conifers, growth becomes more irregular later on and the symmetrical effect is lost (Plate 1).

The Scots pine is an evergreen, and the needle-like leaves are borne in pairs, each pair being protected at the base by a sheath of membranous scales. Many conifers are evergreen, but the larch is not. Also the leaves of many conifers are borne separately, whereas those of others, such as larch, are borne in large tufts.

In the young stages, the root system is that of a typical tap root ; but this later becomes lost in branch roots which attain equal size.

Harold Bastin

Scots Pines growing under Forestry conditions.

D

The leaves of most conifers are needle-like (p. 28) because the trees grow in conditions of exposure and frequently where liquid water is not available. Thus water-loss from the leaves must be reduced. Hence the reduction in leaf surface. Furthermore, the pores (stomata) from which the water evaporates are frequently sunken in the tissue of the leaf, giving them additional protection against the high, drying winds.

In marked contrast with the Angiosperms, vegetative reproduction in the Gymnosperms is exceedingly rare.

THE CONES

The reproductive organs of conifers are borne collectively in cones. These are distinguished according to their sex, so there are female or carpellate cones and male or staminate cones.

The young female cone consists of a central axis upon which the reproductive organs or carpels are arranged in a close spiral. Each carpel is green and soft when young. It is composed of a short stalk and a scale known as the ovuliferous scale on the lower side of which is a still smaller scale known as the bract scale. At the base of the ovuliferous scale are two ovoid ovules.

The male cones are produced in much larger numbers, since a large quantity of pollen is required for the wasteful method of wind-pollination. This cone consists also of a central axis upon which the bulky stamens are borne in a close spiral. Each stamen takes the form of a stalk which bears two pollen sacs on its lower surface.

The ripe stamen splits longitudinally and the pollen is released. In spite of the considerable wastage some pollen reaches the young, un-fertilised female cones which open slightly by pressing their carpels apart for the reception of the pollen. Then the pollen grains are drawn down to the ovules. Soon after this the female cone closes up again and the scales become sealed together by the exudation of pitch. After some time (several months to a year) fertilisation of the eggs in the ovules by the sperms produced by the pollen grains takes place. Thus the seeds are produced.

While all this is going on the female cone has been getting more and more woody, and eventually (when the atmosphere is dry) the thick, woody scales which have now become brown in colour, move apart and expose the seeds. Each seed is brown and bears a large, membranous wing by which means it is dispersed through the air.

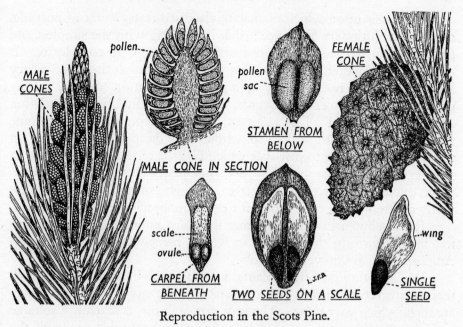

Reproduction in the Scots Pine.

The number of cotyledons (p. 43) produced by the young plant varies; but it is usually very high—sometimes as many as fifty.

The maidenhair tree, yew and juniper should be mentioned here, though they are dealt with fully in Chapters 6, 14 and 16, because their fruits are not borne in cones and are fleshy.

5

CLASSIFICATION OF PLANTS

Although there are many thousands of different plants in the world, some varying considerably from others, so many of them are either closely or distantly related to each other, that it is possible to grade them into various divisions, classes, families and so forth. This is known as plant classification, and no student of the British flora in general or the trees in particular, or indeed anyone with a passing interest in trees, will get very far with his interest unless he makes himself familiar with the elements of this classification.

The basis upon which plants are classified rests, so far as possible, on their evolutionary sequence ; that is, starting with the simplest and graduating, usually upwards, in direct accordance with complexity. It must be remembered, however, that increasing complexity or efficiency are not the only results of evolution. For evolution, though usually upwards, is sometimes downwards, and the latter involves degradation and degeneration of all or some of the plant organs. Some become modified, others vestigial, and sometimes they disappear altogether. In this way, we are able to discover which plant is related to which and to what extent. For example, there are some plants closely related to each other, such as cherry and plum trees. Others, on the other hand, are vastly different from each other, for example, beech and cedar trees.

It was shown in Chapter 1 that the plant kingdom is divided into five main divisions, the last two of which, namely, Gymnosperms and Angiosperms, are flowering plants.

In classifying flowering plants, we must take into consideration all their characteristics ; but it is obvious that the most useful characters are those which vary most. The root, for example, is scarcely a suitable basis for classification, because it is the least changeable organ of the plant. That of the primrose is not very different from that of the dandelion, yet the two flowers are vastly different ; and consequently the two plants are in different families. The root is, in fact, the most conservative organ of the plant. The most changeable organ is the flower, and therefore the classification of flowering plants is based chiefly, though not wholly, on the characters of the flowers and the fruits they bear.

A tree is known by the fruit, and not by the leaves.
                    English Proverbs : JOHN RAY

Plant classification of today follows closely along the lines set forth by the great Swedish botanist, Carl von Linné, usually called Linnaeus (1707-78). He announced his system first in 1735, but it was published in more complete detail in 1753. Though many thousands of plants have been discovered and added to the flora of the world since the days of Linnaeus, we still use his methods in principle though they are frequently modified in the light of more recent knowledge.

There are several somewhat different systems of plant classification in use today, but they differ only in detail. Here, for the Angiosperms, we are adopting (with certain modifications) that originally proposed by Dr. J. Hutchinson of the Royal Botanic Gardens, Kew, and set out in his *Families of Flowering Plants*. So this classification of trees is parallel with that of the other flowering plants dealt with in *Flowers in Britain* (Brimble).

So far as the flowers and fruit are concerned, Dr. Hutchinson points out several trends during the evolution of flowering plants on the earth. A few examples may prove of interest. (1) Hermaphrodite flowers preceded unisexual flowers, and of the latter those produced on two different plants (male on one and female on another) are probably more recent than those produced on the same plant. (2) The solitary flower is more primitive than that borne in groups or inflorescences. The higher form of inflorescence is that of the composite flowers such as daisy and dandelion. (3) Many-parted flowers preceded those with few parts. (4) Those flowers having no petals followed the petalled flowers, the absence of petals being the result of reduction—a common evolutionary trend. (5) The regular flower is an earlier type than the irregular. (6) Free carpels are more primitive than fused. (7) Evolutionary reduction in number of parts makes the few-carpelled flower more recent than the many-carpelled. (8) Aggregate fruits followed single fruit. There are other general principles, and *all* of them have to be considered before assigning a plant its place in the general classification.

Apart from the division of Gymnosperms, to which the conifers and some other plants belong, all other flowering plants (Angiosperms) may first be divided into two great groups. They are the Monocotyledons and the Dicotyledons.

The first leaf present in the embryonic plant embedded in the seed is called the seed-leaf or cotyledon. In Monocotyledons there is usually only one cotyledon and in Dicotyledons there are usually two, though on occasions we come across three or even four. In some plants these cotyledons are pushed above the soil and, though often of a different shape from the foliage leaves, they act as the first foliage leaves in food manufacture (p. 44). In other plants, such as the pea, the cotyledons remain below the soil and gradually disintegrate as the seedling develops. In most Gymnosperms there is a large number of cotyledons to each embryonic plant (p. 44). Besides the difference in number of cotyledons, there are other general differences between Monocotyledons and Dicotyledons. Few Monocotyledons show secondary thickening of their stems and roots, so there are few trees in this group. Most Dicotyledons, on the other hand, display secondary thickening. The leaves of Monocotyledons are usually parallel-veined, whereas those of Dicotyledons are net-veined. The flowers of each group, too, are characteristic within

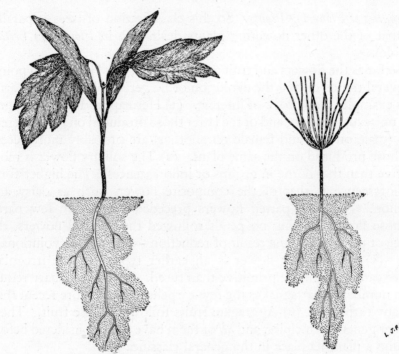

Angiospermous and Gymnospermous Seedlings.
Left, sycamore (angiosperm) showing two cotyledons and two foliage leaves ;
right, Scots pine (gymnosperm), showing many cotyledons.

very wide limits. The parts of the flowers of Dicotyledons are either indefinite or in fours or fives or their multiples. The parts of the Mono-cotyledonous flowers are usually in threes or multiples of three. The tulip and grasses are examples of Monocotyledons, and the rose, elm and horse-chestnut are examples of Dicotyledons.

Every kind of plant is a species. It is easier to illustrate this with a familiar family which contains no trees, for example, the buttercup family. Among the buttercups there are several common types, such as creeping buttercup, bulbous buttercup, water buttercup (or crowfoot) and so forth. Each of these buttercups is a separate species, because each is somewhat different from the other. But all are sufficiently similar to warrant being grouped together, so they are placed in a single group called a genus. Therefore we can say that all kinds of buttercups belong to the same genus but to different species.

In order to assign necessary distinction, yet to emphasise the close relation, Linnaeus suggested each plant having two names, one to designate the genus, the other the species. This is now done for all plants. Every buttercup, for example, belongs to the same genus, which is *Ranunculus*. This is the first name applied to the plant, and is called the generic name. Then each species of *Ranunculus* has a second name called the specific name. Thus the botanical names of the species already mentioned are : creeping buttercup, *Ranunculus repens* ; bulbous buttercup, R. *bulbosus* ; water buttercup, R. *aquatilis*. The lesser celandine is also sufficiently closely related to the buttercup to be placed in the same genus, and its botanical name is R. *ficaria*.

Further details of classification involve subdivision of species, and these subdivisions are known as subspecies and varieties. This applies especially to cultivated plants, for many new varieties are produced by cross-breeding and hybridisation. A variety is usually indicated by a third botanical name, usually preceded by the abbreviation ' var.' There are many varieties of the more well-known species of trees.

Plant genera frequently resemble each other closely, though there is enough distinction in each case to keep them in separate genera. For example, closely related to the buttercup is the garden paeony. But the paeony, though in many respects closely related to the buttercups (*Ranunculus*) is sufficiently different to be placed in a different genus (*Paeonia*). Other genera closely related to *Ranunculus* and *Paeonia* are : *Caltha* (for example, marsh marigold), *Nigella* (love-in-a-mist), *Aquilegia* (columbine), *Delphinium* (larkspur and other well-known garden species and varieties), *Aconitum* (monkshood), *Clematis* (clematis and traveller's joy), *Anemone* (wood anemone or windflower, and many familiar garden varieties), and several other genera. All these genera are so closely related that they are placed altogether in a still larger group called a family. In this case the family is RANUNCULACEAE. A well-known family of trees is FAGACEAE, containing such important genera as *Quercus* (the oaks), *Fagus* (the beeches), *Castanea* (the sweet chestnut) and others.

Families are then arranged in evolutionary sequence, so that those related to each other come near each other in the scheme of classification which thus begins with the most primitive plants and ends with the most recent. For example, other families closely related to RANUNCULACEAE are: CERATOPHYLLACEAE (for example, *Ceratophyllum submersum*, hornwort, an aquatic submerged plant) ; NYMPHAEACEAE (for example, *Nymphaea alba*, white water-lily and *Nuphar luteum*, yellow water-lily) ; and BERBERIDACEAE (for example, *Berberis vulgaris*, barberry).

Finally all families of Angiosperms are segregated into either the Monocotyledons or the Dicotyledons.

The Times

Tree-felling in Scotland.

HOW TO STUDY TREES

A study of trees cannot be made either with pleasure or with profit from a book alone. The only way to understand and appreciate them and their relationship with each other is to go into the country and examine them in their natural habitats, and then study what parts of them are available more closely at home. Then compare and contrast them with related species and varieties available in the gardens and parks. When doing this it must be remembered that trees, like most flowering plants, have been subjected to cultivation by man, and many have been introduced from abroad.

A final word to those who visit our meadows and woodlands. Treat the fields and woods with the respect they deserve. Do not spoil or defile them in any way. It is easy even for a serious student to do so ; but our meadows and woodlands must be preserved and even improved for the benefit and delight of the generations of the future. Especially in the case of trees, we must realize that they usually live longer than we do, and any act of vandalism against them is registered for a long time. Remember, a wood was

> made sacred by the religious mysteries of our fathers, and by ancient awe.
>
> *Germania* : TACITUS

Never collect more than the minimum of leaves, flowers and fruit for study at home, and above all do not cut more twigs than are really necessary, for the future form and beauty of a tree might well be permanently impaired by wanton cutting.

And with those who must fell trees—and perforce there are many today—we would plead for the needs of the future and ask that more attention be paid to afforestation and only the essential minimum to deforestation. Even those of us who are not directly concerned with tree-felling might be reminded of Scott's advice :

> Jock, when ye hae naething else to do, ye may be aye sticking in a tree ; it will be growing, Jock, when ye're sleeping.
>
> *The Heart of Midlothian* : SCOTT

Fox Photos.

Planting out Two-year old Norway Spruce Trees.

PRESENT-DAY NOMENCLATURE OF TREES

Trees have been, and are, an important commercial commodity, and it is not surprising therefore that they, and the timber they yield, often have several different common names according to country, locality, trade or use. Then, sometimes, as botanical and forestry research proceeds, it becomes necessary to transfer a tree from one genus to another or one species to another, and on occasion it becomes desirable to create new genera and new species. In this book it will not prove possible or desirable to give all common or trade names, but the most popular are used. So far as is possible, the generic and specific names have been kept up to date. Those readers who are particularly interested in the different names applied to trees and timber or wish to check certain names should consult the *Empire Forestry Handbook* (Empire Forestry Association, Grand Buildings, Trafalgar Square, London, W.C. 2), and the standardised lists published by the British Standards Institution, namely, *Nomenclature of Softwoods : including Botanical Species and Sources of Supply* and *Nomenclature of Hardwoods : including Botanical Names and Sources of Supply* (British Standards Institution, 28 Victoria Street, London, S.W. 1).

FORESTRY IN BRITAIN

After the War of 1914–18, the Government of the day realised the necessity of ensuring the country's timber supplies, and in 1919 the Forestry Bill made provision for the founding of a Forestry Commission, the main function of which was to develop afforestation in Britain.

In its first twenty-five years of existence, the Commission has acquired about one and a quarter million acres of land, of which half a million have already been afforested. Some of the rest of the land, including mountain tops, will be unproductive ; but now all belong to the State. This includes 263 forests, of which 102 are in England, 39 in Wales and 122 in Scotland.

For the first twenty-five years, that is, until 1945, the Forestry Commission was detached from any State department, and was responsible to the Treasury only so far as funds were concerned. Now, as Sir John Anderson pointed out in the House of Commons on February 15, 1945, the Forestry Commission is to come under the control of the Ministry of Agriculture in England and the Secretary of State for Scotland, thus ensuring "the better co-ordination of the development of agriculture and forestry."

PART II

CONIFERS AND OTHER GYMNOSPERMS

We have still much to learn about that great group of seed-bearing plants, the Gymnosperms. Our present lack of knowledge is due to the fact that some complete divisions of the group are now wholly extinct and have come down to us in fossilised forms only ; and even here the difficulty is sometimes intensified in that the fossils are often very fragmentary. Other divisions are mostly extinct.

Of the seven recognised divisions of Gymnosperms three are wholly extinct, namely, *Cycadofilicales* (the fossils of which bear certain resemblances to living ferns), the *Bennettitales* and the *Cordaitales*.

The division *Ginkgoales* is almost extinct, since it is now represented by only one living species of plant, namely, the maidenhair tree (*Ginkgo biloba*) (p. 51). The *Cycadales* is represented by many fossils and a few living genera, none of which is native to Great Britain.

Perhaps the divisions most closely suggestive of Angiosperms, and therefore the highest in the scale of evolution of Gymnosperms, is the *Gnetales*. This division has so far revealed no fossil representatives ; but there are three living genera of peculiar plants, distributed over the tropical Old and New Worlds, other parts of Africa, and a few areas of Europe. But none of these plants aspires to the dimensions of a tree.

By far the largest and most important living division of the Gymnosperms is the *Coniferales* or coniferous trees. There are five families in this division, namely, ARAUCARIACEAE, PODOCARPACEAE, ABIETACEAE, CUPRESSACEAE and TAXACEAE. Most conifers grow in their native habitats gregariously in forests, especially in temperate and alpine regions of all parts of the world. Some are to be found mixed with broad-leaved (angiospermous) trees. There are about five hundred living species of conifers ; but in past ages there were many more associating with the huge club-mosses and horsetails of those days.

Among the conifers we have the cedars, pines, spruces and firs. Since so much is yet to be learned about these trees, it is not surprising that there is still much confusion in nomenclature—especially among the common names. 'Firs' are called 'pines', and vice versa ; and there are many so-called 'cedars' which are not related to the true cedars at all.

And what a charm is in the rich hot scent
    Of old fir forests heated by the sun,
    Where drops of resin down the rough bark run,
And needle litter breathes its wonderment.

The old fir forests heated by the sun,
    Their thought shall linger like the lingering scent,
    Their beauty haunt us, and a wonderment
Of moss, of fern, of cones, of rills that run.

The needle litter breathes a wonderment ;
    The crimson crans are sparkling in the sun ;
    From tree to tree the scampering squirrels run ;
The hum of insects blends with heat and scent.

The drops of resin down the rough bark run ;
    An riper, ever riper, grows the scent ;
    But eve has come, to end the wonderment,
And slowly up the tree trunk climbs the sun.

Among the Firs : EUGENE LEE-HAMILTON

The firs are ranged in endless dark battalions
    On mountain-side and valley, line on line,
Waiting the winds, that on their viewless stallions
    Are bearing down, at Winter's sudden sign.
The mighty trees are grappling to the rock
With every root, preparing for the shock
    Of that wild cavalry, and seem to hearken
    Silent and sturdy, as the grey clouds darken,
For the first howl of war.

Charge of the Winged Seeds : EUGENE LEE-HAMILTON

6

A 'LIVING FOSSIL': THE MAIDENHAIR TREE

(Ginkgoaceae)

The **maidenhair tree** (*Ginkgo biloba*) is a strange, indeed a unique, tree. It is the only living representative of a division of Gymnosperms—the *Ginkgoales*—which, apart from this plant, has become extinct. The maidenhair tree therefore forms a family of its own, namely, GINKGOACEAE. In fact, among all those living plants which, by their primitive features, display certain linkages with plants of past ages, the maidenhair tree is perhaps the most interesting, because it is still so intriguing even to the botanical specialist. We are told, for example, of former travellers having reported seeing it growing in the wild state in China. Yet, so recently as 1937, Sir Albert Seward cast doubt on this. He wrote: "Does it exist in the wild state today?... Most botanists would probably answer that far-travelled plant collectors in China have never seen a maidenhair growing under conditions in which man was not involved. It would, however, be rash definitely to assert that the question is settled.... A Chinese botanist, W. C. Cheng, in 1933, wrote: ' This tree is very common in Tienmu-Shan, growing in association with coniferous and broad-leaved trees. It seems to grow spontaneously in that region.' The word ' seems ' implies a lack of conviction."

Since ancient times this remarkable tree has certainly been cultivated around Chinese and Japanese temples, for in those countries it was deemed sacred. From those areas it has spread, under erratic cultivation, to Europe and America. The first European specimen was planted in the Botanic Garden at Utrecht about 1730. In Britain it has been cultivated for about two hundred years, and there are particularly handsome specimens in the Royal Botanic Gardens, Kew (this specimen is more than 70 feet high), several London parks, the Oxford Botanical Garden, Frogmore, Windsor, and elsewhere. The tree is perfectly hardy in Britain, though there are no outstanding specimens in either Ireland or Scotland. On the Continent there are finer examples than the British specimens.

But the tree is more interesting in that it is certainly a ' living fossil ', as Darwin called it, having persisted on the earth for ten million years, yet experiencing no evolutionary changes during the whole of that time, thus remaining more closely related to its ancestors of millions of years ago than to any of its contemporaries. Fossil species of the genus *Ginkgo* have been discovered in various geological strata from the Jurassic onwards in Great Britain and in the United States. It is particularly interesting to note that fossilised remains of this genus and other related genera belonging to the same group have also been uncovered in arctic regions, especially Spitsbergen. Still further fossil Ginkgoalean leaves have been found in Franz-Josef Land. But in those days there were several genera in the group *Ginkgoales* ; *Ginkgo* is the only genus remaining alive on the earth today.

The maidenhair tree is not very large, though specimens 80 feet high have been recorded. It is deciduous, and during the winter its slender branches from a fine trunk, covered with greyish bark, make a particularly graceful array.

The leaves are quite unique in several respects (p. 54). They resemble the fronds of the maidenhair fern rather than the leaf of any known flowering plant ; hence the common name of the tree. The leaves are borne in clusters and are pale green in colour. Each leaf has a slender leaf-stalk which fans out into a leaf-blade which may be either entire or deeply divided into two (or sometimes, though not often, more) lobes. The venation, too, is unique. A main vein traverses each half of the leaf-blade close to its lowest margin. Then each of these veins gives off many branches which reach to the far margin of the blade, sometimes forking on the way (p. 54). The leaf turns a beautiful golden yellow before autumn leaf-fall. The male tree sheds its leaves early in November; the female two or three weeks later.

The flowers of the maidenhair tree are unisexual and the sexes are borne on different trees. This explains why the fruit is so seldom seen in Britain, because the trees are so comparatively rare that male and female trees do not grow in sufficiently close proximity to make pollination possible. Kerner in his *Natural History of Plants* has given, however, examples of a female bud being successfully grafted on to a male tree.

The male flowers are borne in groups, resembling catkins rather than cones, on short spur shoots which grow in the axils of scale leaves. Each cone is composed of a central axis which bears the stamens. Each stamen comprises a stalk, swollen at the end and bearing two, or rarely more, pollen sacs beneath the swollen end.

Ginkgo:
The Palace, Wells.

Lonsdale Ragg

Maidenhair Tree at the Bishop's Palace, Wells, Somerset.

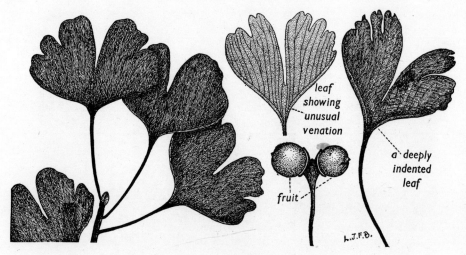

Leaves and Fruit of the Maidenhair Tree.

The female flowers are the simplest imaginable. They also are borne in clusters, and each flower takes the form of a long stalk towards the end of which are two ovules, each borne on the side near the apex. Each ovule is naked, but it is supported by a collar.

After fertilisation (which is effected through the agency of wind), each ovule produces a woody seed which becomes surrounded by a swollen, yellow, fleshy layer about the size of a small plum. In fact, *superficially*, the fruit resembles a plum; but the fleshy pulp has an unpleasant and persistent smell. The seeds are edible, and in China they are sold as articles of diet.

As might be expected, the timber of the maidenhair tree is not used very much, for naturally it is always in short supply. In the Far East it is sometimes used in wood-carving. But on the whole it may be said that the usefulness of the maidenhair tree lies in its graceful form (during both summer and winter), and therefore in its ornamental beauty, and also in its exceptional botanical interest.

There are several cultivated varieties of *Ginkgo biloba*; for example, *G. biloba* var. *variegata*, having green leaves streaked with yellow; *G. biloba* var. *pendula*, a weeping form; and a few others. Dwarf specimens are raised in China.

It is a pity that this tree is so little known and therefore so infrequently cultivated in Britain, for it is very easily grown in a rich, well-drained soil. Furthermore it is easily transplanted and is also tolerant of hard pruning. It will thrive in the atmosphere of towns.

7

MONKEY PUZZLE OR CHILE PINE
(*Araucariaceae*)

The **monkey puzzle** or **Chile pine** belongs to the family ARAU-
CARIACEAE, which contains only two living genera, namely, *Araucaria* and *Agathis*, these genera being remnants of a much larger number
of genera now extinct. All members of the family ARAUCARIACEAE are
large trees.

The monkey puzzle (*Araucaria araucana*) is the only representative
of the family commonly seen in this country. It is a strange-looking
tree—almost sinister in appearance. No wonder it is so frequently
seen dominating the entrance to cemeteries. The trunk is straight
and the branches come off in whorls, each whorl consisting of four to
six branches. Each branch begins from the trunk growing obliquely
upwards but soon curves downwards by virtue of its weight; then
the ends again curve upwards. Loudon describes the branches as
like " snakes partly coiled round the trunk, and stretching forth their
long slender bodies in quest of prey." The lower branches frequently
die off, and then they become covered with brown withered leaves
which do nothing towards enhancing any beauty which might be there.

The leaves are very pointed and broad at their bases (p. 57).
They are inserted on the stem in such a close spiral that they overlap like
the tiles of a roof, thus completely hiding the stem which bears them.
All the leaves are dark green in colour. Each leaf lasts up to fifteen
years, so the tree is evergreen. Even on the trunk itself some leaves
remain, though they are usually withered and brown.

Both male and female cones are large. The male cone takes the
form of a catkin borne in the axil of a leaf towards the end of a branch.
Sometimes there are small groups of male cones. Each cone is about
four inches long. The female cone is more or less spherical in shape,
though it usually assumes a point at its distal end. Each cone is
covered with pointed scales which overlap like the tiles of a roof—as
the foliage leaves do. After fertilisation, the female cone attains a diameter of about six inches (p. 57). It then becomes brown in colour.
On the lower side of each scale is a seed about an inch long. When

Eric J. Hosking

Monkey Puzzle (Chile Pine) in Somerset.

Eric J. Hosking

Cones of the Monkey Puzzle (Chile Pine).

completely ripe, the scales fall apart and the seeds are thus released. Each seed, which is about twice the size of an almond and is edible, is enclosed in a thin but tough outer case.

The wood of the monkey puzzle is yellowish-white and is attractively veined. It is easily polished. At one time it was used for shipbuilding; but now, though a certain amount of the timber is imported into Britain, it is not of any great importance.

The whole tree is impregnated with a white resin which exudes as a gum. This is still used by the inhabitants of certain parts of South America for various medicinal purposes; but not to the extent that it was at one time: in any event, there is considerable doubt about the curative properties of this gum.

The monkey puzzle is a native of South America, mainly Chile. Its generic name, *Araucaria*, is derived from Arauco, the Chilean district where it was first discovered by a Spaniard in 1780. In its native haunts, especially the Cordilleras of Chile, this tree often attains a height of 150 feet, and, especially when growing among other forest trees, it succeeds in looking impressive and even attractive. But even in its native habitats, it usually loses its lower branches when growing in exposed positions, and then it is far from beautiful.

In South America, the edible seeds are still highly prized as articles of diet, especially by the Indians. The Rev. C. A. Johns, in his *Forest Trees of Britain*, estimated that eighteen monkey puzzle trees would maintain one Indian for a whole year.

The monkey puzzle was introduced into Britain in 1796, when Menzies, the famous botanist who (in that capacity) accompanied Captain Vancouver on his voyages along the Chilean coast, collected some of the seeds and presented a few of the plants raised from them to the Royal Botanic Gardens, Kew. There they flourished for many years, but the last of them died in 1892.

Though the tree flourishes in Britain provided it has a well-drained soil and plenty of fresh air and sunshine, it does not succeed in built-up areas where it is so often seen. There it seldom grows to any height and no oftener does it look healthy. But further afield, given satisfactory conditions, it will thrive and attain a height of 80 feet. Some very successful groups of monkey puzzle trees are to be seen in various parts of Britain and of Ireland, though conditions in Scotland do not seem to encourage it. Above all, it cannot withstand sharp frosts, especially if they are sustained. For this reason, many young trees have been known to perish during certain hard winters.

Another member of the genus *Araucaria*, namely, *A. excelsa*, the **Norfolk Island pine**, is sometimes cultivated in Britain as an ornamental pot plant. Of course, in this condition, it is seen in its youth only ; but it is an attractive sight by virtue of the bright green foliage. This tree was first discovered in its native habitat (Norfolk Island and New Caledonia) by Captain Cook during his second voyage, and introduced into Britain by Sir Joseph Banks in 1793. In its native haunts this tree attains a height of more than 200 feet. A rarer member of the genus, *A. brasiliana*, the **Brazilian** or **parana pine,** was introduced into Britain in 1819 ; but, since it needs considerable protection, it has not achieved popularity.

Other species of *Araucaria* are to be found in South America, Australia and Polynesia. The timber of some of these is imported into Britain ; for example, **bunya pine** (*A. bidwillii*) and **hoop pine** (*A. cunninghamii*), both from Australia.

8

PINES

(*Abietaceae*)

Like two cathedral towers these stately pines
Uplift their fretted summits tipped with cones ;
The arch beneath them is not built with stones,
Not Art but Nature traced these lovely lines,
And carved this graceful arabesque of vines ;
No organ but the wind here sighs and moans,
No sepulchre conceals a martyr's bones,
No marble bishop on his tomb reclines.
Enter! the pavement, carpeted with leaves,
Gives back in softened echo to thy tread!
Listen! the choir is singing ; all the birds,
In leafy galleries beneath the eaves,
Are singing! Listen, ere the sound be fled,
And learn there may be worship without words.

My Cathedral : LONGFELLOW

The pines, of which the Scots pine (sometimes erroneously called ' fir ') is the most typical example in Britain, belong to the genus *Pinus*, a very important member of the family ABIETACEAE. The name ' pine ' is loosely applied even today (just as is the word ' fir ') ; in ancient times, ' pine ' was applied to a large number of coniferous, resin-yielding trees. But today it is, or should be, limited to those conifers comprising the genus *Pinus*.

The pines differ from the firs in that the former produce their leaves from sheathing bases, each sheath bearing two, three, four, or five leaves. The number of leaves produced in each sheath is not necessarily diagnostic of the species, though very frequently it is. In most British pines the number is two. The sheathing base of a pair of Scots pine needles is easily visible (pp. 28 and 41). It is interesting to note that the needle-like foliage leaves of pines are really of secondary origin ; the primary leaves are modified into inconspicuous brown scales.

Another distinctive feature of pines is that the distal ends of the scales of the female cones are thick and woody. This contrasts with the scales of the cones of firs which are thin and often membranous.

The male cones of a pine are usually borne in dense clusters towards the apices of young shoots (p. 41). The female cones develop on short stalks which grow out laterally near the ends of branches. There are one or two to each end. A ripe cone usually takes at least two years to develop. Pollination, which, of course, is by wind, takes place in the young green cone during June of the year of its formation. Then the scales of the cone close up again, and the cone grows but very slowly until the spring of the following year. After this, development proceeds apace, and by the autumn of the second year the seeds of the cone are ripe and the cone itself has turned brown. In the following spring these brown cones open, and the winged seeds are released to be dispersed by the wind.

After germination of the seed, the young seedling displays many cotyledons (up to fifty)—quite unlike those of Monocotyledons which usually have only one cotyledon or Dicotyledons which usually have only two (pp. 43 and 44).

It is common observation that pines can obviously withstand the rigours of extremely harsh climates. They are tolerant of high winds because the leaves offer almost the minimum of resistance and the root system is widespread and deep. Furthermore, pines are equal to the exacting conditions of an arid soil and dry air because the leaf surface is almost minimal. This is essential to trees frequently growing where water is not plentiful, either because the soil is particularly loose or the soil water is in the frozen state for many months of the year. Pines, like most other conifers, prefer light, well-drained soil.

The pines are distributed throughout the north temperate and subtropical zones, and a few are indigenous to the tropics themselves. No pine is native to the southern hemisphere, though several have been introduced with success.

> This fashionable watering-place [Sandbourne–Bournemouth] with its eastern and its western stations, its groves of pines, its promenades, and its covered gardens, was, to Angel Clare, like a fairy place suddenly created by the stroke of a wand, and allowed to get a little dusty . . . Within the space of a mile from its outskirts every irregularity of the soil was prehistoric, every channel an undisturbed British trackway; not a sod having been turned there since the days of the Cæsars.
>
> The sea was near at hand, but not intrusive; it murmured, and he thought it was the pines; the pines murmured in precisely the same tones, and he thought they were the sea.
>
> *Tess of the D'Urbervilles* : THOMAS HARDY

SCOTS PINES

PLATE I

SCOTS PINE

The **Scots pine** (*Pinus sylvestris*) is a native of northern Britain and the countries of northern Europe. It is the most important British coniferous tree, and is the only conifer indigenous to this country. A general description of this plant is given on pp. 39-41.

Though frequently seen growing in southern England, the Scots pine is not really indigenous to that area. Plantations are, however, now very common, and the tree has become naturalised. The tree can be seen growing either in groups or forming forests all over northern Europe and into Siberia and as far south as Spain, Italy and on to Persia. But it is most abundant in Scandinavian countries. It is the ' fir ' referred to in Norse mythology and used so much by the old Norsemen. In these countries, and in the U.S.S.R., northern Germany and Poland, huge forests of this pine are still to be seen.

Under favourable soil and climatic conditions in Britain, the Scots pine will attain a height of 100 feet, the erect trunk often being bare of branches for nearly three quarters of its length. The tree does not usually succeed in urban areas, though the group at Hampstead immortalised by the painter Constable still seems to be in fairly sound condition.

The bark is rough and irregularly fissured : towards the top of the tree it becomes a glowing red. Though, as in the case of most pines, the root generally goes deep, its growth might be checked by unfavourable conditions and then the tree is unstable against high winds. In many old specimens, the tree loses all semblance of a pyramidal habit and the crown becomes irregular and quite flattened. In very old trees, the trunk is often gnarled and twisted (p. 134).

Today, the Scots pine is planted not only for ornamental purposes or for the timber it produces, but also on slag heaps for binding the loose soil. Prof. A. Henry, in his *Forest Woods and Trees*, also recommends it for the afforestation of water catchment areas, especially in the north. But in times past, this tree played a much larger part in British forestry. From neolithic times it was widespread and itself formed large forests : today, such forests are confined to the Scottish Highlands. The Rev. C. A. Johns, in his *Forest Trees of Britain*, gives a picturesque description of the Scots pines in Scotland by quoting Sir T. D. Lauder : " In the forests of Invercauld and Braemar, the endless Fir woods run up all the ramifications and subdivisions of the tributary valleys, cover the lower elevations, climb the sides of the higher hills, and even in many cases approach the very roots of the giant mountains which

Pinus Sylvestris
Girth 11 ft
Luscombe. 21-6-41
LR

Lonsdale Ragg

Scots Pine in Somerset.

tower over them ; yet with all this, the reader is mistaken if he supposes that any tiresome uniformity exists among these wilds. Every movement we make exposes to our view fresh objects of excitement, and discloses new scenes produced by the infinite variety of the surface. At one time we find ourselves wandering along some natural level under the deep and sublime shade of the heavy Pine foliage, upheld high overhead by the tall and massive columnar stems, which appear to form an endless colonnade . . . hardly conscious that the sun is up, save from the fragrant resinous odour which its influence is exhaling, and the continued hum of the clouds of insects that are dancing in its beams over the tops of the trees." Alas! Even in Scotland these trees are now suffering considerably from the ravages of the forester's axe. Fortunately, the Scots pine develops quite easily from seed—a characteristic which those responsible for re-afforestation are now noting.

The bluish-green leaves are sheathed in pairs, and are short (compared with those of other pines) with a slight twist. They remain on the tree two or more years (p. 41 and Plate 3).

The male flowers are characteristic of pines (p. 41 and Plate 3) and ripen during May and June, when the pollen is disseminated in clouds. The buoyancy of each pollen grain is enhanced by two wing-like outgrowths which are filled with air. The young female flowers at this time are soft and reddish purple (Plate 3). Although pollination takes place in the first year of their formation, fertilisation does not occur until about the middle of the following year (p. 40). Then the cones mature, but they do not open and release their seeds until the following spring, that is, when the cone is two years old (p. 41 and Plate 3). The seeds (p. 40) are distributed by wind and by birds.

The tree, as one would imagine, is extremely hardy ; in fact, it is perhaps the hardiest of all British trees, being able to withstand wide extremes of wind and weather. It prefers dry, sandy soil and must have plenty of light.

The wood of the Scots pine is useful for all sorts of indoor and outdoor purposes, especially because the resin present in large quantities, particularly in the heart-wood, makes it durable. Railway sleepers, pit props and wood pavings are often made from this wood ; but in such cases it must be treated with some form of preservative to ensure its durability. Since growing conditions in Scandinavia, the U.S.S.R., and other north European areas reduce the rate of growth of the Scots pine, the timber imported from these regions is tougher, stronger and much more durable than the British-grown timber.

AUSTRIAN PINE

The **Austrian pine** is one of the most well-known of the varieties of **black pines** (*Pinus nigra*), all of which are native to Central Europe and the Mediterranean regions. Since it is a variety of several, the Austrian pine is therefore designated *P. nigra* var. *austriaca*. The native haunts of this particular variety are confined to Austria and the Balkan mountains; but the tree has been successfully introduced into Britain where it frequently figures in landscape architecture. Often, too, it may be seen together with specimens of Scots pine. It is rather bushy and of irregular habit, forming a not very handsome adult tree. The leaves are very dark green. They are somewhat longer than those of Scots pine, but they too are sheathed in pairs. When ripe, the female cones are not quite so dark in colour as are those of the Scots pine.

The tree averages 60 to 80 feet in height.

The Austrian pine grows well in maritime regions, and is therefore useful in those parts exposed to strong sea gales. It is also useful for binding sand-dunes, slag-heaps and other loose sloping ground. It is frequently grown in plantations as a nurse or shelter tree for other young trees, especially certain hardwoods. Seldom is it grown to form plantations of its own. The timber is coarse. This, together with the fact that it contains an excessive number of knots, renders it practically useless except as a fuel. Nevertheless, a certain amount is imported from southern Europe for rough and general purposes.

CORSICAN PINE

The **Corsican pine** (*Pinus nigra* var. *corsicana* or *calabrica*) is one of the noblest of the group of black pines (p. 67). It is very common in Corsica (its native habitat) and also thrives well in Spain and along the Mediterranean shores to Greece.

This tree is more slender and cylindrical, and attains a greater average height (80 to 120 feet) than the Austrian variety of *Pinus nigra*. In fact, it is proving itself to be a valuable tree and has figured more and more in British forestry since its introduction in 1759, more especially because it can withstand our soil and climatic conditions better than such trees as the Scots pine.

The bright green leaves, sheathed in pairs, are twisted in a characteristic manner, and by this the tree may be identified. Furthermore,

Austrian Pine in Westmorland.

Eric J. Hosking

the leaves have slightly toothed margins, and they are packed less densely on the stem than those of the Austrian pine.

Like the Austrian pine, the Corsican pine flourishes in maritime regions, and the two varieties are often seen growing together near the sea-shore and elsewhere. There is a handsome specimen of Corsican pine more than 90 feet high in the Royal Botanic Gardens, Kew.

STONE PINE

The **stone pine** (*P. pinea*), a native of Mediterranean regions, especially Spain and Italy, is not a particularly beautiful tree. Its cumbersome, umbrella-like appearance does, however, make it an impressive sight and an intriguing subject for landscape artists (p. 68). In fact, it figures so often in the Mediterranean landscape and coast-line scenery that pictorial artists have been quite unable to resist its appeal; often, therefore, does the stone pine find itself depicted on the canvasses of those artists who have chosen the Mediterranean scene as the object of their inspiration. The unusual shape of this tree has earned for it the alternative common name of **umbrella pine.**

The stone pine does quite well in Britain, provided conditions are suitable ; but it is grown in this country solely for decorative or sentimental reasons. It is not known for certain when the stone pine was

first brought to Britain, though there is evidence that it has been known here for well-nigh four hundred years. (The Rev. C. A. Johns, in his *Forest Trees of Britain*, definitely gives 1548 as the date of its introduction.)

In Britain, the tree will attain a height of more than 50 feet, though it often falls far short of this. There is a specimen in the Royal Botanic Gardens, Kew, just about 50 feet high and about 9 feet in girth. In its native habitats the tree will grow to a height of 90 to 100 feet.

During the younger stages of the tree, the leaves are borne singly; later they emerge in sheathed pairs borne in clusters. Each leaf is bright green and nearly six

Foliage and Cone of Stone Pine. inches long.

Corsican Pine.

Lonsdale Ragg

LR
7-9-33

Umbrella Pine
St Mary's Bersted

Stone Pine in Sussex.

The scales of the cone are rhomboidal in shape when viewed at the surface of the cone (p. 66). The cone takes three years to ripen. The seeds are enclosed in a very hard shell (which inspired the common name ' stone ' pine); in fact, from the days of Pliny they have been erroneously called ' nuts ' because of the hard outer casing and the edible kernel or seed inside. Each seed is about the size of a hazel nut, though longer, and it has a somewhat similar taste. Since the days of the early Romans these seeds, called pignons or pinocchi, have been eaten as a sweetmeat, especially by the Italians. They are usually stored while still in the cone, for the oil which they contain easily becomes rancid when exposed to the air. The empty cones are used as fuel.

An inferior kind of turpentine is sometimes obtained from this tree; but apart from this and its edible seeds the tree is of little commercial value.

Among other interesting pines which, however, are not commonly seen under cultivation in Britain, is the **pinaster** or **maritime pine** (*P. pinaster*). The vigorous growth and penetrating capacity and spreading nature of the roots of this tree have made it especially valuable in binding sand-dunes, particularly in the Bay of Biscay. Even on the most unstable sand, this tree soon becomes firmly established. In France the maritime pine is a valuable source of resin and turpentine, and its timber supplies pit-props. It has not found favour in Britain, though here and there it may be seen growing on sand-dunes. At Purbeck and other parts of the south of England it seems to have become firmly established. There are several unimportant varieties of this pine.

The **cembran** or **Swiss stone pine** (*P. cembra*) is not a success in this country, though it may sometimes be seen growing under careful cultivation. It is a native of the Swiss Alps and of Siberia, and is distinguished by having the leaves sheathed in groups of five. In Siberia a fine oil is extracted from the seeds, and this is used as a food and for illumination.

Of the North American pines there are about thirty-five species. These are grouped under ' soft pines ' and ' pitch pines '. The soft pines are usually deciduous, and their leaves are borne in five-leaved sheathes. The pitch pines are in three-leaved sheathes. The **Weymouth pine** (*P. strobus*) (p. 70) is a large tree, with leaves borne in clusters of five and having narrow cones about six inches long. It was introduced into Britain by Lord Weymouth in 1710; but since then it has never achieved popularity. The **sugar pine** (*P. lambertiana*) is a huge tree,

Weymouth Pine.

and is valuable for its timber especially in California. It has very long cones—sometimes as much as two feet in length. The **long-leaf pine** (*P. palustris*) abounds in the southern States, where it is one of the chief lumber-producing trees. The **loblolly pine** (*P. taeda*) is also widespread in the southern States, and is a useful timber tree.

Not so frequent in cultivation in British parks and gardens is the **blue pine** of the Himalayas (*P. excelsa*). Its needles are sheathed in groups of five. As the name implies, they are of a bluish-green colour. In its native habitat, this tree produces useful timber and resin.

The **bull pine** or **western yellow pine** (*P. ponderosa*), from many parts of North America, including Canada, may sometimes be seen in this country. Its leaves are sheathed in groups of three. They also, like those of the blue pine, are bluish-green in colour.

There is a golden form of the Scots pine, namely, *Pinus sylvestris* var. *aurea*, sometimes cultivated in Britain. This tree is at its best during the winter months, which is all to the good, for then the only trees with leaves are the evergreens, most of which are sombre enough.

There are many other pines indigenous to the Americas and to Asia which might well be tried in Britain provided their individual characters have been sufficiently studied in order that they may be cultivated under suitable conditions. Dwarf pines are not common.

9

CEDARS

(*Abietaceae*)

A cedar spread his dark-green layers of shade.
The Gardener's Daughter : TENNYSON

The name 'cedar' has been, and still is, applied to a considerable number of coniferous trees some of which have no close affinities and which have therefore been assigned to different genera. Apart from the well-known cedar of Lebanon (*Cedrus libani*) and other trees of the same genus, there are, for example, the Port Orford cedar or Lawson cypress (*Chamaecyparis lawsoniana*) (p. 107), the red or American pencil cedar (*Juniperus virginiana*) (p. 104), the Jamaican red cedar (*Cedrela odorata*), and others, some belonging to still different genera.

F

So the common name cedar, which is of Greek origin, is popularly applied not only to the true cedar of the genus *Cedrus*, but also to other conifers and even to some broad-leaved angiospermous trees. For the sake of botanical clarity, the tendency today is to confine the term ' cedar ' to those cedars which belong to the genus *Cedrus*. This will be done here ; nevertheless, those so-called ' cedars ' not belonging to the genus *Cedrus* will be mentioned as such, though in their correct botanical genera.

Although foresters recognise four different cedars and have nominally raised each to specific rank, it is most probable that they are all geographical forms of one species only, namely *Cedrus libani*. The differences between the four forms are, indeed, so slight, that some botanists still include them all under the species *C. libani*. All four forms are mountain trees. The **cedar of Lebanon** (*C. libani*) grows on Mount Lebanon, in Cyprus and in the Orient ; the **Indian cedar** or **deodar** (*C. deodara*) (p. 78) is Himalayan ; the **Mount Atlas** or **Algerian cedar** (*C. atlantica*) is African and grows mainly on the Atlas Mountains ; the fourth (recognised by some authorities but not by all) is the **Cyprus cedar** (*C. brevifolia*), which is found at the eastern end of the Mediterranean.

There are several varieties of these cedars, including the very lovely **blue cedar** (*C. atlantica* var. *glauca*), the **golden cedar** (*C. atlantica* var. *aurea*) an attractive golden form, several varieties of the **deodar** (*C. deodara*), namely, the **golden deodar** (*C. deodara* var. *aurea*) and the **silver deodar** (*C. deodara* var. *argentea*), and others. All the cedars so far mentioned are grown in gardens in Britain.

Then there are certain dwarf forms to be seen growing in rock gardens. Some of these develop the habit of almost spherical bushes ; one dwarf form of deodar, namely, *C. deodara* var. *nana*, makes an attractive compact flat-topped bush. The genus *C. libani* has produced several dwarf forms. For example, *C. libani* var. *nana pyramidata* is a compact dwarf pyramidal tree. There are several others, some of which have been raised to specific rank by certain botanists. A full account of these, together with other dwarf conifers suitable for rock gardens, is given in M. Hornibrook's *Dwarf and Slow-growing Conifers*.

Since the cedar is so frequently mentioned in the Scriptures, it is not surprising that it, too, has been claimed by tradition as having supplied the timber for the Cross of Calvary. Solomon is supposed to have buried a cedar where the pool of Bethesda once existed. Just before Christ's crucifixion this wood floated to the surface and was utilised for the upright portion of the Cross.

Cedars of Lebanon in Kent.

Lonsdale Ragg

CEDAR OF LEBANON

Cedars, that high upon the untrodden slopes
Of Lebanon stretch out their stubborn arms,
Through all the tempests of seven hundred years
Fast in their ancient place, where they look down
Over the Syrian plains and faint blue sea,
When snow for three days and three nights hath fall'n
Continually, and heaped those terraced boughs
To massy whiteness, still in fortitude
Maintain their aged strength, although they groan ;
The Death of Adam : LAURENCE BINYON

The cedar of Lebanon (*C. libani*) varies considerably according to environment. Though it has been known to attain a height of well over 100 feet, the usual height in Britain is between 50 and 80 feet. The tree branches profusely. The largest branches spread out majestically, giving excellent umbrage ; in fact, the lowest branches frequently touch the ground. The bark is rough and markedly fissured on the bole, but is very thin on the branches.

This tree is evergreen, and the leaves are deep bluish-green in colour. They are arranged mainly in dense clusters, each of about thirty leaves, on short shoots (p. 77), and sparsely in spiral fashion on the older shoots. The leaves are comparatively short (about one inch) and remain on the tree for from three to five years.

The male cones are borne, not in clusters, but singly and stand erect (p. 77). The female cones are also erect and, when young, are green. Later they become greyish. The seeds are ripe when the cone is two years old. The scales of the cone are membranous but are pressed very closely together (p. 77).

The cedar of Lebanon is frequently mentioned in the Bible where it symbolises longevity and power.

The righteous shall flourish like the palm-tree : he shall grow like a cedar in Lebanon. *Psalm* 92

The beams of our house *are* cedar, *and* our rafters of fir.
Song of Solomon, 1

Behold, the Assyrian *was* a cedar in Lebanon with fair branches, and with a shadowing shroud, and of an high stature ; and his top was among the thick boughs. *Ezekiel*, 31

cedrus
Libani:
Compton,
Surrey.

Lonsdale Ragg

Bole of a Cedar of Lebanon in Surrey.

21-7-34

This tree is native to the eastern Mediterranean, and though there are still many growing on the famous Mount Lebanon, the glorious groves which used to exist there have disappeared. In Biblical times, as already indicated, this tree was certainly well recognised. It was largely used in the construction of Solomon's Temple, and masts of ships were made from it. But the people of those days over-rated the durability of the timber (nothing to that of the timber of the Indian cedar or deodar, p. 79). Today the timber of the cedar of Lebanon is scarcely used, at any rate in Britain. Yet, despite the doubtful nature of the wood, the stately cedars of Lebanon have inspired the inhabitants of the eastern Mediterranean regions (and this includes North Africa) for centuries. Referring to the cedars on Mount Lebanon, Lamartine (quoted by Johns) writes : " These trees are the most renowned natural monuments in the universe ; religion, poetry, and history, have all equally celebrated them. The Arabs of all sects entertain a traditional veneration of these trees. They attribute to them, not only a vegetative power, which enables them to live eternally, but also an intelligence, which causes them to manifest signs of wisdom and foresight, similar to those of instinct and reason in man. They are said to understand the changes of the seasons ; they stir their vast branches as if they were limbs ; they spread out or contract their boughs, inclining them towards heaven or towards earth, according as the snow prepares to fall or melt."

The cedar of Lebanon has also been a favourite with British poets and painters on account of its stateliness and strength.

> Thus yields the cedar to the axe's edge,
> Whose arms give shelter to the princely eagle,
> Under whose shade the ramping lion slept,
> Whose top-branch overpeer'd Jove's spreading tree,
> And kept low shrubs from winter's powerful wind.
> *III Henry VI*, Act V, Sc. 2 : SHAKESPEARE

The early Classical authors of Greece and Rome also made many references to this tree.

It is not definitely known when the cedar of Lebanon was introduced into Britain ; but it probably first arrived some time during the seventeenth century. Johns, in his *Forest Trees of Britain*, gives a colourful account of how a traveller first introduced it into France by bringing a young specimen from the Holy Land, using his hat as a flower-pot and tending it with meticulous care during a very rough sea voyage. He eventually got it safely to the Jardin des Plantes in Paris where it

Leaves and Cones of the Cedar of Lebanon.
Above, a twig showing clusters of leaves ; below, left, a cone of male flowers ;
below right, a cone of female flowers ; below centre, a ripe cone.

thrived for about a hundred years and was then cut down to make room for a railway. The actual facts on which this story is based cannot now be verified, though there seems to be some truth in this version of how the first cedar of Lebanon arrived in France.

In Britain, the tree has been more valued in the past than it is today ; so now we see many specimens disappearing from our midst with little effort to replace them. The sacred associations of the tree no doubt explains why it is so often seen in cemeteries and churchyards, bishops' palace grounds and the lawns of country parsonages. Even in this country, the tree is a very quick grower, and several grand specimens have figured in the history of British arboriculture. Those which were planted in the Apothecaries Garden at Chelsea in 1683 have now disappeared. The famous Enfield Cedar was planted in the grounds of Enfield Manor House by Dr. Uvedale, a master of Enfield Grammar School, also in the seventeenth century ; but, alas, this was felled in 1927. Still other handsome cedars of Lebanon are with us, and it is to be hoped that, unless necessity absolutely demands, they will be preserved, and above all that more will be planted if only for ornament and umbrage.

Harold Bastin

Deodar or Indian Cedar.

INDIAN CEDAR OR DEODAR

Like the cedar of Lebanon, the Indian cedar (or deodar) (*C. deodara*) grows in Britain solely as an ornamental tree, though in its native Himalayas it achieves gigantic proportions and thrives under forestry conditions, yielding a valuable and durable timber. It has been used considerably for the building of Indian temples and palaces.

The botanical distinction between this cedar and the cedar of Lebanon is, as already stated, very slight ; but the branches of the former are less long and spreading, and the result is a tree of more pyramidal form.

The tree was introduced into Britain in 1831 by the Hon. William L. Melville and later in larger quantities by the East India Company, in the hope that the timber resources of Britain would be amplified. But this hope was never realised. All the same, the deodar, even in Britain, is a lovely tree and frequently attains a height of 50 feet or more.

It is not possible to distinguish between the timbers of the four recognised forms of cedar. That of the deodar (*C. deodara*) is the only kind imported to any extent into Britain, though certain quantities of the timber of the Algerian cedar (*C. atlantica*) are also imported. The wood of these true cedars is useful for indoor decorative work ; that imported is very durable.

10

LARCHES

(*Abietaceae*)

It seems incredible to at any rate one lover of graceful trees that the writer of the lines :

> To the solid ground
> Of nature trusts the Mind that builds for aye ;
> Convinced that there, there only, she can lay
> Secure foundations.

could ever pen a deprecatory description of such a lovely thing as a larch tree. Yet Wordsworth—to use his own words, " So long a worshipper of Nature "—did so in the following words : " the Larch, till it has outgrown the size of a shrub, shews, when looked at singly, some elegance in form and appearance, especially in spring, decorated as it then is by the pink tassels of its blossoms ; but, as a tree, it is less than any other pleasing. Its branches (for boughs it has none) have no variety in the youth of the tree, and little dignity even when it attains its full growth. Leaves it cannot be said to have ; and consequently it affords neither shade nor shelter. In spring the Larch becomes green long before the native trees ; and its green is so peculiar and vivid, that finding nothing to harmonize with it wherever it comes forth, a disagreeable speck is produced." For some reason or other, the great Nature poet was hypersensitive about the larch ; but few could agree with him entirely. Of course the larch is not dignified, but its slender drooping branches in tall pyramidal form are most certainly graceful ; and it is difficult to consider any larch tree (unless it be some monstrosity) a " disagreeable speck " in any environment. Furthermore, surely we do not appreciate trees solely for the " shade and shelter " they might offer us.

The larches form a small group of conifers comprising the genus *Larix*, though one exotic form is sufficiently different to warrant another genus, *Pseudolarix* (see p. 84). All larches differ from the firs in that their leaves are completely deciduous, thus making the tree quite bare of foliage during the winter. Furthermore, unlike the firs, the larch leaves, though borne singly on the younger shoots, are grouped in pronounced whorls or tufts on the older shoots, each tuft growing at the end of a very short shoot (p. 82). There are about thirty needles to each tuft. Larches differ from the cedars not only in the deciduous character of the leaves, but also in the scaly, membranous nature of their cones. The larches are the only deciduous conifers in Britain.

EUROPEAN LARCH

There are about a dozen species of larch distributed throughout Asia, Europe and North America. The **European larch** (*Larix decidua* or *europaea*) is the most common larch in Britain. This species is also very abundant on the Continent, especially in Switzerland, where it is a striking feature of the Alpine scenery, and there are large forests of it in the U.S.S.R. It is also very common in Central Europe. It is essentially a tree of mountainous areas, where it grows at an altitude as high as seven thousand feet.

The European larch is a tall and stately tree, pyramidal in shape, with very slender branches borne in attractive, pendulous whorls. Actually, the branches begin horizontally from the trunk, then droop and

Winter.   Summer.

Harold Bastin

Larch.

eventually curve upwards towards their tips. The tree attains a height of anything from 80 to 140 feet. Its trunk becomes comparatively stout if the tree has plenty of space in which to grow; but more often in Britain the trunk is slender because the trees are cultivated in plantations or form large woods. The bark is dull red in colour, and is deeply fissured in older trees.

The larch does not begin bearing flowers until it is about twenty years of age. The male flowers open out in the spring (April and May) just at about the same time that the new leaves are beginning to develop.

> I have looked on the hills of the stormy North,
> And the larch has hung his tassels forth.
> *The Voice of Spring* : FELICIA D. HEMANS

The male flower is composed of a mass of golden yellow stamens cupped in a number of scales (Plate 2). The female flowers are very conspicuous, taking the form of bright red catkins (Plate 2). Sprays of larch bearing these red catkins in the spring make a particularly charming sight. The female flowers are pollinated and fertilised, and

Harold Bastin

Old Cones of Larch.

also become ripe during the first year. The brown, ovoid cones also develop during the same year, towards the autumn. Each cone eventually attains a length of about an inch and has membranous scales quite unlike those of the pines. The cones seldom open to release their winged seeds until the spring of the following year, when the weather is dry. Sometimes, however, if the weather is particularly fine, they release their seeds during the autumn of the first year. After the seeds have been disseminated, the old cones remain on the tree for several years. They are quite a pleasing sight.

The larch was introduced into Britain from the Continent early in the seventeenth century, but it was used for nothing but ornamental purposes for the whole of that century and well into the next. During this time it seemed to catch a morbid side of the imagination of the public and, like the cedar of Lebanon, was often planted in churchyards. Then, during the last quarter of the eighteenth century, some people, encouraged by the Society of Arts, began a more extensive planting of this tree with the view of obtaining a useful timber. Even earlier than this, in 1728 (according to Step in his *Wayside and Woodland Trees*, revised by A. K. and A. B. Jackson), the Duke of Atholl began cultivating larch on a big scale until, during the time of the fourth Duke, fifteen thousand acres of barren land became populated by twenty-seven million larch trees. Since those days, the cultivation in Britain of larch (especially under the auspices of the Forestry Commission) has met with outstanding success, though the tree does best in forests mixed with broad-leaved trees rather than in pure forest. It requires plenty of sunlight.

Nevertheless, it must not be thought that the larch can be cultivated with little or no attention, for it has its enemies from which it needs protection. It is seldom subject to such attacks in its native Switzerland and Bavaria. Several insect pests are responsible for severe depredation of larch trees; among these are the wood-wasp (*Sirex* species), the larvae of which penetrate the wood, and the larch-miner (*Coleophora* species), the larvae of which attack the leaves. Perhaps the most destructive disease is larch canker caused by the attack of a fungus (*Dasyscypha* species) through wounds and cracks in the bark. This results in serious deformations of trunks and branches wherever the disease occurs.

The durable timber is yellowish if taken from the sap-wood; but the dry heart-wood is red. Since it can withstand unfavourable weather conditions it is much in demand for outdoor constructional purposes. It is also immune to the effect of immersion under water. It is therefore frequently used for various forms of marine construction especially since it is not very prone to splitting. On the Continent (especially in certain parts of Switzerland) it is used for constructing log-houses, and most of the buildings in Venice are constructed on larch piles. Bridges were built of larch wood even in the times of the ancient Greeks and Romans.

A good turpentine can be extracted from larch trees which have grown in warm sunny climes, as in Switzerland and other parts of Europe, especially around Venice.

OTHER SPECIES OF LARCH

Apart from the European larch (*Larix decidua* or *europaea*), which is extremely common in Britain, certain other species are sometimes cultivated in this country, the most popular of which is the **Japanese larch** (*L. kaempferi*). It is not such a tall or strong tree: but it is sometimes grown for its ornamental beauty, and in certain areas it is cultivated in plantations because it is of quicker growth than the European species. Its leaves are not of such a bright green colour. Its cultivation in Britain is now being exploited by the Forestry Commission.

There is also a hybrid larch (*L. eurolepis*), the result of a chance crossing between the European and Japanese larches in Scotland. It is somewhat variable, but in general character is intermediate between the two original parents. No doubt other examples of this hybrid will appear where the European and Japanese larches are growing together or near each other.

Certain other exotic larches are cultivated in Britain for ornamental purposes, but none is common. One of the most beautiful is the very rare **weeping larch** (*L. pendula*). Then there is the **golden larch** (*Pseudolarix amabilis*) from China, whose beautiful light green foliage turns a golden colour before falling in the autumn.

Only a few dwarf varieties of larch exist and none of these is extensively cultivated in British gardens.

II

ABIES FIRS

(*Abietaceae*)

> I love to lie, when lulling breezes stir
> The spiry cones that tremble on the fir.
>
> *Noontide* : J. LEYDEN

The name ' fir ' is still vague in meaning because throughout history it has been applied to many different conifers. In fact, it is still often loosely applied to all coniferous trees. The name was probably originally given to the Scots pine, when it was known as Scotch fir (p. 89) : but now it seems better to confine it to the genus *Abies* of the family ABIETACEAE, at any rate when no other distinguishing word is also used, such as in the case of the spruce firs or the Douglas firs.

The leaves of firs are borne separately on the stem, in contradistinction to those of the pines which are borne sheathed in groups of two, three, four or five, and of the cedars and the larches which grow in clusters of many. The trunk is very tall and straight, and the branches are given off in whorls. The leaves are arranged spirally on long shoots, and when they fall or are pulled off they leave distinct scars on the stem. The cones are usually erect and their scales are membranous, overlapping each other like the tiles of a roof. Beneath each bract on the cone there is often a large scale. After the cone has ripened and the seeds disseminated, the scales drop off, leaving the bare axis of the cone still on the branch where it remains for a long time.

The firs are distributed spasmodically throughout the northern hemisphere. There are about thirty species altogether, and some varieties have arisen through accidental crossing or controlled scientific breeding.

SILVER FIR

It is possible that the tree recorded by John Evelyn, the great seventeenth-century diarist and man of science, in his classic book on trees, *Sylva*, as having been planted in Harefield Park in 1603 was the first specimen of **silver fir** (*Abies alba* or *A. pectinata*) to appear in Britain. The tree is now distributed throughout the whole of Europe except the very north. It is abundant in the Caucasus and the Ural Mountains, and there are extensive forests of it in the Alps, the Rhine Valley, the Black Forest, the Vosges and the Pyrenees. In Germany it is known to reach a height of 200 feet; but the average height in Britain is 80 feet, though specimens up to 150 feet are known.

The tall, tapering trunk of the silver fir has a smooth bark of a greyish-brown colour. The lowest whorls of branches begin to fall off after about fifty years, and from then on the tree begins to lose its pyramidal form and assumes a more flattened crown.

The leaves are about an inch long and are arranged spirally but in distinct longitudinal rows on the stem. They are not arranged radially, but are almost completely flattened into one horizontal plane (p. 86 and Plate 2). Each leaf lasts from six to nine years on the tree.

The male flowers (p. 86 and Plate 2) are about three-quarters of an inch long and comprise a collection of stamens enclosed at the base in a cup of scales. The young female flowers, which are produced on the same tree as the male, are longer (p. 86 and Plate 2). The very attractive ripe cone is upright and about eight inches in length. Beneath each scale is a pronounced pointed bract which is visible externally because it is longer than the scale itself and ultimately turns downwards (p. 86 and Plate 2). The cone is at first green, but eventually turns brown when ripe, that is, within two years. Although the silver fir does not produce fertile cones until it is about forty years old, seedless cones make their appearance on a tree no more than twenty years old.

Foliage and Cones of Silver Fir.
Male flowers are borne at the tips, and female flowers on the sides of the shoot. A large ripe cone is also shown.

Unfortunately the young trees are so often attacked by an insect (*Chermes*) that foresters have not felt very disposed to plant them extensively as a commercial proposition, which is a pity, because, given adequate protection against disease, it would well repay cultivation since, after about the first ten years of life, it grows quickly and then produces a clean bole 9 feet in circumference yielding much useful timber. This is soft in texture and yellowish in colour and useful mainly for indoor work since it cannot withstand extremes of weather.

Large amounts of resin collect in the trunk during the summer months and this is sometimes extracted and refined as Strasbourg turpentine.

The silver fir has been valued as an ornamental and timber-yielding tree for many centuries. Virgil greatly admired it, and the Romans used it extensively for ship-building. Pliny also refers to it; he records that the ship used for removing an obelisk from Egypt to Rome had a mast twenty-four feet in circumference made of silver fir.

From the abundant silver fir forests on the Continent, much timber has been obtained in the past and used not only for ship-building but also for under-water constructional purposes, since this timber withstands prolonged immersion. For centuries the Dutch have taken advantage of this fact.

Apart from its timber and the turpentine, this fir has proved valuable in other respects. The bark has been used for tanning leather, especially in Switzerland, and in times past the young cones were boiled to a pulp and then treated with sugar to make a sweetmeat.

GIANT FIR

The **giant** or **grand fir** (*A. grandis*) is a native of North America, and today it is largely taking the place of the silver fir in European forestry. In America it is known as the **Oregon** or **white fir,** and it thrives throughout the north of that country, spreading so far south as California.

Like those of the silver fir, the leaves of the giant fir lie flat on the horizontal branches. There are two types of leaves—long and short, the former being much larger than those of silver fir ; and the buds, in contradistinction to those of the silver fir, are resinous.

In its native country this, the tallest of all the *Abies* firs, reaches a height of 250 feet, though, as might be expected, specimens in Britain fall far short of this. Nevertheless, many giant firs in Britain exceed 100 feet in height. It does very well in this country, so one might look forward with confidence to extended cultivation of this valuable timber-yielding (none the less ornamental) tree.

OTHER *ABIES* FIRS

The silver fir and the giant fir are the only two *Abies* firs usually cultivated in Britain for economic purposes. But, together with these two, several others (chiefly indigenous to the United States) are grown in parks and gardens for their ornamental beauty.

The **Japanese common silver fir** or **nikko fir** (*A. brachyphylla*) hails from Japan and is a hardy and adaptable species. Somewhat similar, though not so well adapted to conditions in Britain, is the **Indian silver fir** (*A. webbiana*).

The **Colorado fir** (*A. concolor*) is a beautiful tree which attains a height of 80 feet in this country. It has very lovely glaucous green foliage. The leaves are arranged irregularly on the stem, not following any particular pattern.

Abies firma is another Japanese importation, and is quite hardy and of vigorous growth.

The well-known **Balsam fir** (*A. balsamea*) of the eastern United States, from which Canada balsam is obtained, does not thrive in Britain ; but the smaller **southern balsam fir** or **she-balsam** (*A. fraseri*) of the Allegheny Mountains is sometimes cultivated in this country.

The beautiful *A. forrestii* was introduced into Britain from western

G

China. Its foliage is of a rich green colour above and bright silver beneath.

The **red fir of California** (*A. magnifica*), native to the mountains of south-western Oregon, northern and eastern California and western Nevada, is a lovely tree with curved glaucous foliage. It is not very successful in Britain, though it may be seen here and there in parks and gardens.

The **noble fir** (*A. nobilis*) is a tree of dense habit, having light green foliage which is silver beneath. It is indigenous to Washington, Oregon, and northern California, where it forms large forests. Like those of *A. magnifica*, the upper leaves on the horizontal branches have characteristically recurved tips. The cones of the noble fir are very large and globular. The tree is grown in Britain for ornamental purposes only, though it thrives so well here that its commercial possibilities might well be considered. There is also a glaucous blue form of this tree, *A. nobilis* var. *glauca*.

The **Algerian fir** (*A. numidica*), one of the rare North African conifers, is quite successful as an ornamental tree in Britain.

The **Caucasian fir** (*A. nordmanniana*) is a hardy, rapidly growing tree with dark glossy foliage, silver beneath. It is a native of the Crimea and the Caucasus, but is very susceptible to insect pests, such as *Chermes* (p. 86). Closely resembling this tree is the **amabilis fir** (*A. amabilis*) which is indigenous to the Cascade Mountains of California.

The **pinsapo** or **Spanish fir** (*A. pinsapo*) has dark green foliage which is not flattened but is arranged radially on the stems. It hails from the Sierra Nevada and thrives in the limestone areas of southern England.

A. veitchii, from Japan, is not common in Britain, but it is none the less attractive, especially by virtue of the silver streaks on the under surfaces of the leaves.

The **Greek fir** (*A. cephalonica*) has very sharply pointed leaves. It is hardy throughout Britain, though not common.

There is a dwarf form of the silver fir, namely *A. alba* (or *pectinata*) var. *compacta* which forms a round bush, but under cultivation in Britain it tends to revert to the arborescent type. Another dwarf form—of very irregular habit, however—is *A. alba* (or *pectinata*) var. *tortuosa*; its branches are very twisted. Of the several dozen other dwarf forms of almost every species of *Abies*, not one is cultivated in Britain to any extent because they so frequently revert to their specific prototypes.

Some other exotic species of *Abies* firs are also cultivated in Britain, though solely for ornamental purposes.

12

SPRUCE FIRS
(*Abietaceae*)

In the literature of today and of the past, the term 'fir' (like other common names applied to coniferous trees) has been very loosely applied. Johns, for example, used the common name 'Scotch fir' for the Scots pine. Even today, the term 'fir', without any other qualifying name might mean one of several totally different kinds of conifers; so in this book we are not using the term alone (except in Chapter 11), thus, it is hoped, reducing the confusion to a minimum.

The spruce firs were at one time placed in the genus *Abies* (p. 84), but now they are all included in the genus *Picea*, the name given them by the classic authors. In fact, the genus *Picea* contains nothing but spruce firs, and there are altogether about forty species of them.

COMMON OR NORWAY SPRUCE

The **common** or **Norway spruce** is one of the most familiar coniferous trees in Britain today (p. 90). The botanical name now accepted for it by international agreement is *Picea abies*, though it is still frequently referred to as *Picea excelsa*.

This tree is the 'Christmas tree' so beloved at that festive season by children of all ages. The origin of the use of the Christmas tree as such is somewhat obscure because it dates back to antiquity. There seems little doubt, however, that the use at Christmas time of some form of tree, as also the maypole, is reminiscent of the Scandinavian ash, known as the Tree of Time. The Egyptians, on the other hand, used branches of palm, during their winter solstice festivities, each branch bearing twelve leaves representing the completion of the year. Then, of course, the Romans, during their Saturnalian celebrations, used evergreens; and many of our Christmas customs have been brought forward from those pre-Christian days.

The modern custom of using the actual spruce fir for Christmas is of Teutonic origin. According to an old German legend a forester and his family were sitting around their fire one wild winter night when

Harold Bastin

Common or Norway Spruce.

a knock came on the door. When the peasant answered it he was surprised to find a child, shivering with the cold, tired out and hungry. The man took the child in, and decided to keep him there for the night. His wife gave the child some warm milk, and when the question of a bed for him arose, Hans, the peasant's son, gave up his own and he himself slept on the floor. In the morning the peasant awoke to glorious singing outside as if the cottage were surrounded by some celestial choir. Then he looked at his little visitor and saw his face was dazzling in its brightness. It was the Christ-Child Himself. As the Child departed from the cottage He tore a bough from a nearby fir tree and planted it firmly in the ground, telling the peasant that for his kindness the tree would always bring him abundance in the depths of winter.

The practice of decorating the spruce tree at Christmas time is certainly Teutonic in origin. In Germany it is usually placed in the window when illuminated. There was a time when in Germany it was also decorated with lights and placed in the streets at Christmas time; some even placed an illuminated tree on the graves of their relatives on appropriate days.

> And now the fir tree . . .
> Acclaimed by eager, blue-eyed girls and boys,
> Bursts into tinsel fruit and glittering toys,
> And turns into a pyramid of light.
> EUGENE LEE-HAMILTON

Owing to the religious significance of the custom, only presents which bring joy and pleasure should be hung on the Christmas tree. Purely utilitarian gifts should be placed around its base as in the days of old.

Though it is known that Prince Albert set up a Christmas tree at Windsor in 1841, it is not true that this was the first occasion in Britain, for Princess Lieven did so in this country several years before (see Greville's Diary). Though in Britain the tree is usually set up indoors, in the New World it is frequently placed outside the door where its bright illuminations give a festive and welcoming air to the whole house.

The Norway spruce is distributed throughout Europe except Holland and Denmark. Although ages ago it was prevalent in Britain (according to fossil evidence), it was re-introduced probably just before the sixteenth century. The tree is indigenous to Europe only, though it now grows in the eastern United States also.

In the mountainous regions of Norway, Sweden, Finland, the U.S.S.R., Central Europe and Switzerland, this tree often reaches a height of 200 feet; but in Britain, though it frequently achieves 120 to 150 feet, its average height is round about 80 feet with a bole about 10 feet in circumference.

The tree assumes a pyramidal form with a pronounced leading shoot—rather different in this respect from the silver fir.

> Out of the golden-green and white
> Of the brake the fir-trees stand upright
> In the forest of flame, and wave aloft
> To the blue of heaven their blue-green tuftings soft.
>
> ROBERT BRIDGES

The bark is brownish, thin and scaly. The roots are very shallow and the upper ones may often be seen above the ground-level acting as buttresses to the trunk. In spite of the latter, and because of the former, the tree frequently succumbs to fierce gales. The branches come off from the trunk in regular whorls.

The dark green leaves are almost an inch long and each remains on the tree for about six years. They are arranged on the stem in a spiral fashion; but owing to a twist in their bases they lie more or less in a horizontal plane which, however, is not so pronounced as in the silver fir.

The flowers are borne on last year's shoots (p. 93 and Plate 2). The male flowers are about three-quarters of an inch long and occur singly or in groups of two or three (p. 93 and Plate 2). The female flowers (p. 93 and Plate 2) are at first green and form erect cones. Later, the fertilised cones become larger and pendulous—another distinction from the silver fir in which the cones are more or less erect. The ripe cones are not so elongated as those of the silver fir. The

Foliage and Cones of Common or Norway Spruce.
The male flowers are at or near the tips ; the female further down the shoot.
Two ripe cones are also shown.

scales are thin and, though they overlap, they are rather loosely arranged.
The seeds are ripe about a year after the flowers have been formed. The
old cones remain on the tree several years after the seeds have been
disseminated and then eventually fall off intact.

Unlike many conifers, the spruce fir is tolerant of deep shade,
though when tucked among other trees it tends to lose its lowest
branches. In its first years it is slow in growth, but later it grows at a
rate of about three feet a year, especially if growing on light, moist soil.

The timber of the Norway spruce fir is tough but rough, and is
therefore used for many general purposes such as telegraph poles,
scaffolding, planks for all kinds of uses, packing-cases, and so forth.
Commercially it has several names such as ' spruce fir ', ' white deal ',
' Baltic whitewood ', ' northern whitewood ', ' white ', etc. From this
galaxy of names, it is easily deduced that the wood is white in colour.
The wood is also used for making cheap kinds of paper. In northern
European countries, however, the spruce fir is one of the most important

economic forest trees. It is also grown as a nurse for other trees, as a shelter for crops and for ornamental purposes.

The resin extracted by tapping living trees is called Burgundy pitch, and this is used in making varnish. In Germany and the surrounding countries, a drink called spruce beer is brewed from its leaves and branches with the help of sugar, water and other ingredients. This concoction is supposed to have medicinal properties.

SITKA SPRUCE

The **Sitka spruce** (*P. sitchensis*) was brought to Britain little more than a century ago. It is native to the Pacific coast of North America, stretching from Alaska to northern California. It is abundant in Alaska whence its common name ' Sitka ' is derived, though there and elsewhere it is sometimes called the **tideland spruce.** Since it was discovered by Archibald Menzies, it is sometimes called the **Menzies spruce,** though this name is no longer encouraged. Another synonym is **silver spruce.**

Though the Sitka spruce is by no means as common in Britain as the Norway spruce, its cultivation is now being encouraged by the Forestry Commission, for it is a quick grower in the most trying conditions. However, though specimens here have exceeded 100 feet in height, the tree never reaches the dimensions in Britain that it does in its native America where it is the largest of the spruces, often growing nearly 200 feet high.

Apart from its massiveness, it is not difficult to distinguish the Sitka spruce from the Norway spruce because the needles are stiffer and very pointed and they have a bluish tinge. Although the adult tree is handsome in its very massiveness, the young tree is rather misshapen and ugly. The cones are rather small—about two inches long.

The whitish wood is very strong yet light, so it is particularly valuable in joinery and in the building of aircraft and making plywood. It is also used in the United States for the production of wood-pulp.

OTHER SPRUCE FIRS

No other spruce firs are cultivated in Britain for economic purposes, but several species are grown for their ornamental effect. Among these is the very lovely **weeping spruce** (*P. morinda*), a native of the Himalayas. The **Serbian spruce** (*P. omorika*) is also popular on account of its dark green leaves and its rapid growth. The distinctive **blue spruce** (*P. pungens*), of the Rocky Mountains, is of splendid pyramidal form, and attains a height of 80 feet. There are also some varieties of this tree, attractive by virtue of their foliage covered with a blue-white bloom, for example, *P. pungens* var. *glauca* and *P. pungens* var. *kosteriana*.

The **tiger tail spruce** (*P. polita*), of Japan, is another pronounced pyramidal form, and,

Harold Bastin

Picea abies var. *dumosa.*

though small, it is suitable for isolated growth in landscape architecture. Other pyramidal forms, attractive in isolation, are *P. hondoensis*, of Japan, the **oriental spruce** (*P. orientalis*), and *P. albertiana*.

Then there are the very intriguing dwarf spruces, especially suitable for rock gardens. There are more than fifty different forms of these, some of which are extremely popular. The favourites are *P. pygmaea* of dense habit, *P. pumila*, *P. abies* var. *dumosa*, and *P. abies* var. *remontii*, the last-named being perhaps the most popular of all.

13

DOUGLAS FIRS

(*Abietaceae*)

The **Douglas fir** belongs to the small genus *Pseudotsuga*, which is indigenous to North America and eastern Asia, though it is in the United States that the best-known species, *Pseudotsuga taxifolia*, grows. This species is one of the most magnificent of trees ; but impressive though it is by the very fact of its tremendous height, it can scarcely be called beautiful.

In its native habitat this tree is sometimes also known as **red fir, yellow fir** and **Douglas spruce** : no doubt the last name can be attri-

E.N.A.

Lumbering Douglas Firs in Washington State, U.S.A.

buted to the fact that this fir more closely resembles the spruce firs than it does the *Abies* firs. In America the tree flourishes from the State of South Dakota in the west to as far as British Columbia in the north, and then to the south reaching Texas and Mexico. It is at its best in the two far-western States of Washington and Oregon, where it is frequently referred to as the **Oregon pine.** In the United States, the Douglas fir is the second tallest tree, the giant *Sequoias* or redwoods being the tallest of all.

The common name, 'Douglas fir', might conceivably be attributed to the supposition that the tree was discovered by David Douglas (1798-1834), the Scottish botanist who visited the State of Oregon and British Columbia, among others, in search of new plants on behalf of the Royal Horticultural Society. But though his name was given to the tree by the British botanist, Dr. John Lindley, the supposition would be wrong, for Archibald Menzies first collected parts of the tree and thus brought it to the knowledge of botanists in the Old World in 1792,

The Director, Royal Botanic Gardens, Kew

The Flagstaff at the Royal Botanic Gardens, Kew.
This is from a Douglas fir presented by the Government of British Columbia.

when he accompanied Vancouver on his visits to the western United States. Douglas was, however, the first to send seeds of the tree to Britain in 1828. Though the botanical name *Pseudotsuga douglasii* has been given to the tree, priority demands that the designation *P. taxifolia* be now accepted.

In its native habitats, the Douglas fir varies considerably in dimensions. In the forests of Washington State it often reaches a height of 250 feet, with a girth of 36 feet. There, trees so high as 300 feet have been seen. These trees are therefore more than twice the height of Nelson's Column in Trafalgar Square and would even overshadow the Boston Stump. Trees even much loftier than this have been seen, some of them almost reaching the height of the Spire of Salisbury Cathedral which is a little over 400 feet. Specimens have been known to be more than 750 years old. But further north in America, especially in the Rockies, where conditions are drier, the tree seldom surpasses 100 feet. A clearer idea of the size of these plants, which might seem almost incredible to the average Briton so used to much smaller trees, can be gleaned from a visit to the British Museum (Natural History), to the museums in the Royal Botanic Gardens, Kew, and to other museums in Britain, where sections of large trunks are exhibited. An even clearer conception can be obtained from the famous flag-staff at Kew Gardens, which is a landmark for miles around. This flagstaff is of Douglas fir and replaces a smaller one (also of the same

Douglas Fir growing in Britain.

Eric J. Hosking

wood). The present one was presented by the Government of British Columbia, and was erected in 1919. It is 214 feet high, nearly a yard in diameter at the base and a foot at the top, and weighs eighteen tons.

Though a large number of these trees have been planted in Britain during the past hundred years and more, it is obviously still too early to say with any degree of precision what dimensions it might attain under British conditions. Some specimens are already proving themselves quite acclimatised, one at Powys Castle being about 170 feet high and therefore one of the tallest trees in Britain. Another at West Dean in Sussex is nearly 160 feet high.

Foliage and Ripe Cone of Douglas Fir. Note the long, pointed buds on the shoot; and the three-toothed bracts on the cone.

In Britain the Douglas fir assumes a pyramidal form, though in America, where it grows so much higher and is closely accompanied by others of its kind, the nether branches drop off and then the trunk stands out boldly. In this country the tree thrives best in moist soil though it is very resistant to dry conditions; in fact it will grow in many parts of the country where other kinds of trees would not thrive at all.

The branches of the tree are arranged in more or less horizontal whorls which droop somewhat. The branches are covered with bright green needles about an inch long. These are spirally arranged on the stem; but, like those of the silver fir, they are so twisted as to fall in a pronounced horizontal plane.

A distinguishing feature of the Douglas fir is the buds, which are extremely long and pointed. The male flowers are borne on the underside of last year's shoots, usually in clusters. The cone, which first appears when the tree is about fifteen years old, grows at or near the tips of new branches, and is pendulous. The ripe cone is anything up to four inches long. A very diagnostic feature of the long loose scales is the bract which develops behind them. Each bract takes the form of a three-toothed extension, the middle tooth being much longer than the other two ; but the entire bract is longer than the scale so that the former projects beyond the latter and is clearly visible on superficial examination of the cone.

The Douglas fir is another conifer very prone to attack by the insect *Chermes* (p. 86).

The timber is very tough and resinous. It is yellowish in colour, though the heart-wood is yellow or red. In America it is used for all kinds of constructional purposes—telegraph poles, railway wagons, pit-props, buildings, plywood, furniture, etc.—and for paper-making.

It should have been made clear from this account of the Douglas fir that here we have an American tree which will undoubtedly do well as a timber-yielding tree in Britain. Those particularly interested in this tree as a cultivated forest tree are recommended to read an account of it by E. R. Yarham in the *Gardeners' Chronicle* of November 4, 1944. It has been grown in Britain for more than a century, and the first tree is mentioned by H. J. Elwes, the great British arboriculturist, and Prof. A. Henry in their *Trees of Great Britain and Ireland*. The Forestry Commission has proved itself alive to the possibilities of this remarkable tree, and before the War, one eighth of the coniferous trees used for afforestation were Douglas firs. As Mr. Yarham claims, it has greater commercial possibilities than any other conifer, so in view of the considerable demands for all sorts of timber which will surely be made for many years during the immediate future, it is good to know that the Douglas fir is being given a chance in Britain.

OTHER DOUGLAS FIRS

There is another species of *Pseudotsuga* in America—the **big-cone spruce** (*P. macrocarpa*), which is considerably smaller. It is indigenous to southern California ; but it has not found favour in Britain.

The **blue Douglas fir** (*P. glauca*), also of America, has handsome glaucous foliage, though, despite its name, it is not easy to distinguish its foliage from that of *P. taxifolia*. The blue Douglas fir is sometimes cultivated in British parks and gardens for ornamental purposes, and there is an attractive variety of it, *P. glauca* var. *elegans*, having pendulous branches. Another rarer form, suitable for rock gardens, is a variety of *P. taxifolia*, namely, *P. taxifolia* var. *fletcheri*, which grows to a height of about two feet and also has handsome glaucous green foliage. Many other dwarf varieties of both *P. taxifolia* and *P. glauca* are known.

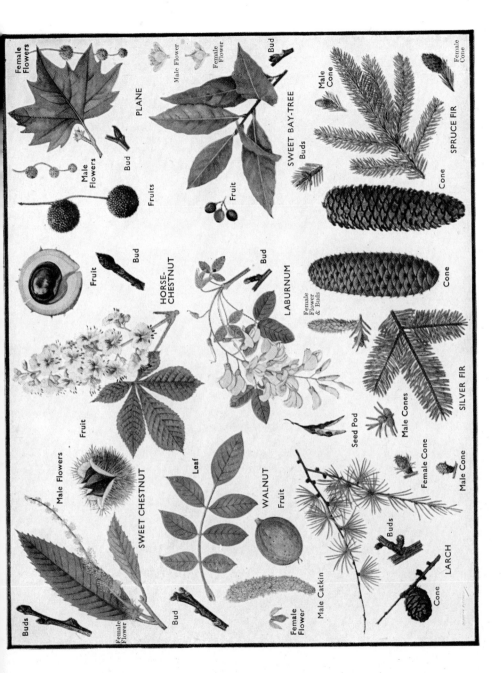

Female Flowers

PLANE

Male Flower

Female Flower

Bud

Male Flowers

Bud

Fruits

SWEET BAY-TREE

Fruit

Buds

Male Cone

Female Cone

SPRUCE FIR

Cone

Fruit

Bud

HORSE-CHESTNUT

Bud

LABURNUM

Cone

Female Flower & Buds

Cone

Male Flowers

Fruit

SILVER FIR

Leaf

Seed Pod

Male Cones

SWEET CHESTNUT

WALNUT

Fruit

Female Cone

Male Cone

Buds

Female Flower

Male Catkin

Bud

Buds

Female Flower

Bud

LARCH

Cone

PLATE 2

14

JUNIPERS

(Cupressaceae)

The slope is darkly sprinkled
With ancient junipers,
Each a small, secret tree :
There not a branch stirs.

I fear those waiting shapes
Of wry, blue-berried wood.
They make a twilight in my mind,
As if they drained my blood.

The Junipers : LAURENCE BINYON

The junipers are the first members of the next family of the *Coniferales* to be considered here, namely, CUPRESSACEAE. There are about twenty-two genera and about a hundred and fifty species in this family ; the junipers have been assigned to the genus *Juniperus*. Perhaps the most distinguishing feature of this genus is the succulent fruits, which, as in the case of the yew (p. 116) take the place of the familiar cones of other conifers.

The juniper is mentioned in the Bible, when Elijah was flying from the persecution of Jezebel :

> But he himself went a day's journey into the wilderness, and came and sat down under a juniper tree : and he requested for himself that he might die ;
>
> 1 *Kings*, 14

But it is very probable that the English translation is at fault, for there are no junipers in the Arabian desert. Johns, in his *Forest Trees of Britain*, gives various arguments supporting the view that the tree in question was a species of broom (*Genista*).

There are about forty different species of *Juniperus* spread all over the temperate and sub-arctic zones of the northern hemisphere. They are most abundant around the Mediterranean, in the islands of the North Atlantic and in the United States—chiefly on the eastern side. The only species native to Britain is the common juniper and a variety.

Common Juniper on Box Hill, Surrey.

COMMON JUNIPER

The **common juniper** (*Juniperus communis*) is not only native to Britain but is also widely distributed elsewhere. It occurs abundantly over northern Europe, northern Asia and North America, where it is sometimes known as the **ground cedar**. In southern Europe it also thrives high up in the mountains, such as the Alps, the Apennines and the Pyrenees. In Britain it occurs chiefly as a shrub, though it sometimes assumes the habit of a small tree. It does best on the chalk downs of southern England and in the mountains of Wales and Scotland.

> Of all the trees in England,
> Past frankincense and myrrh,
> There's none for smell, of bloom and smoke,
> Like Lime and Juniper.
>
> *Trees* : WALTER DE LA MARE

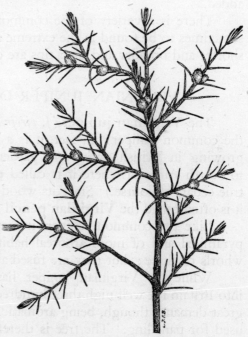

The needles of the common juniper are particularly sharp and are borne on the stem in whorls of three. The whole tree, especially the leaves, is aromatic. The bark is of a reddish colour and frequently scales off the trunk.

The juniper is unisexual and the male and female flowers are most often borne on separate plants. The male flowers take the form of small greenish catkins ; but the yellow pollen is very evident when it is ripe in May (Plate 3). The female flowers are greenish and compact (Plate 3), and are borne in the axils of leaves, thus forming groups of three on the stem where they occur. Surrounding the female flower are

Shoot of Common Juniper in Fruit.

fleshy scales (Plate 3), and after fertilisation the upper scales become even more fleshy and eventually form a structure resembling a berry (Plate 3). The lower scales usually remain as they are. The berry is

H

at first green, and remains so during the first year; then in the second year it turns a deep blue covered with ' bloom ' (Plate 3).

Whereas some foreign junipers are sufficiently large and tree-like to yield useful timbers, the common juniper in Britain is practically useless in this respect, though its wood is sometimes used for ornamental work. Nevertheless, the common juniper has its uses, for a strong diuretic, oil of juniper, is extracted from the berries. These are also used for flavouring gin. In fact, the name ' gin ' is abbreviated from ' geneva ' which is in turn a corruption of *genièvre*, the French for juniper, or *junever* its Dutch equivalent. The utilisation of juniper berries in the making of gin dates back many centuries, and it may be that the popularity of this beverage throughout the centuries is due to the diuretic effect of the juniper extract present in it. British gin is prepared by distilling a fermenting mixture of maize, rye and malt. Then the resulting liquid is redistilled after juniper and sometimes coriander have been added.

There is a variety of the common juniper, *J. communis* var. *nana*, sometimes to be found in the extreme north of Britain. The leaves are shorter and broader and their tips are curved backwards.

VIRGINIAN JUNIPER OR PENCIL CEDAR

The **Virginian juniper** (*J. virginiana*) is a much larger plant than the common juniper; in fact, it is a tree. It may frequently be seen growing in British parks and gardens, though it is actually native to North America where it is called **eastern red cedar.** (It is not a true cedar, of course.) Since its wood is used in the making of pencils it is often called the **Virginian pencil cedar.**

Like the common juniper, it may be short and shrubby or tall, pyramidal and of more arboreal habit. Its leaves, too, are borne in whorls of three; but they are fused at their bases.

While the Virginian juniper has been imported spasmodically into Britain for well-nigh three hundred years, it has never been in very great demand, though, being aromatic, the wood has on occasion been used for panelling. The tree is therefore seen mainly as a decorative plant in Britain, though in its native America, where it usually attains a height of 40-50 feet, it is cultivated for its timber, used in pencil-making and for fences, etc. In this respect, the Virginian juniper is now supplanting the juniper from Bermuda (*J. bermudiana*)—a tree at one time extensively used for making pencils.

OTHER USEFUL AND ORNAMENTAL JUNIPERS

Several other species of *Juniper* are of economic value ; but they are not to be found in Britain since they are intolerant of our soil and climate.

The **savin** (*J. sabina*), native of the mountains of Switzerland and parts of Central Europe, is poisonous, and from it powerful drugs were at one time prepared. The **incense juniper** (*J. thurifera*), a native of the Iberian Peninsula, is sometimes burned as incense, though incense is also prepared from many kinds of wood, bark, dried flowers, fruits and seeds. Cedar-wood oil is extracted not only from *J. virginiana* but also from *J. oxycedrus*, an inhabitant of the Mediterranean regions. The berries of *J. drupacea*, of Asia Minor, are large and edible ; and the American Indians eat those of the **California juniper** (*J. californica*).

Apart from the common juniper, the Virginian juniper and the savin, several other species and many varieties of juniper are frequently grown for ornamental purposes in the parks and gardens of Britain, especially in rock gardens. In fact, there are so many different varieties that only a representative few can be mentioned. The **golden juniper**

Harold Bastin

Juniperus japonica var. *aurea*.

(*J. chinensis* var. *aurea*) is a golden variety of the **Chinese juniper**. It is of a very dense habit. Another variety of the same plant (*J. chinensis* var. *pendula*) is attractive in that the ends of its branches droop. Still another (*J. chinensis* var. *sargentii*) is a creeper and forms a very dense, procumbent growth. *J. japonica* var. *aurea* is another favourite in British rock gardens. A variety of the Virginian juniper (*J. virginiana* var. *glauca*) bears lovely silver-grey foliage which turns green as the year advances towards the autumn.

There are several other variegated, dwarf and compact varieties of juniper, easy to cultivate and very attractive additions to a large or small rock garden. Perhaps the most popular of all is *J. communis* var. *compressa*, a plant which presents itself as a pleasing column of silver-green foliage. *J. communis* var. *nana aurea* is a shrub with pendulous branches bearing golden foliage all the year round. It spreads easily. There are about a score of different dwarf and procumbent varieties of *J. communis*.

A prostrate trailing species of the juniper is *J. horizontalis*, of which there are quite a dozen different varieties.

The pencil cedar (*J. virginiana*) also contributes its share of dwarf bushy and prostrate varieties—quite a dozen altogether ; and the Chinese juniper has given us about two dozen varieties, including those mentioned above.

15

TRUE CYPRESSES

(*Cupressaceae*)

The true cypresses are members of the genera *Cupressus* and *Chamaecyparis* (CUPRESSACEAE)—a genus comprising about a dozen species indigenous to the southern parts of Europe, to Asia and to North America. All are evergreen, aromatic trees. The leaves are very characteristic, being scale-like and closely overlapping each other in four longitudinal rows (though the leaves of the genus *Thuya*, see p. 122, are similar in this respect). The cones are very small, and consist of six to eight scales which are shield-shaped and attached to the axis from their centres. These scales open very widely when the cones are ripe (p. 108).

Most cypresses are tolerant of clipping and cutting back, and for that reason alone, many varieties are popular in the gardens of Britain.

LAWSON CYPRESS

The most well-known cypress in Britain is the **Lawson cypress** (*Chamaecyparis lawsoniana*) which is indigenous to south-western Oregon and north-western California. This tree assumes a beautifully symmetrical pyramidal form, and in its native habitat it attains a height of well over 150 feet, that is, higher than Nelson's Column in Trafalgar Square; and on occasions trees nearly 200 feet high are to be seen.

The Lawson cypress was discovered in the western United States in 1852; there it is usually known as the **Port Orford cedar** (after Port Orford on the Oregon coast where the tree thrives particularly well). It is sometimes also known as the **Oregon cedar**. A few years later, seeds of the tree were sent to Lawson's, the Edinburgh nurserymen, and it was then named after the head of that firm.

In Britain, this tree is grown solely for ornamental purposes, and a handsome sight it makes especially when standing alone or in homogeneous groups in

Eric J. Hosking

Lawson Cypress.

parks, cemeteries, etc. But in this country it usually only grows about half the height that it attains in its native Oregon. Nevertheless it is quite hardy here, and, being tolerant of clipping, and comparatively immune to attack by pests and frosts, is very useful for making ornamental hedges; but it is at its best when standing alone. Unfortunately it grows very slowly.

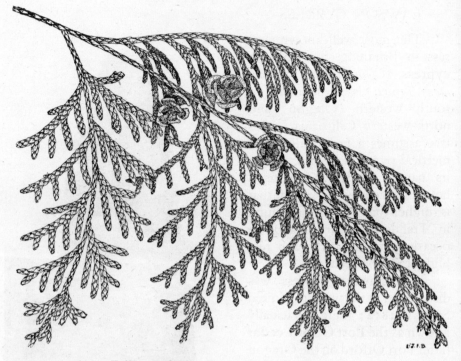

Foliage and Ripe Cones of Lawson Cypress.

Actually the Lawson cypress is quite typical of the genus *Cupressus*. The bark is particularly thick. The leaves are dark green. They are like scales and are arranged along the stem in four rows closely overlapping each other. They remain on the stem for several years, then fall off, not singly, but in small branches. The male flowers are borne at the tips of the young branches and take about a year to mature. They are of a pronounced crimson colour. There are about eight scales on the ripe female cones, and these open very wide to release the ripe seeds.

In the United States, the Lawson cypress is a valuable timber-producing tree. It never grows sufficiently massive in Britain for this purpose, and therefore does not figure in British forestry. Nevertheless, the timber is imported, chiefly from Oregon and California. The timber is yellowish or reddish-brown in colour, and is strong and very durable. Since it stands up well to dampness, it is frequently used for making storage vessels, in shipbuilding and for other purposes where the wood is constantly subjected to high humidity.

OTHER TRUE CYPRESSES

There are several other true cypresses, some of which are cultivated for their ornamental purposes in Britain, but none is of any economic value, at any rate in this country.

The **common** or **Italian cypress** (*C. sempervirens*) is interesting because it is the cypress which has figured so much in prose and poetry since classic times.

> Know ye the land where the cypress and myrtle
> Are emblems of deeds that are done in their clime;
> Where the rage of the vulture, the love of the turtle,
> Now melt into sorrow, now madden to crime?
>
> *The Bride of Abydos* : BYRON

This tree has been known in Mediterranean regions for many centuries, but though it has been cultivated in Britain for well-nigh four hundred years it does not thrive except in the south and the south-west of England. A tall and tapering tree, it attains a height of 90 feet in its native habitat.

Once this tree is cut down it seldom grows again, and this, coupled with the fact that the foliage turns almost black as the tree ages, is the reason why the tree was a symbol of death in classic times. As a tree of death it was dedicated by the Romans to Pluto.

> Cypresse garlands are of great account at funeralls mongst the gentiler sort, but rosemary and bayes are used by the commons both at funeralls and weddings. *Introduction to the Knowledge of Plants* : COLES

For the same symbolic reason, the Italian cypress is sometimes seen growing in cemeteries, though in general it does not take kindly to conditions in Britain. But to the peoples of the past the common cypress was not only symbolic. According to Johns, certain parts of the Temple of Diana at Ephesus were made of cypress wood. So also were the ships with which Alexander the Great formed a huge fleet ; he obtained the timber from Assyria. In this connexion, it is of interest that the theological author Thomas Fuller believed that the " gopher " wood from which Noah's Ark was constructed was really some form of cypress. Johns, too, appears to have believed this, since " being at once light, and not subject to rot, it was often used in ship-building." But it is not likely that this will ever be confirmed, especially in view of the conflicting opinions of other authorities ; for example, Arabian authors claimed it was box-wood ; Bockart considered it was ebony ;

Castellus says it was juniper; the Religious Tract Society believed it to be acacia; and still other authorities suggest pine, deal, cedar, wicker-wood and even bulrushes bound with slime.

The **Monterey cypress** (*C. macrocarpa*) is now very popular in British gardens, both as a solitary tree and for making ornamental hedges. It is native to Monterey in southern California where it became close to extinction. It is, however, one of the finest of the cypresses when growing in its native country, where it attains a height of 150 feet and a girth of 8 to 10 feet. Since it thrives on almost any soil, no matter how poor, and especially near the sea, it is again being cultivated in California, where it is able to withstand the fierce Pacific gales.

Cupressus macrocarpa

Eric. J. Hosking

Among the more ornamental forms of cypress in Britain is the **weeping cypress** (*C. funebris*), of China. This tree is not very hardy, but it makes an attractive indoor tree especially in conservatories and ' winter gardens '. Then there is the **cedar of Goa** (*C. lusitanica*), a native of Mexico. The **sawara cypress** (*C. pisifera*) of Japan and Formosa is represented in British gardens by many varieties, most of which are thin-growing trees.

There is a very large number of different species and varieties of *Cupressus* to be seen under ornamental cultivation in Britain, ranging through colours of blue, green, yellow, gold, variegated, etc. Some are handsome trees, others are dwarfs.

16

YEW

(*Taxaceae*)

The yew tree is massive though never very tall, of a very dark green colour and sombre in aspect. No wonder it is so closely associated with death, for in by-gone days it was used for making the long-bow, and to this day it is frequently seen growing in churchyards and cemeteries. It is almost sinister; or, as Pliny wrote, " neither verdant, nor graceful, but gloomy, terrible, and sapless." Further-more, it is poisonous to man and other animals, especially after the twigs and leaves have been left to ferment for some time. No wonder, therefore, that classic authors such as Caesar, Virgil and Livy and many other poets and writers since their day have associated this tree with mysticism and death.

> Beneath those rugged elms, that yew-tree's shade
> Where heaves the turf in many a mouldering heap,
> Each in his narrow cell for ever laid,
> The rude forefathers of the hamlet sleep.
>
> *Elegy* : GRAY

> Dark Yew, that graspest at the stones
> And dippest towards the dreamless head,
> To thee, too, comes the golden hour,
> When flower is feeling after flower.
>
> *In Memoriam* : TENNYSON

For centuries, our forefathers have planted this tree as an emblem of death, or a " fit shelter for the dead." As the Rev. C. A. Johns writes : " there is far greater probability that at the period when crosses were erected in those sacred spots as emblems of the victory over death achieved by the Author of our faith, the yew-tree was stationed not far off, to symbolize, by its durability and slowly altering features, the patient waiting for the resurrection, by those who committed the bodies of their friends to the ground in hope. . . . The yew, then, we may safely conclude, is not an unmeaning decoration of our churchyards, much less a heathenish symbol, or, as some will have it, a tree planted with superstitious feelings, but an appropriate religious emblem."

24 8 36 The Tandridge
Yew.

The Tandridge Yew, Surrey.

Lonsdale Ragg

In the days of the long-bow, this tree was protected, and its cultivation encouraged, by royal decree, for the yew was the main source of supply. Much yew was even imported for the purpose. Thus was the yew the mainstay of the national weapon of the England of those days, and mightily did it figure at Cressy, Poictiers and Agincourt.

> There is a Yew-tree, pride of Lorton Vale,
> Which to this day stands single, in the midst
> Of its own darkness, as it stood of yore;
> Not loth to furnish weapons for the bands
> Of Umfraville or Percy ere they marched
> To Scotland's heaths; or those that crossed the sea
> And drew their sounding bows at Azincour,
> Perhaps at earlier Crecy, or Poictiers.
> Of vast circumference and gloom profound
> This solitary Tree! a living thing
> Produced too slowly ever to decay;
> Of form and aspect too magnificent
> To be destroyed.
>
> *Yew-Trees*: WORDSWORTH

It has been claimed by many that the fact that the yew supplied England's long-bows explains why it was for centuries grown under cultivation in churchyards; but as Johns points out, there is not sufficient evidence that English yew was particularly prized since a great deal was imported, so it seems that this view which held considerable sway is not tenable. No: it is more probable that the tree was planted as an emblem of protection over death, especially since yew trees were venerated in Britain even before the Christian era.

The yew is a representative of another family in the *Coniferales*, namely TAXACEAE. This family comprises small trees and shrubs, most of which are unisexual and bear their male and female flowers on separate trees. There are five genera and about a dozen species, with a host of varieties produced under cultivation. The **common yew** belongs to the genus *Taxus*, and the most common form is *Taxus baccata*.

This tree is native to Europe, Asia and North Africa. In Britain, though usually seen under cultivation, it grows wild in such areas as the Lake District and on the chalk downs of the south, especially in Surrey and Sussex. It was formerly very much more widespread than it is today.

The bole of the yew is very short and misshapen. This irregularity is due to the fact that the lower parts frequently give off new

Sprays of Yew.
Left, female spray bearing female flowers and ripe seeds surrounded by arilli ;
right, male spray bearing male flowers.

branches which grow upright and eventually become absorbed into the general trunk system. Though its massive limbs are wide-spreading, the tree never exceeds more than 60 feet in height in Britain (though in Asia it often grows much higher and assumes a more pyramidal habit). The tree is evergreen.

On the upright main branches the leaves are borne spirally all round the stem ; on the horizontal branches they form two lateral rows (Plate 3).

The yew is unisexual, and the male and female flowers are borne on separate trees ; though on rare occasions one comes across a tree with a few branches bearing flowers of the opposite sex. The flowers appear during March. They are borne on the lower surface of the twig of the previous year, in the axils of the leaves. The male flowers bear scale leaves at the base, and at the top about ten rosette-shaped stamens joined to the main axis by stems shooting from their centres. Each stamen has five to ten pollen sacs. The pollen is distributed by wind—in " faithful cloud and living smoke ", as Tennyson says—as in the case of all conifers. The female flowers develop in the axils of the scale leaves on the young shoot. Each flower contains one ovule.

Eric J. Hosking

Irish or Florence Court Yew.

After fertilisation the seed develops and becomes surrounded by a fleshy red structure called an arillus. This is ripe by September of the same year. Specimens having yellow arilli are known (p. 119).

Though the leaves and the seed of the yew are poisonous, the arillus is not, and sometimes children eat it though it is not altogether palatable. Anyhow, the edible arillus is useful in attracting birds by which the seeds are disseminated.

The length of life which the yew can attain is open to doubt, nevertheless it obviously can live to a very ripe old age. Yet the claims that this tree has been known to last for as long as two thousand years are most probably based on myth rather than fact. There is little doubt, however, that some yews in Britain are nearly a thousand years old, for even in a gnarled or decayed condition they still seem to linger for years. Neither is the yew always a solitary tree. Near the beginning of the nineteenth century, three hundred of them were felled on one small island in Loch Lomond. Furthermore there are still some very famous collections and avenues of yew trees. The yews on the estate of the Earl of Radnor in Wiltshire, those forming the famous walks at Midhurst, the large number at Castle Eden Dene in Durham, and the yew walk at Hatherop Castle, Gloucestershire, are all worthy of mention. Then of the solitary veterans, there is the yew in the churchyard at Fortingal in Scotland—perhaps the oldest tree in that country ; the very old specimen in the churchyard at Darley Dale in Derbyshire ; and the even more famous yew in Crowhurst churchyard (p. 118). There are many others.

Yew also makes thick, very efficient hedges, but owing to the poisonous character of the foliage they have never been grown on land

A Case against Topiary (A).

frequented by domestic animals. Many ornamental hedges have been devised from yew, and not a few of these are now justly famous, for they are very old and very large; but there are so many, to be seen especially on large country estates, as to preclude individual description.

Yew hedges are very thick because this tenacious plant seems to thrive on clipping; and therein lies the reason for its being used for making the labyrinths or mazes of past days. Perhaps the finest example of this curious feature in Britain today is in the grounds of Hampton Court Palace. It is believed that this maze was originally made of hornbeam (p. 242) but this was later replaced by hollies and yews.

The yew in its natural form is sinister yet impressive; clipped as a hedge it has its uses; arranged and clipped to form a maze it is intriguing: but when it is clipped in the fantastic forms of animals and birds (called topiary work), as it has been for many years, then it is the victim of the cult of the ugly. There seems neither rhyme nor reason in it, and never has man been able justifiably to claim the right to mutilate any tree for such puerile reasons. Though topiary is not often practised today, examples of the hideous fashion still exist (usually with yew or box (p. 197) as the victims), and it seems almost incredible that the great John Evelyn should be associated with the introduction of it to the end that it became fashionable in the early eighteenth century. Among the several objections to this form of landscape gardening are those set out by W. Robinson who wrote so strongly against the practice in his *English Flower Garden* (eighth edition, 1900). His objections included: loss of natural form; absence of movement, one of the most welcome characters of trees; risk of disease and death of the trees; cost. To this might well be added, the cultivation and perpetuation of ugliness.

A Case against Topiary (B).

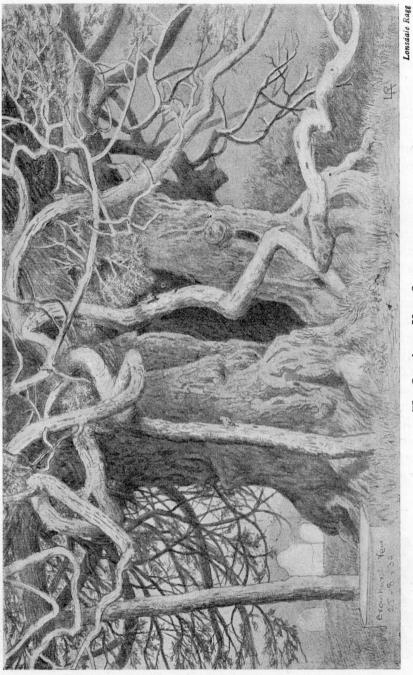

Lonsdale Ragg

The Crowhurst Yew, Sussex.

VARIETIES OF YEW

Several species and many varieties of yew are cultivated in the ornamental gardens and parks of Britain. Perhaps, apart from *Taxus baccata*, the most popular is the **Irish** or **Florence Court yew**, which is a variety (*T. baccata* var. *fastigiata*) (p. 115). This variety originated about 150 years ago. Its branches are much nearer the erect than those of its progenitor. It averages a height of 20 to 35 feet. Another distinguishing feature is the arrangement of the leaves, for they are arranged spirally all around the stem—even the branchlet stems : no leaves are arranged in horizontal rows.

Then there is another variety, *T. baccata* var. *adpressa*, having very short leaves which are closely adpressed to the stem. There is also a golden form of this variety, just as there are golden forms of the common yew and the Irish yew.

T. baccata var. *dovastonii* is a particularly impressive pendulous form. The variety *T. baccata* var. *elegantissima* bears leaves which are of an attractive silver colour when young. Though the arils of most yews are pinkish red, those of the variety *T. baccata* var. *fructu luteo* are yellow. The species *T. cuspidata* is a Japanese form of a spreading habit.

The forms of yew above mentioned are only some of the species and varieties available ; but enough has been said to give some idea of the versatility of this tree which offers a wide choice to the gardener who fancies it for his garden.

17

MISCELLANY

Although the most important conifers which are to be found in Britain to any considerable extent have already been dealt with in the previous chapters (6 to 16), there are many other species and a host of varieties to be seen under cultivation in this country. Some of them are to be considered here. Furthermore, there are others of outstanding interest, for example, the giant redwoods and big trees of western America, which, though not familiar to most people of this country, are of such unique interest that they cannot be entirely ignored.

I

HEMLOCKS
(*Abietaceae*)

The hemlock trees are very common in America ; but they must in no circumstances be confused here with the common hemlock, which is a very poisonous herbaceous plant belonging to the parsley family (UMBELLIFERAE).[1]

Hemlock-spruce in Britain.
Below, sprays showing young cones (left), and silvery under-sides of leaves (right).

Harold Bastin

Hemlock trees belong to the coniferous genus *Tsuga*. They are all very handsome, pyramidal evergreens with a striking red bark. The leaves are of varying lengths, mixed in a haphazard fashion in two horizontal rows. The cones are pendulous.

The **Canadian hemlock** (*Tsuga canadensis*), known also as the **eastern hemlock** and **hemlock-spruce,** is widespread in eastern Canada and the United States. It attains an average height of 60 to 80 feet in its native haunts. This tree is sometimes cultivated in British parks and gardens ; but here it betrays a tendency to lose its pyramidal form by developing several trunks, the branches of which intertwine to form an irregular dense dome. There is a dwarf weeping form of this tree—*T. canadensis* var. *sargentii pendula* —which is eminently suitable for rock gardens. It forms a very compact mass of pendulous branches.

The **western hemlock** (*T. heterophylla*), sometimes also

[1] See *Flowers in Britain*, p. 185.

called **hemlock-fir** and **Prince Albert's fir,** is a valuable timber tree attaining a height of sometimes 200 feet in its native country—the Pacific coast of North America. It is grown in Britain more frequently than the Canadian hemlock, and even here it attains a height of 100 feet provided it is subjected to suitable conditions, especially a moist climate.

Incense Cedar in Britain.

INCENSE CEDARS
(*Cupressaceae*)

The **incense cedars** belong to the genus *Libocedrus*—a genus closely related to the genus *Thuya*, the next to be considered in this miscellany. The most commonly cultivated incense cedar in Britain is *L. decurrens*, and this makes a fine ornamental tree (up to 70 feet) of a particularly narrow columnar habit. This tree hails mainly from California, though other members of the genus are to be found growing in many Pacific areas such as New Zealand, New Guinea and China.

The needles of the incense cedar are very dark green and exceptionally sharp. The cones have only a small number of scales. The bark is of a deep red colour.

In certain parts of the United States the incense cedar is a valuable timber tree. The wood is soft, though very durable. The tree is also prized there, as elsewhere, for its ornamental qualities. Certain other species also yield useful timber.

Eric J. Hosking

THUYA
(*Cupressaceae*)

The genus *Thuya* is not a very large one, and it is confined in its indigenous habitats to China, Japan and North America. Nevertheless it is a popular genus in the ornamental parks and gardens of Britain (where it is known as arbor vitae or 'tree of life', a name originally given by Clusius—though there would appear to be no particular reason for the name). So popular is this genus in Britain that many varieties have arisen as the result of cross-breeding.

The **American arbor vitae** (*Thuya plicata*), sometimes known as the **canoe cedar, western red cedar** or **Pacific red cedar** is native to the western areas of the North American continent, and there it grows frequently associated with the Douglas fir. Though it often attains a height of 200 feet in its native haunts (especially on the western American coast and on Vancouver Island), seldom does it reach even half that height when growing in Britain.

This tree was discovered by Née while on his voyages round the world during 1789-94, and the specimen which he gathered at Nootka Sound is now in the British Museum (Natural History). Archibald Menzies also collected specimens of American arbor vitae, and it was eventually introduced for cultivation in Britain in 1853.

The foliage of the American arbor vitae, like that of all species of *Thuya*, is similar to that of the Lawson cypress (*Cupressus lawsoniana*, p. 108), with which it might easily be confused. The small cones bear five or six pairs of scales; the second, third and fourth pair only are fertile.

In its native habitats, this tree yields a valuable timber; but in Britain it figures mainly as a plant of interest or decoration, though it does sometimes play a minor part in forestry programmes. In North America, the wood is used particularly for making shingles for the roofs of buildings, and it is also used for packing-cases, posts and general building purposes.

Although cultivation of the American arbor vitae in Britain has not been carried out with any particular enthusiasm, some successful plantings have been recorded, especially in Scotland where the tree has been planted in association with the Douglas fir as it so frequently occurs in Nature. It is singularly free from disease; but against this it suffers from exposure to high winds and often yields very knotty poles. Like the Lawson cypress (*Cupressus lawsoniana*) and *C. macrocarpa*, this plant is very useful for hedge-making. Some fine solitary specimens of American arbor vitae may be seen in parklands and on estates in the south and south-east of England and also in Eire.

The **white cedar** (*T. occidentalis*), also native to Canada and the United States, is a valuable timber tree in those countries. (Elwes and Henry, in their *Trees of Great Britain and Ireland*, call this tree the ' western arbor vitae ' ; but this, and the other name which caused considerable confusion, namely ' eastern arbor vitae ', have now fortunately fallen into disuse.) Though not established commercially in this country, it, and several of its varieties, have found favour with British landscape gardeners. *T. occidentalis* itself is used extensively for hedge-making, though it sometimes grows as a pyramidal tree 50 feet high but less dense than American arbor vitae. Then of the many varieties there is a golden form (*T. occidentalis* var. *aurea*). The narrow columnar habit, coupled with a curious twisted growth, of the variety *T. occidentalis* var. *douglasii*, make this form of peculiar interest. On the other hand *T. occidentalis* var. *reedi* is a globose dwarf, especially useful in rock gardens. There are also other pyramidal and dwarf varieties of this species of *Thuya* ; but they are too numerous to justify further space here.

The **Chinese arbor vitae** (*T. orientalis*) is indigenous to China, though, unlike *T. dolobrata* and *T. japonica* (see p. 124), it is not native to the islands of Japan. Like its Japanese relatives, the Chinese arbor vitae is grown in Britain solely for ornament. Sometimes in this country it assumes the habit of a small tree ; but more often it is scarcely anything but a dense shrub.

The leaves are aromatic. The cones are ovoid and bluish when young, but become woody when mature.

According to Elwes and Henry, in their *Trees of Great Britain and Ireland*, this tree attains a height of 50 to 60 feet when growing wild on the mountains of China. Though it is now frequently seen in Japan, the Japanese botanists do not consider it indigenous to their country, but that it was introduced from China by Buddhist missionaries. The first specimen in Europe was cultivated in the famous Botanic Garden at Leyden early in the eighteenth century, and this tree attracted the attention of Linnaeus ; but there is no record of how it arrived there, though it seems probable that it was sent by a Dutchman in Japan. Some specimens were collected even earlier (1690-92), and these are now preserved in the British Museum (Natural History). During the eighteenth century, too, French Christian missionaries sent specimens to Paris. Other specimens arrived in Britain.

As might be expected, this tree yields no useful timber here.

The variety *T. orientalis* var. *aurea* has its branches tipped with gold which turns bronze towards the end of the year. Another similar golden variety which, however, is narrow in general habit, is *T. orientalis* var. *elegantissima*.

Among other species of *Thuya* found in ornamental gardens in Britain, the Japanese species, *T. dolobrata*, is rather popular. It is a thick tree attaining a height of 40 feet. There is also a variety of this, *T. dolabrata* var. *variegata*, having young foliage sprays of an off-white colour. *T. japonica* is another Japanese species sometimes to be found in Britain.

THE MARSH CYPRESS
(*Cupressaceae*)

The **marsh** or **swamp cypress** belongs to the genus *Taxodium* which is closely related to the *Sequoias*, a genus which comprises the giant redwoods and big trees (see p. 126). The swamp cypress itself (*T. distichum*) is one of the most beautiful of all the conifers. It is a deciduous tree (it is frequently called the **deciduous cypress**), and its lovely green foliage turns to an impressive bright red before falling in the autumn.

The tree is native to the United States where it is also known as the **bald cypress** and **Louisiana cypress**; but it is also cultivated in Britain chiefly on account of its highly decorative character.

In its native habitat it often reaches a height of 170 feet with a bole 15 feet in diameter. As its common name implies, it thrives best near water; those who wish to cultivate this beautiful plant in Britain should bear this fact in mind. When growing actually in water, as it often does in the wild state, the bole is supported by massive buttresses from which branches arise beneath the water. These branches send up hollow aerial breathing roots called ' knees ' through which the rooting system of the tree can, while itself submerged, carry out the gaseous interchange essential to any living thing.

The leaves are arranged in two rows when borne on the youngest branches, but on the older branches they are inserted in a spiral fashion. During the season these light, feathery leaves are very bright green. The cones are about an inch long and bear many scales arranged spirally and overlapping each other. But this tree seldom bears flowers, or, therefore, cones in Britain.

Winter.   Summer.

Harold Bastin

Marsh Cypress.

On occasions one may see a specimen of this lovely tree as much as 100 feet high, even in Britain, especially if growing on river banks or near a lake. Those at Syon House in Middlesex are famous, and there are some particularly attractive examples (though not very tall) in Whiteknights Park, Reading. Other interesting examples are to be seen in various parks and on certain estates, and the strange thing about them is that they often betray a variety of habits. Seldom does the swamp cypress succeed in the north of England or in Scotland, though there is a specimen in the Royal Botanic Garden, Edinburgh.

Though the swamp cypress was introduced into Britain three hundred years ago it is not cultivated very much today though it is not difficult to rear provided it is near a plentiful supply of water.

In its native countries, this tree yields a valuable timber. This applies especially to Mexico, where the tree seldom grows in water and consequently produces no respiratory 'knees'. The sap-wood is almost white, and the heart-wood reddish. As one might expect, this wood stands up well to damp conditions; in America it is therefore utilised for buildings, doors, window-sashes, verandahs, and so forth. Since the tree is not cultivated except for ornamental purposes in Britain, the wood is not very well known here; all the same, a certain amount of the timber is imported.

JAPANESE CEDAR
(*Cupressaceae*)

The **Japanese cedar** is the only species belonging to the genus *Cryptomeria* (*C. japonica*). It is a handsome tree reaching a height of 100 feet and terminating in a pyramidal head, but the lower part of the trunk frequently becomes denuded of its branches. In Japan it is a valuable timber tree though it is often used for ornament and may frequently be seen lining city streets.

In Britain the Japanese cedar demands plenty of moisture but adequate shelter. It is cultivated here purely for decorative purposes and has a foliage similar to that of *Sequoia gigantea* (see below) to which it is closely related, though the leaves of the Japanese cedar are more bluish-green. In this country the tree attains a height of 60 feet provided it is carefully nursed.

Then there are several varieties of it. *C. japonica* var. *elegans* is a shrubby plant, useful in rock gardens, where it turns a delightful russet in the winter. *C. japonica* var. *nana* is an intriguing dwarf, very compact and turning a bronze shade in the winter. *C. japonica* var. *alba variegata* is a dwarf whose young shoots have white leaves which gradually turn green as they become older.

There are about two dozen varieties and monstrosities of the Japanese cedar; but they are either too specialised or too unstable to warrant further discussion here.

GIANT REDWOODS AND BIG TREES

The genus *Sequoia* comprises the tallest, heaviest and oldest trees in the world, namely, the **big tree** or **giant redwood** (*S. gigantea*) and the giant **Californian redwood** (*S. sempervirens*). Though seen in many parts of the world under cultivation, both species are indigenous to the State of California and its environs.

E.N.A

Group of Californian Redwoods (*Sequoia sempervirens*) in the
Pepperwood Grove, California.
Some of these have a diameter of 25 feet and are 370 feet high.

Spray of Californian Redwood (*Sequoia sempervirens*) showing Cones.

The genus *Sequoia* may be looked upon as the only surviving link between the true firs and the true cypresses. Their trunks are very massive, usually with gigantic clean boles when growing in their native habitat. The ripe cones have very thick woody scales.

The Californian redwood (*S. sempervirens*) is the most important lumber tree in California, and it abounds in a short part of its coast. A road called Redwood Highway runs through forests north of San Francisco, and penetrates several groves which have been acquired by the State, aided by the Save-the-Redwoods League. The tree was really discovered by Archibald Menzies in 1795, though it had been seen in 1769 by Don Gaspar da Pabola during his voyages of discovery in and around San Francisco Bay. David Don named it *Taxodium sempervirens*, but a new genus, *Sequoia*, was assigned to it by Endlicher in 1847. This generic name is derived from Sequoyah, a Cherokee Indian who invented an alphabet. The tree is gigantic, attaining a height of 200 to 350 feet and a diameter of 10 to 15 feet at the base of the bole if it is cylindrical and sometimes twice as much if the

Transverse Section of a Trunk of a Californian Redwood (*Sequoia sempervirens*). The labels give the thickness of the trunk at the dates indicated : 55 B.C., Roman invasion of Britain ; A.D. 98, Rome in its heyday ; A.D. 452, Venice founded as a city ; A.D. 612, the Koran first published ; A.D. 800, Charlemagne crowned emperor of the new Western Empire in Rome ; A.D. 890, University College, Oxford, supposed to have been founded by Alfred the Great (now discounted) ; A.D. 1066, Hastings, and Norman Conquest of England ; A.D. 1769, redwood first seen by white man—Gaspar da Pabola.

bole is buttressed. The older trees have boles clear of branches for many feet. One tree at Big Basin, called the Chimney Tree, is 100 feet high, but its wood has been almost completely destroyed by fire, so it is hollow and several people can stand inside and look up through it to the sky; yet it still bears many living branches. The bark is brown in colour and of a soft, fibrous texture, being exceedingly thick. The needles are arranged in a manner similar to those of the silver fir or yew.

Californian Redwood (*Sequoia sempervirens*) in Britain.

Eric J. Hosking

The Californian redwood does well in Britain where, so far, it has been cultivated for reasons of ornament or interest. Here it thrives best in sheltered positions and attains a height of 150 feet and a diameter of about 7 feet. Investigations into the possibilities of its cultivation on a commercial scale in Britain are now proceeding.

There is also a purely ornamental variety of this tree (*S. sempervirens* var. *alba spica*), the tips of the young shoots of which are an off-white colour.

The big tree (*S. gigantea*), indigenous to the Sierra Nevada, is the only other species in the genus *Sequoia*, and it is the largest of all conifers. It is known also as *Wellingtonia*, *Washingtonia* and **Mammoth tree**. A feature distinguishing it from the redwood is the spiral arrangement of the leaves. These are somewhat like those of *Juniperus*, though not quite so sharp—scaly and pointed.

Big trees, though familiar to most botanists owing to their unique size and longevity, are

E.N.A.

Motor Road through the Mariposa Grove in the Yosemite National Park, California. This Park contains 200 large and many small species of *Sequoia*. Note that the road passes through the bole of one of these trees (see also p. 5).

not really very common. In fact, they were not discovered until 1841 by Bidwell and introduced to the botanists of Britain by John Lindley. The average height is 275 feet, though specimens so high as 320 feet have been known. The average girth is 20 feet with an extreme maximum of 35 feet. One of the most famous groups of this tree is the Mariposa Grove of the Sierra Nevada, which comprises ninety large trees and many smaller ones.

The present-day big trees are the oldest of all living trees. One at a thousand years would be a mere youth. Many are two thousand years old, and there are some known to be at least three thousand years of age.

The big tree has been grown with success in Britain, chiefly in the southern and western areas. Here it is quick-growing provided it is subjected to mild conditions, and it attains a height of 150 feet, though the lower branches usually remain, thus giving the tree a pyramidal and more formal appearance. It makes a good avenue tree; indeed, there are some very fine avenues of big trees or *Wellingtonias* (as they are usually called) in the south of England.

The wood of both *Sequoias* is of considerable commercial value. Both trees were much more widespread throughout the world of past ages : in fact, fossil representatives were known to science long before the living survivors were discovered in California. These fossils have been unearthed even in Britain and other parts of Europe, besides various places in America. In Yellowstone Park there are still to be seen erect fossil trunks, 30 feet high and 6 to 10 feet in diameter.

This ends the review of the Gymnosperms, which comprise, mainly coniferous trees. It has been quite impossible to deal with the majority of these trees, so only a representative number have been considered, though it is hoped that no important conifer has been omitted and that those chosen will give the reader a good general idea of coniferous trees.

It should be noted that very few of these trees are actually indigenous to Britain, but during the past, their beauty of form (in most cases) has inspired our ancestors to cultivate exotic examples here. We are the beneficiaries of the foresight thus displayed. It is therefore up to each one of us to do what we can to encourage the cultivation of coniferous trees, and wherever possible to foster the importation of still further genera and species.

It is true that the Forestry Commission and others are now carrying out extensive planting programmes of such softwoods as Scots and

Harold Bastin

Big Trees or Giant Redwoods (*Sequoia gigantea*) in Britain.

Corsican pines, European and Japanese larches, Norway and sitka spruce, and Douglas fir, among others ; but encouraging though all this is, it must be realised that the ultimate aim of such programmes is economic ; there is also the aesthetic point of view, and here we can all do our share. There must be many points of a landscape where an Austrian pine, for example, would fit into the general scene. If so, then someone should make an effort to see that one is planted.

All this might savour of too much interference by man with the natural flora of the country, but it must be borne in mind that the control of Nature by man is essential today, and since this cannot be avoided, it is our business to see that our control is as rational as possible, and that it aims at producing the best possible results.

This can best be done by making a thorough survey of those conifers which might conceivably thrive in Britain and then proceed with their cultivation both on estates and in forests for economic purposes and in public parks and gardens and on private grounds for their aesthetic value. But it is doubtful whether we shall be able to depend upon the enthusiasm of a few private individuals.

Seton Gordon

Scots Pine.
This veteran, in Glen Lui, Scotland, shows the phenomenon of spiral growth.

PART III

BROAD-LEAVED TREES (ANGIOSPERMS)

We now come to the trees belonging to the great division known as Angiosperms which was reviewed in general in Chapter 3. Though the order in which the angiospermous flowering plant families containing arborescent forms are dealt with here may differ somewhat from the order chosen in other works, we are following rather closely that scheme of classification set out by Dr. J. Hutchinson in his *Families of Flowering Plants*—a scheme which was also followed by another book in this series, namely *Flowers in Britain*, in the hope that the two books, *Trees in Britain* and *Flowers in Britain*, will dovetail together to form a general review of flowering plants—herbs, shrubs and trees.

As might be expected, the broad-leaved trees can often be identified by the size and especially the form of their leaves ; in winter, when these have fallen (with the exception of the evergreens), the winter buds often prove to be a diagnostic feature. Both these organs may therefore be used as bases for a general, though admittedly rough, key to the identification of the more common broad-leaved trees.

The bark of the trunk is also a useful aid to identification, as again are the general form and detailed branching of the tree. Flowers and fruit are not always available, and very often inaccessible ; but these are very diagnostic of a species, though not of a variety. All these characters of the trees to follow will be considered in some detail.

18

TULIP-TREES AND MAGNOLIAS

(Magnoliaceae)

TULIP-TREE

Among the many handsome trees introduced into Britain from abroad, the tulip-tree is most outstanding. It is of American origin, and there, especially in the eastern States, it thrives, frequently attaining a height of nearly 200 feet and a bole diameter of 10 feet, especially in Ohio and Florida. In the United States it is sometimes called **yellow poplar** and **whitewood**. It occurs but rarely in Canada also. It belongs to the genus *Liriodendron* (*L. tulipifera*), a member of the family MAGNOLIACEAE—a very primitive flowering plant family. An even more familiar genus of this family is *Magnolia* itself (p. 139), and to it *Liriodendron* is closely related.

This handsome exotic frequently attains a height of 80 feet in Britain. It was introduced from the United States some time during the seventeenth century; a specimen was cultivated by the then Bishop of London in the grounds of Fulham Palace in 1688.

The tree is covered with a grey bark, slightly grooved, and this surrounds a particularly fine long bole extending to a trunk bearing large limbs.

The winter buds are long and pointed and are borne on short stalks spirally arranged on the twigs. Each bud is protected by two long scales.

The leaves are very characteristic—in fact, they are almost unique (p. 138). Each leaf is borne on a slender stalk about three inches in length. The leaf-blade is characteristic in shape, though it varies somewhat. It is fairly large, and has several big lobes (usually two, but sometimes four) on the side margins, often with some smaller ones also; but instead of terminating in a point it is cut off almost square; in fact, there is even a slight re-entrant notch where the mid-rib ends. The earliest leaves of a seedling are not lobed at all but have smooth margins; nevertheless even these have the unusual notch at the distal ends. The leaves turn a bright yellow before falling in the autumn.

The tulip-tree blossoms freely and often luxuriant during June and July, sometimes even extending into August. Then it makes an impressive sight, for it seems bedecked with thousands of tulips, greenish-white on the outside and yellow inside with orange-white nectaries at the bases of the petals (p. 138). From the appearance of these flowers the common name of the tree has been derived, though botanically the flowers do not resemble tulips at all—the former are Dicotyledons, whereas tulips are Monocotyledons. There are six petals, each about two inches long, and it is these that render the flower so conspicuous. When the flowers are in bud, these petals are enclosed in a sheath. The stamens and the carpels closely resemble those of the *Magnolia*. That is, the stamens are numerous and are deep yellow in colour. The carpels, too, are numerous. They are simple in structure

Liriodendron
60'
Chevening
2-9-26
LR

Lonsdale Ragg

Tulip Tree in Kent.

Foliage and Flowers of the Tulip Tree.

and are free from each other, arranged spirally on a slightly elongated axis.

After fertilisation each carpel forms a long, light brown, winged fruit borne on a short stalk, so that the collection of fruit forms a dense cone. By means of the wing on each fruit the seeds are dispersed far and wide by the wind. Unfortunately the fruit seldom ripens in Great Britain.

Though the timber produced by this tree in the New World is used for various constructional purposes, the tulip-tree is not cultivated for commercial use in Britain. The timber is imported, however, under the name 'white poplar', 'yellow poplar', 'tulip-wood' or 'canary white wood'. So the tulip-tree is grown in Britain solely for ornamental purposes, and when it is in flower a particularly fine sight it makes. It is distributed from the north Midlands southwards. The largest tree in Britain is still growing at Woolbeding, Sussex; but there are many other beautiful examples, especially in private parks in the south of England.

There are several good specimens in the Royal Botanic Gardens at Kew, in Kensington Gardens and in other London parks. The specimen growing in Golders Hill Park is probably the largest in London.

Among the varieties of tulip-tree, the gold-leaved form (*L. tulipi-fera* var. *aurea*) is to be recommended for ornamental planting. Its flowers are more yellow than those of the common species. *L. tulipifera* var. *pyramidalis* is more pyramidal in shape than its progenitor.

MAGNOLIAS

Exotic stranger, whose most costly scent
Might, with sweet odour, flood a Continent,
Whose opulent voluptuousness looks down
Amazed upon an English country town,
(So Messalina, exiled, might we see
Brooding, astonished, at a Parish tea)—
What do you here, lost Empress? How old
Our sun must seem, our warmest winds, how cold!
What thoughts are yours? Those petals of thick cream
Lie lapped and laved in a continuous dream
Of forests, dark as death, yet shining bright
With tropic blooms, all insolence and might,
Which poison with hot breath the violent air,
Their frantic perfume heavy like despair!

Magnolia : LADY MARGARET SACKVILLE

The lovely exotic **magnolia** scarcely needs any introduction to British readers, though they are probably familiar with it more as a very small tree or as a bush rather than as a tree of reasonable dimensions, which, indeed, it often is in its native habitats. Most species are deciduous, though there are some evergreens.

The species of magnolia are distributed widely throughout both Old and New Worlds, though only in the northern hemisphere. There are luxuriant examples in tropical America and northern India especially.

The common name has been taken from the botanical generic name (*Magnolia*) which was given in honour of Prof. Pierre Magnol (1638-1715), professor of medicine and botany at Montpelier. There are about two dozen species of this genus.

Like that of the tulip tree, the flower, though very large, is simple in construction. Quoting from the description in *Flowers in Britain* : " Most members of the genus are deciduous, that is, they shed all their leaves in the autumn ; and the flowers open out before the new leaves do. The species, *M. grandiflora*, however, is evergreeen. Most members of the genus have white or cream flowers, though a few have white flowers flushed with purple."

" Each flower is borne singly, and, in spite of its large size, it is very simple in structure. When in bud it is protected by sheathing stipules of the unopened leaves. These are shed later. There are several whorls of sepals and petals, all of which are alike—usually white. The outer whorls are, however, sometimes sepaloid. Inside the innermost whorl of petals are several whorls of stamens making up a large indefinite number altogether. Inside the stamens is a large number of simple, free carpels arranged spirally on an elongated axis which is really an extension of the receptacle. The fruit is a collection of follicles, which in due course split. As each follicle splits, the seeds are exposed hanging each on a single thread. The outer layer of each original ovule becomes fleshy after fertilisation, and this fleshy layer which now surrounds the seed enables the latter to be distributed by birds."

Owing to the superficial resemblance of the flower to a lily, the magnolia is sometimes called the **lily tree.**

The most commonly cultivated magnolia in Britain is the evergreen *M. grandiflora*, often seen growing as an isolated shrub or as a small tree up against walls. This was introduced into Britain from the southern United States (where it is often called the **laurel magnolia**) in 1734. In its native country it often attains a height of 80 feet. The leaves are large, dark and glossy. The flowers are creamy white and frequently measure eight inches across. They have a delicate perfume.

Another native of the southern United States is the **big-leaf magnolia** (*M. macrophylla*) ; but this is not often seen in Britain. Its leaves are one to three feet long and eight to ten inches broad ; they are deciduous.

The **sweet bay magnolia** (*M. virginiana*) was the first of the American magnolias to be introduced into Britain. John Bannister brought the first specimen in 1688. Its flowers are more globose and are white.

The **cucumber magnolia** or **cucumber tree** (*M. acuminata*) is widespread in the United States (chiefly the north), and is so called because its young fruits resemble small cucumbers. It grows to a height of 60 feet in its native habitat. The flowers are greenish tinted with yellow.

Another American species, the **umbrella tree** (*M. tripetala*), is so called because those leaves at the ends of the branches present a mosaic resembling the ribs of an umbrella. They are large and sometimes grow two feet in length. The flowers also are large and are

Magnolia grandiflora.

creamy white with a strong scent. This species was introduced into Britain in 1752.

The **mountain magnolia** (*M. fraseri* or *M. auriculata*), native chiefly to the southern part of the United States, is cultivated as a garden shrub in Britain. In its native home it attains a height of 50 feet. The leaves are large, and the flowers are somewhat smaller than those described so far and almost yellow in colour.

The **yulan tree** (*M. conspicua*) is Chinese in origin, and is perhaps the oldest in cultivation. The Chinese use its buds as a medicine and for flavouring rice dishes. This species was introduced into Britain in about 1790, and here it has developed the habit of an exquisite shrub or small tree. Its white flowers appear in abundance before the leaves open, and they have a delightful perfume. One variety of the yulan tree (*M. conspicua* var. *soulangeana*) blooms later in the year. It has chalice-shaped flowers (because the petals are recurved) which are purplish. An even darker form is *M. conspicua* var. *soulangeana nigra*. There are several other forms of this species. A closely related species is *M. fuscata* which will thrive only in greenhouses.

There are three Japanese species of magnolia. *M. kobus* was brought to Britain in 1709 ; it has small, white, stellate flowers and large leaves. Another, *M. obovata*, was brought to this country in 1804. Yet another, *M. hypoleuca*, attains tree-like proportions even in this country. Its creamy white flowers appear during summer, whereas a related species, *M. lennei*, has massive flowers, pinkish on the inside and purple outside, which appear later in the summer.

M. stellata is the earliest flowering of all magnolias in Britain, and it is so prolific with blooms that the bush becomes a cloud of white in March, that is, before the leaves open. This species is very sweetly scented.

M. watsonii also hails from Japan. It is of a shrubby habit, and bears exquisite flowers, five inches across and ivory white with red centres. Several other species of magnolia indigenous to Japan are now cultivated in Britain.

Of the Indian species of magnolia, none of which is in general cultivation in Britain, the most important are *M. globosa*, *M. sphaerocarpa* and *M. campbellii*. The last-named is the most magnificent of all magnolias, contributing largely to the Indian scene, especially around Darjeeling. It attains the dimensions of a forest tree, up to 150 feet in height and 12 feet in girth. Its flowers, which appear before the leaves, are six to ten inches across and are of various shades of white to red.

It seems a pity that magnolias are not more widely cultivated than they are, for they are not difficult to cultivate—at any rate in the south ; given a well-drained, loamy soil they flourish and flower freely.

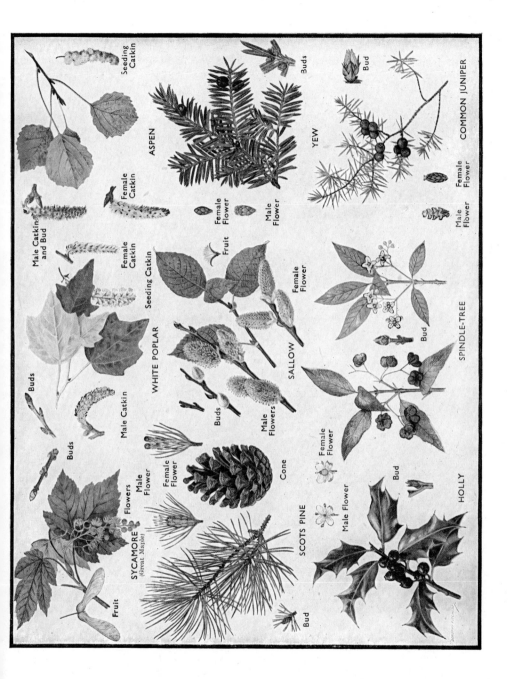

Seeding Catkin

ASPEN

Buds

YEW

Bud

COMMON JUNIPER

Male Catkin and Bud

Female Catkin

Female Catkin

Female Flower

Male Flower

Female Flower

Male Flower

Seeding Catkin

WHITE POPLAR

Fruit

Female Flower

SALLOW

SPINDLE-TREE

Buds

Buds

Male Catkin

Buds

Male Flowers

Bud

Buds

Flowers

Male Flower

Female Flower

Female Flower

Cone

Female Flower

Bud

HOLLY

SYCAMORE
(Great Maple)

Fruit

SCOTS PINE

Male Flower

Bud

PLATE 3

19
SWEET BAY-TREE
(*Lauraceae*)

The **sweet bay** is the true laurel. It is important to realise this, for the name ' laurel ' is applied to several plants which are not in any way related to each other. Most of them, however, are sturdy shrubs which are very frequently cultivated in gardens, shrubberies and ornamental hedges. Indeed, the term ' laurel ' is the cause of considerable confusion in gardening circles unless the true designation of the plants under discussion is clearly stated. There is, for example, the **cherry laurel** (*Prunus laurocerasus*), often simply called ' laurel ', which is cultivated everywhere as an ornamental shrub or in hedges and as coverts for game. But this plant is not related to the true laurel ; in fact it belongs to the natural order ROSACEAE (p. 166), and is scarcely ever seen except as a bushy shrub with dark green lance-shaped leaves. Then there is the very familiar **Japanese laurel** (*Aucuba japonica*) which again is not a true laurel ; it belongs to the very advanced family CORNACEAE to which the **dogwood** (*Cornus sanguinea*) also belongs (p. 320).

The sweet bay-tree or true laurel belongs to the family LAURACEAE, which is a family consisting mainly of tropical trees and shrubs, many of which are beautiful ornamental plants and others of which are of varying commercial value. For example the genus *Cinnamomum* contains the **cinnamon plant** (*C. zeylanicum*) and the **camphor plant** (*C. camphora*). The **avocado pear** belongs to the genus *Persea* (*P. gratissima*).

The family LAURACEAE is closely allied to the family MAGNOLIACEAE, and is therefore comparatively simple and primitive. In fact, the LAURACEAE family shows considerable evolutionary reduction from the MAGNOLIACEAE.

The sweet bay-tree belongs to the genus *Laurus*, and it has been assigned the botanical name of *Laurus nobilis*. It is native to Mediterranean regions in both Europe and Africa, though it is now commonly cultivated in Britain where it was introduced some time in the early sixteenth century. In its natural habitat it often attains a height of 60 feet, though it usually takes its form more a shrub than a tree because it sends up so many suckers, by means of which it spreads, that the original trunk is often lost.

Eric J. Hosking

Sweet Bay-Tree.

I have seen the wicked in great power, and spreading himself like a green bay tree.   *Psalm* 37, v. 35

Under cultivation in Britain this plant may either assume the form of a shrub or, by constant pruning, of a standard tree. Though it thrives in Britain it cannot withstand extreme or continuous cold, and it therefore does best in the south and south-west of England. Further north it usually has to be housed indoors during the winter months.

The leaves are evergreen and lance-shaped with smooth whitish margins (Plate 2). They are aromatic though bitter, but not poisonous. The aromatic character renders the leaves a valuable ingredient in soups, broths and meat dishes. The leaves are also used for flavouring fish, especially pilchards, in the south-west of England. Bay rum is not obtained from the sweet bay-tree but from the **bay-rum tree** (*Pimenta acris*) which belongs to the more advanced family MYRTACEAE—a family of tropical and Australian plants containing the well-known *Eucalyptus*.

The sweet bay-tree is unisexual, and the sexes are segregated on different plants. The male flowers, which appear during April and

May, are greenish-yellow, and are borne in clusters in the axils of the leaves (Plate 2). Each flower has four perianth segments and nine stamens. The female flower also has four perianth segments, together with three carpels joined to form a single ovary, which, after fertilisation, ripens to form a berry (Plate 2). This is green when immature but eventually turns dark purple. The berries are sometimes used in veterinary medicine.

The sweet bay has been the laurel of the poets since classical times; it is the laurel of victors and conquerors; hence the present-day term ' laureate ', which signifies eminence, as in the case of the poet attached to the Royal household and of Nobel prize-winners. Victorious Roman generals were crowned with a wreath of sweet bay to mark their victories. In Greek mythology the sweet bay was sacred to Apollo. Pliny, in his *Natural History*, Book XV, sets out the various characteristics which the laurel symbolised. Like the olive it was a sign of truce; it denoted victory and courage.

> Yet laurels, drench'd in pure Parnassian dews,
> Reward his memory, dear to ev'ry muse,
> Who, with a courage of unshaken root,
> In honour's field advancing his firm foot,
> Plants it upon the line that justice draws,
> And will prevail or perish in her cause.
>
> *Table Talk* : COWPER

It had the power of purification and protection. It was held by the Romans as a protection against lightning, and it is said that for this reason Tiberius wore a wreath of sweet bay laurel.

> Reach the bays—
> I'll tie a garland here about his head ;
> 'Twill keep my boy from lightning.
>
> *Vittoria Corumbona* : JOHN WEBSTER

When a bay-tree withered, it was an omen of death.

> 'Tis thought the king is dead. We'll not stay—
> The bay-trees in our country are withered.
>
> *Richard II*, Act. 2, Sc. 4 : SHAKESPEARE

The reason for the protective powers of the sweet bay over Apollo is ascribed to his love for Daphne, and the result of Apollo's hasty actions. Daphne had dedicated her life to one of complete virginity, but Apollo was in love with her. On one occasion he chased her, but her father came to her aid and converted her into a bay laurel. From that time onwards Apollo wore a wreath of bays on his head, and requested others to do the same.

> When we have run our passion's heat
> Love hither makes his best retreat ;
> The gods, who mortal beauty chase,
> Still in a tree did end their race ;
> Apollo hunted Daphne so
> Only that she might laurel grow ;
> And Pan did after Syrinx speed
> Not as a nymph, but for a reed.
>
> A. MARVELL

20

TAMARISK
(Tamaricaceae)

The **tamarisk** is a member of the family TAMARICACEAE—a small family which is distributed mainly in the northern hemisphere. There are five genera, one of the most important of which is *Tamarix*. The tamarisk which grows wild in Britain is *T. gallica*. It is deciduous and thrives best on sandy soils in maritime areas. But it is a delicate plant and rare in Britain except along the coasts of the south-west of England.

Seldom does it aspire to an arboreal habit, and never in this country; here it is of bushy form. In its native habitats—mainly southern Europe, western Asia, Arabia and as far east as Japan—it assumes a variety of habits, and on occasions takes the form of a small tree. The tamarisk seen in Britain is sometimes called **French tamarisk,** for it flourishes in France and in North Africa, where, though usually of shrubby habit, it sometimes grows as a tree 30 feet high. It is not known exactly when or how the plant was introduced into Britain, but, according to Johns in his *Forest Trees of Britain* it might have been brought over from France by smugglers. It seems that it has thrived in south-west England for at least three hundred years. All this seems quite probable since tamarisk is very easily regenerated from cuttings.

The French tamarisk has very attractive long slender branches which bear numerous small, bluish-green leaves. In fact the foliage gives a graceful feathery appearance because the tamarisk is one of the very few 'broad-leaved' trees the leaves of which closely approach

Tamarisk on Durlston Head, Dorset.   *Eric J. Hosking*

the needle-like appearance of the leaves of conifers (hence the frequent confusion with *Cupressus*). The reason for this is not far to seek. Leaves transpire water from their surfaces, and since tamarisk grows in dry and sandy, almost arid, regions, its water-loss must be reduced. So, like the leaves of many other plants growing under such conditions, the surface of the tamarisk leaf has become reduced almost to the minimum. Frequently a small number of leaves is retained through-out the winter.

The flowers make a handsome display for about six weeks during May and June. They are borne in long, rose-pink spikes. In each flower there are four to six sepals, the same number of petals which are free, and either the same number or twice as many stamens. There are four or five joined carpels bearing the corresponding number of free styles. The fruit is a capsule and contains numerous seeds, each of which has a tuft of hair at the end.

Since time almost immemorial, the tamarisk has been valued for its medicinal properties which were probably more apparent than real. It yields no timber of any commercial value. The plant's greatest value lies in the fact that it will sometimes flourish in those seaside areas where nothing else will succeed owing to the arid and exposed conditions. A related species, *T. articulata*, has been introduced from Asia to the desert areas of California for use as wind-breaks.

A variety, *T. gallica* var. *mannifera*, an inhabitant of Egypt and the intervening countries to Afghanistan, produces a white, honey-like secretion when it is punctured by an insect. This white substance is edible and is the manna of the bedouins. It usually drops from the branches during June, but does not occur every year. It is not the manna of the Israelites.

Although the tamarisk is more happy in maritime regions it can be seen growing in certain inland parks in this country. For example, there are some trees 20 feet high in Battersea Park, London. In private gardens several other varieties are to be found; for example, *T. gallica* var. *hispida aestivalis* is very free-flowering with plume-like sprays of carmine pink, and *T. gallica* var. *parviflora* presents crimson flowers.

Among other species of *Tamarisk* sometimes cultivated in Britain are the **Chinese tamarisk** (*T. chinensis*) and a species from the Caucasus (*T. tetrandra*).

21

LIMES OR LINDENS
(*Tiliaceae*)

Sweet lime so hushèdly at the height of noon
Diffusing dizzy fragrance from your boughs,
Tasselled with blossoms more innumerable
Than the black bees, the uproar of whose toil
Fills your green vaults, winning such metheglin
As clouds their sappy cells, distil, as once
Ye used, your sunniest emanations . . .
. . . Scatter your fumes, O lime,
Loose from each hispid star of citron bloom,
Tangled beneath the labyrinthine boughs,
Cloud on such stinging cloud of exhaltation
As reeks of youth, fierce life, and summer's prime.

The Sprig of Lime : ROBERT NICHOLS

The lime or linden is a thing of beauty and delight. The form of the whole tree, whether it be in winter or in summer, is Nature at its best; the delicate leaves are perfect and cast a welcome shade especially during the summer months when the flowers are exuding their seductive perfume. Furthermore this tree lasts for at least five hundred years.

Our ancestors, living in more leisurely days, when time was not estimated in man-hours, seemed to realise the paramount importance of all this more than we do today, for, alas, most of us seldom even dream of the value of beautiful trees unless they be in a formal park or garden. Yet even this is better than nothing; and when deciding what to plant for man's enjoyment in park or on estate, the lime is well worthy of consideration. It is said that it was the great John Evelyn himself who, during the middle of the seventeenth century, proposed planting those lime trees in St. James's Park, London, which we of today may now appreciate and enjoy. But this lovely tree was then being planted in groups or avenues in many parts of the country. Some of the best-known avenues of limes still in existence include that on the Backs at Trinity College, Cambridge, and those at Bushey Park and on the Clumber Estate in Nottinghamshire. The famous limes (400 of them forming four avenues) at Shrewsbury Quarry, which were planted by Thomas Wright in 1719, were condemned as dangerous and felled early in 1945. The limes which formerly graced the streets of Berlin and gave the name to the famous *Unter den Linden* were eventually replaced by younger trees; these latter have recently been subjected to rather trying conditions.

Those who have visited the Continent, especially the countries of central and western Europe, can testify that the older generations there also held the lime in high esteem as a shade and ornamental tree in parks, on estates and along the roads. Unfortunately, on the Continent they have been too prone to cut this tree into fantastic shapes. The custom of planting lime avenues leading up to country chateaux began in France during the reign of Louis XIV; and many splendid avenues of lime may still be seen in that country.

In Holland and Germany there are some of the largest lindens in the world. In 1826, J. G. Strutt wrote in his *Sylva Britannica*: "In Holland ... they not only shelter and adorn the highways, but are planted in many towns in even lines before the houses, throughout the streets, filling the air with the fragrance of their blossoms, and screening the passengers from the sun, with the luxuriance of their shade. It is particularly adapted for avenues, from the straightness of the stem, and the luxuriant spreading of its branches, which are likewise so tough as to withstand the fury of the gales that would dismember most other trees." Again, in 1776, Evelyn, describing these Continental giants in his *Dis-*

course on Forest Trees, wrote : " But here does properly intervene the Linden of Schalouse in Swisse, under which is a bower composed of its branches, capable of containing three hundred persons sitting at ease ; it has a fountain set about with many tables, formed only of the boughs, to which they ascend by steps, all kept so accurately, and so very thick that the sun never looks into it. But this is nothing to that prodigious Tilia of Neustadt, in the Duchy of Wirtemberg, so famous for its monstrosity that even the city itself receives a denomination from it, being called by the Germans *Neustadt an der grossen Linden*, or Neustadt by the great Lime Tree. The circumference of the trunk is twenty-seven feet four fingers ; the ambitus, or extent of the boughs four hundred and three *fere* ; set about with divers columns and monuments of stone . . . which several Princes and Noble Persons have adorned, and celebrated with inscriptions, arms and devices ; and which, as so many pillars, serve likewise to support the umbrageous and venerable boughs ; and that even the tree had been much ampler, the ruins and distances of the columns disclose, which the rude soldiers have greatly impaired."

In the German heroic epic *Nibelungenlied* it was a linden leaf which fell on Siegfried when he was bathing in the blood of the dragon which was to give him immunity from all weapons ; and it was through this one vulnerable spot that Hagen struck and murdered Siegfried in the forest.

The lime has several uses apart from the timber which it yields— though the latter is not very useful. From the inner bark the Russians make mats which have been familiar to British housewives for a long time. In former days, according to Johns, in his *Forest Trees of Britain* (1849), the lime had many other uses. " The Russian peasants weave the bark of the young shoots for the upper part of their shoes, the outer bark serves for the soles ; and they also make of it baskets and boxes for domestic purposes. The fishermen of Sweden make nets for catching fish of the fibres of the inner bark, separated by maceration, so as to form a kind of flax ; and the shepherds of Carniola weave a coarse cloth of it, which serves them for their ordinary clothing. The sap drawn off in the spring affords a considerable quantity of sugar, and the seed may be converted into an oily substance perfectly resembling chocolate, but unfortunately of little value, as it soon becomes rancid."

Pliny records that the Romans made agricultural implements of the timber ; they also made their shields of lime wood. The bark was used for writing upon and for making head-dresses.

Honey produced from the nectar of lime flowers is much prized by

British Museum (Natural History)

Winter.   Summer.

Lime.

apiarists and the gourmet as being of a particularly delicate flavour. The purest lime honey is made among the dense lime woods on parts of the southern Baltic coast.

It is said that the lime tree was introduced into Britain from Germany in the reign of Queen Elizabeth by Sir John Spelman, who was also responsible for the introduction of paper-making in this country.

The lime belongs to the natural order TILIACEAE, a family distributed throughout the world and comprising many trees and shrubs though rarely herbs. The family is well advanced among the Dicotyledons with free petals, forming one of a group of families of trees and shrubs coming between the St. John's wort and the mallow families.[1]

Economically the family TILIACEAE is of importance, since, apart from the limes of this country and the Continent which belong to the genus *Tilia*, there is the well-known timber-producing **basswood** (*T. americana*) of North America. Then several other genera of the family yield valuable fibres, for example, *Corchorus capsularis*, an Indian annual plant which supplies the jute of commerce, and *Grewia*, a tropical genus

[1] See *Flowers in Britain*, p. 118.

L

of Africa, Asia and Australia. Fibres are also extracted from tropical herbs and shrubs of the genus *Triumfetta*, another member of the same family.

There are three species of lime to be found in Britain, namely, the **large-leaved** or **red-twigged lime** (*Tilia platyphyllos*), the **small-leaved lime** (*T. cordata*), and the **common lime** (*T. vulgaris*). The common lime is now considered to have originated as a hybrid of the other two. Seldom are any of these trees found growing wild ; in fact, it is probable that none of them is really native of this country but was originally introduced as recorded on p. 151. The trees attain a height of 100 to 140 feet, and are deciduous.

The spreading crown of the lime tree is supported by a tall, usually clean, bole covered with a rather smooth grey bark which tends to roughen with age. The winter buds are arranged alternately, and each bud is protected by two bud-scales of unequal size.

The foliage of the lime is a sheer delight, though, alas, it falls very early in the autumn after giving us only a very short treat in the form of golden autumnal coloration. Each leaf is bright green above, and duller green beneath owing to the presence of fine hairs. It is heart-shaped, though the lobes are of unequal size and the margins are slightly serrated. The leaves of the large-leaved species are about four inches across, those of the small-leaved species are about half that size, and those of the common lime are intermediate in size. The leaves are arranged alternately on the twig, and each leaf-blade is borne at the end of a long, gracefully curving leaf-stalk.

The flowers, which appear annually, but not until the tree is nearly forty years of age, are inconspicuous in size and colour, but not in fragrance. They open in July (when the tree is in full leaf) and then their fragrance makes a walk under the limes a real pleasure. The perfume of flowers generally attracts bees more surely than their colour, and the visits of the insect to the lime flower are not unrewarded, for much nectar is secreted at the base of the sepals. The flowers are borne in clusters called cymes, each flower growing at the end of a short stalk and then all the stalks joining at the end of a longer stalk which, for half its length, is fused with a curious, oblong, light green bract (Plate 5). These bracts are very diagnostic of the lime tree, and by their means the tree should be easily identified.

Each flower is of a dull yellow colour, and is composed of five, free, boat-shaped sepals ; five, free, lance-shaped petals ; an indefinite number of stamens ; and an ovary with a comparatively long style end-

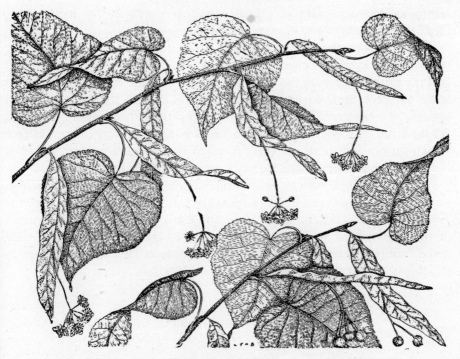

Large-leaved Lime.
Above, a twig bearing flowers ; below, a twig bearing fruit.

ing in five stigmas. Almost invariably the stamens of one flower ripen
before the ovary of the same flower, so that cross-pollination by the
visiting bees is ensured.

The fruit of the lime is a small, almost spherical nut, yellowish-
brown in colour and covered with very fine hairs. Those of the large-
leaved lime are more oval than the others, and they are ribbed. The
fruits of the small-leaved lime are less conspicuously ribbed, and those
of the common lime are not ribbed at all.

The lime does not yield a particularly valuable timber, for the
wood is soft and therefore not very durable. It is yellow in colour. For
decades it has been used for the sounding-boards of pianos and certain
other musical instruments. For wood-carving it is particularly suitable
since it is easily cut and thus gives considerable sharpness of detail.
The famous wood-carver, Grinling Gibbons (1648-1721) used lime as the
main medium for his art. He was introduced to Charles II by Evelyn,
and then proceeded to carve his masterpieces such as those in the choir
of the chapel at Windsor Castle, the choir of St. Paul's Cathedral, the

ceiling at Petworth, and various ornamental works in Trinity College, Cambridge, Chatsworth House, and other famous buildings.

Apart from the three species of lime described so far, there are several other species sometimes cultivated for their ornamental beauty ; and the number of varieties produced in Britain and also imported is so large as sometimes to create confusion. There is the very beautiful species, *T. euchlora*, having graceful, pendulous branches : then the **white lime** (*T. argentea*) bears leaves having a silvery under-surface which cannot fail to attract the eye when the leaves are disturbed by a breeze. Other species and varieties are too numerous to mention.

Among other genera belonging to the family TILIACEAE which supply plants for ornamental purposes should be mentioned the genus *Tricuspidaria* which hails from Chile and Peru. Seldom do any species of this ornamental plant attain the height of trees in Britain, but they make handsome shrubs with white or crimson flowers. All species should, however, be grown on sheltered sites.

22

TREES OF THE ROSE FAMILY

(*Rosaceae*)

Perfection is my goal
And nothing less can satisfy my soul :
But I await
Haltingly that blest state
Wounded by human hate ;
How lovely now to see
Perfection flowering in a blossoming tree.

Be ye therefore Perfect : MARIE C. STOPES

The all-important rose family (ROSACEAE) is as cosmopolitan in distribution as it is heterogeneous in organisation, being distributed throughout the world (though chiefly in the northern hemisphere), and composed of trees, shrubs and herbs, many of which are familiar and a very high percentage of which are of value to man. The family contains some of our loveliest wild and cultivated flowers, and it also produces an unusually large number of edible fruits, most of which are now bred and cultivated for food.

Among the well-known wild herbs belonging to the rose family are the wild strawberry, silver-weed, salad burnet, wood and water avens and meadowsweet. Those herbs cultivated for their ornamental beauty include the genera *Geum* and *Potentilla* ; and perhaps the most favoured of all rosaceous fruit is the herbaceous strawberry. Then many shrubs belonging to the rose family are particularly familiar because they are so attractive. Among these we have the many varieties of dog-rose and bramble (or blackberry), the dewberry and the wild raspberry. Rosaceous shrubs also play a highly important part in the decoration of our flower gardens. First and foremost is the garden rose in all its varying habits, forms and varieties. Certain species of the genus *Rubus* are also cultivated for their floral beauty. Of the rosaceous shrubs of economic importance may be mentioned the cultivated blackberry, dewberry, raspberry and loganberry ; the last-named is probably a hybrid of the blackberry and raspberry.

But consideration of any of these very important herbs and shrubs of the family ROSACEAE has no place in this book, and the reader is referred to the companion volume *Flowers in Britain,* where they are more fully discussed and illustrated. Here we must confine ourselves to the trees of the family.

There are several representative wild trees of the rose family, including the sloe (or blackthorn), the hawthorn (or may), the crab-apple, the wild plum and pear, and the rowan (or mountain ash). Some of these are themselves of a certain economic importance ; but most have been progenitors of still more important cultivated forms, including the apple, pear, plum, damson and cherry. Then also, a large number of rosaceous trees are now cultivated purely for their ornamental value, and the popularity of these is increasing. They include the so-called ' flowering ' almonds, cherries, and crabs, and the white beam and the service tree. In fact, there is no other flowering plant family in Britain which provides so many different trees—wild or cultivated—which present so many conspicuous and lovely flowers, or indeed so many different edible fruit.

> For in the morning the tall pear stands white
> With fragile petals that are shed at night,
> And the apple wears her trembling sweet array
> For hardly longer than a short spring day.
> Would they might further live or would that I
> Might see three springs without a break go by!
> *The Flowering Trees* : EDWARD SHANKS

SLOES, DAMSONS AND PLUMS

Sloes, damsons and plums are all members of the genus *Prunus* and are so closely related that they sometimes merge insensibly, especially in view of the fact that there are several thousand varieties altogether. There are nearly a hundred species of *Prunus*, most of which are distributed over north temperate areas, though a few are tropical.

The **sloe** or **blackthorn** (*Prunus spinosa*) sometimes assumes the habit of a small tree though more frequently it appears as a large bush having no pronounced bole; in fact, most frequently it is found growing as such in hedgerows.

Its leaves are rather small, elliptical and simple, and the stem bears thorns. The stem and its branches are irregular and very twisted, and the bark is black—hence the common name. The white flowers appear during March to May. The flower buds are formed during the August and September of the previous year, which explains why the flowers open before the leaves appear.

The flower of the blackthorn is comparatively small. There are five free, boat-shaped sepals, five free, white petals and fifteen to twenty stamens. There is only one carpel in a sunken receptacle. After fertilisation, this ripens into a large, fleshy, black fruit, and the remains of the rest of the flower wither away (Plate 7). The fruit is often covered with a bloom. It is sometimes used in making jellies, and also in the preparation of the liqueur sloe gin. In its early state the fruit is unpleasant to the taste, being very sour and dry, but when fully ripe it is quite palatable. The dried leaves of the blackthorn have in the past been used for adulterating tea.

> O blackthorn myriad-budded,
> Lifting your tiny fists of clenched white!
> Be braver, Bush, for Winter is vanished quite!
> Your fears forget, and open your hands shut tight!
> Now for eyes' delight
> Your treasures unlock, that our ways be flooded
> With beauty! With snowy blossom thick
> Each naked bough, each bare sharp stick
> Cover, that hither whoever strays
> May shout unawares, as he stands at gaze!
> *Barren Sloe* : EDWARD THOMPSON

The blackthorn is one of the first of our wild shrubs to bloom. Each year during March to May its white flowers enveloping the black leaf-

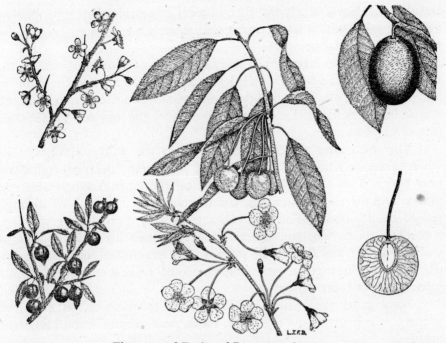

Flowers and Fruits of *Prunus* species.
Left, blackthorn, flowers above, fruit below ; centre, wild cherry, fruit above,
flowers below ; right, cultivated plum, above, section of cherry, below.

less branches in a cloud of white make a welcome sight in the still comparatively barren landscape. Small wonder, therefore, that this plant has so often inspired the poets.

> White of the blackthorn
> That the March winds toss,
> Where the sunlight falls
> On laughing petals,
>
> Dancing whiteness
> On the stiff branches,
> Dear as the first thought
> Of love to come.
>
> *Blackthorn in March 1939* : R. C. ORMEROD

Less common than the blackthorn is the **bullace** (*P. inistitia*) which is of a generally more robust habit. Its leaves are larger and broader and hairy on their under-surfaces ; the flowers have larger petals, and they bloom somewhat later in the year. Furthermore, the branches of the bullace are more or less straight and are covered with a brown bark, and there are not so many thorns. In most cases, this plant is probably a garden escape, which is not surprising since the cultivated form is the well-known **damson**.

Another close relative of these members of the genus *Prunus* is the **wild plum** (*P. domestica*) which has straight-growing brown branches but no spines at all. The flower is somewhat, though not much, larger, and as in the cultivated forms, it opens before the leaves. This species is not very common.

The cultivated plum is derived from the wild plum; but its varieties are too numerous and varied to warrant detailed consideration here. There are the small varieties, the large Victoria and egg plums, and the greengages. In colour they vary from yellow through red to deep purple. The cultivated trees may be bush or standard according to choice, site and training. **Prunes** are dried plums of varieties grown chiefly for the purpose in certain Mediterranean countries such as Yugoslavia, Spain and the south of France, and in certain warm parts of North America.

Some cultivated plums are produced from seeds, others from suckers which grow up from the roots, and others by budding and grafting.

The fruit of all species of the genus *Prunus*, which includes those already discussed, and others, such as almonds and cherries (pp. 158 and 161), is very characteristic. It is called a drupe. In view of the structure of the flower, the fruit is formed from one carpel only. The kernel inside the stone of the fruit is the actual seed. It is surrounded by a thin papery seed-coat. Surrounding the seed are three layers. Immediately enveloping the seed or kernel is a woody layer or stone. On the very outside of the fruit is another layer taking the form of a tough skin. Between these two layers is a thick, fleshy layer—the edible portion. In some cases, such as the almond, it is the kernel or seed which forms the edible portion.

The origins of the three species of *Prunus* so far considered are interesting. In spite of the fact that the ancient Romans cultivated a large number of different sorts of plums, no seeds of these have been found there or in the Swiss lake dwellings, although in those dwellings stones of the blackthorn and the bullace have been found. The plum (*P. domestica*) originated from Anatolia and the Caucasus, but may now be looked upon as being naturalised in other parts of the Old and New Worlds. Both the other species are most probably true natives of southern Europe and western Asia.

Though other species of *Prunus* (pp. 160, 164 and 166) have given us some of our most ornamental flowering trees and shrubs, those so far considered are useful mainly in supplying edible fruit. Seldom is their timber utilised commercially. There are a few interesting 'flowering' plums, some having white flowers and others pink, and certain species and varieties bearing attractive purple foliage. There is also a double-flowered sloe or blackthorn (*P. spinosa* var. *flore pleno*), though this plant is almost invariably of bushy habit only.

ALMONDS

Almonds are not native to Britain, but since they have become so very popular as ornamental trees and shrubs in gardens, parks and even along modern roadways, we can scarcely ignore them altogether here, especially since they too belong to the genus *Prunus* (*P. amygdalus*). The fruit takes the form of a typical drupe, though in this case the edible portion is not the green fleshy layer surrounding the seed, but the seed itself within the stony layer. The seed is highly nutritious, for it contains up to 55 per cent oil or fat. The objectionable taste to the seed of the bitter almond is due to the presence of a chemical substance called amygdalin from which prussic acid (a strong poison) and benzaldehyde can be extracted.

The almond originated in western Asia, but, through the agency of man, it has spread far and wide. Cultivation of almonds for their edible seeds is an extensive industry in certain parts of the Pacific coastal regions of North America. The seeds ripen even in the south of England. For centuries the plant has flourished in its native habitats of the Mediterranean regions and especially Syria and Palestine. There, particularly in the Holy Land, it blooms early in the year—that is in January, which perhaps explains the following quotation from the Bible :

> Moreover, the word of the Lord came unto me, saying, Jeremiah, what seest thou? And I said, I see a rod of an almond tree.
> Then said the Lord unto me, Thou hast well seen : for I will hasten my word to perform it.
>
> *Jeremiah* 1

The almond became symbolical in the days of the Old Testament, and even today rods of almond are used during certain important Jewish festivals.

And Moses laid up the rods before the Lord in the tabernacle of witness.

And it came to pass, that on the morrow Moses went into the tabernacle of witness; and, behold, the rod of Aaron for the house of Levi was budded, and brought forth buds, and bloomed blossoms, and yielded almonds.

Numbers 17

The bitter almond is a slightly different form from the sweet, but the differences involved do not warrant its being placed in a separate species. Both are *Prunus amygdalus*. The sweet almond bears pink flowers; those of the bitter almond are white. In Britain the flowers appear during March to May, before the leaves open, though in some seasons the leaves are well on the way to opening out when the tree is in full bloom.

> Almond blossom, sent to teach us
> That the spring days soon will reach us,
> Lest, with longing over-tried,
> We die, as the violets died.
>
> *Almond Blossoms* : EDWIN ARNOLD

Structurally, leaves, flowers and fruit of the almond closely resemble those of other members of the genus *Prunus*, though the leaves are somewhat narrower.

So popular as ornamental flowering trees and shrubs in Britain have almonds become that it is no cause for wonder that many attractive varieties have been produced chiefly by hybridisation. Some have large white flowers, whereas others bear masses of pink bloom. Then there are many double varieties and some forms bearing coloured foliage—mainly red or purple.

Longitudinal Sections through Flowers of Plum (left), Cherry (centre) and Apple (right).

Geans in Full Bloom.   *Eric J. Hosking*

CHERRIES

Sweet is the air with the budding haws, and the valley stretching
    for miles below
Is white with blossoming cherries, as if just covered with lightest
    snow.   *The Golden Legend*, Pt. 4 : LONGFELLOW

Three species of cherry now grow wild in Britain, namely : **gean**
(*Prunus avium*), the most widely spread ; the **bird cherry** (*P. padus*) and
the **wild** or **dwarf cherry** (*P. cerasus*).

It is not possible to say for certain whether these wild cherries are
really native to Britain, though it is probable that they are. Furthermore, although cultivated cherries were probably introduced about the
beginning of the Christian era, it is also certain that wild species have
also been the progenitors of cultivated forms (p. 164). The generic
name of the former botanical designation for the wild cherry—*Cerasus
vulgaris*—is derived from Cerasus (now Kerasund), a town in western
Asia from which Lucullus first took wild cherries for cultivation in
Italy and eventually elsewhere in Europe. Some authorities consider

Eric J. Hosking

Foliage and Fruit of Gean.

that what Lucullus took to Italy were only improved forms of the cornel (or wild cherry, *not* present-day cornel or dogwood, p. 320) which was already growing there. It is still further claimed that the Romans brought cherries to Britain; but though this is probable, it is just as likely that British wild cherries were also domesticated. It is said that the cherries of Kent were introduced from Flanders during the reign of Henry VIII, and this may be true; but it is also just as likely that cherries now under cultivation in other parts of Britain were adapted from the wild species in the vicinity. According to Johns, the first mention of the sale of cherries by hawkers in London was in the year 1415.

The leaves of all three species of cherry mentioned are simple, oval, with serrated margins, and pointed at the tip. Those of the gean are slightly hairy on the under-surface.

The flowers appear shortly after the leaves have broken bud, that is, during April and May. In the case of the gean and the wild cherry, they are borne in clusters called umbels; but those of the bird cherry grow in looser racemes. The basic structure of the cherry flower is similar to that of other species of *Prunus*, though the receptacle which encloses the single carpel growing up from its base is more vase-shaped and less open than those of the blackthorn and plum (p. 160). In all cases the flowers are white. The petals of the gean are heart-shaped; those of the wild cherry are not so open and are more oval in shape; and the margins of the petals of the bird cherry are notched.

The fruit of the cherry is the well-known drupe, very similar in fundamental structure to that of the blackthorn and plum, and is borne at the end of a long, thin stalk. That of the gean may be either red or black. It is usually sweet to taste and its juice stains the skin. The fruit of the wild cherry is more spherical and is always red in colour and bitter to the taste. The drupes of the bird cherry are comparatively small, black and very bitter.

The gean (*P. avium*) is perhaps the most lovely of all our wild cherries (p. 161); it is also the largest. Given good conditions it will grow anything from 80 to 110 feet high, though it usually falls far short of that. The large spreading branches produce a crown which, especially when in flower, makes a never-to-be-forgotten sight. When the leaves begin to open (that is, just before the flower-buds burst forth) they are very deep red in colour; then they turn a bright green, and eventually, just before leaf-fall, they turn a fiery red.

The gean would produce a valuable timber if it were cultivated. The heart-wood is brown in colour, and is used in cabinet-making, whereas the wood of the smaller branches is used for the manufacture of tobacco pipes.

No owner of a cherry tree needs to be told that birds are a perfect pest when the fruits are ripe, and this applies to the gean also. Among the worst culprits are thrushes and blackbirds. Furthermore, this tree attracts the woodpecker seeking the larvae of insects beneath its bark and a haven for its nest.

The bird cherry (*P. padus*) rarely attains arboreal habit; more often does it take the form of a shrub, though trees up to 30 feet in height have been known. It is confined to the northern parts of Britain, sometimes also occurring in midland districts. As already stated above, the drupes are small and bitter; in fact they are quite useless to man, though birds eat them. The red wood takes a high polish, and on the Continent it is used for cabinet-making.

The wild or dwarf cherry (*P. cerasus*), like the bird cherry, does not often appear as a tree, especially since it is so prone to produce suckers. This species is confined mainly to the south of England, and though it sometimes appears in the north of the country it never occurs in Scotland.

> Under pure skies of April blue I stood,
> Where, in wild beauty, cherries were in blow ;
> And, as sweet fancy willed, see there I could
> Boughs thick with blossom, or inch-deep in snow.
>
> *The Cherry Tree* : WALTER DE LA MARE

As already indicated on p. 161 there is considerable doubt about the true origin of the cherries ; but once they had become naturalised on the Continent and eventually in Britain, there seems little doubt about the origin of cherries now grown under cultivation. May duke and morello or brandy cherries and the cherries of the south-east of England are most probably forms of the wild cherry (*P. cerasus*), while geans, black-hearts and bigarreaus arose from the wild gean (*P. avium*).

Today cherries are cultivated for their delicious fruit in all the temperate regions of the world. Apart from supplying a natural dessert, the fruit is used for many culinary purposes and for the making of such liqueurs as cherry brandy, kirschwasser and maraschino.

The number of ' flowering ' cherries cultivated for their decorative value in gardens, parks and streets is now legion. By far the majority of them originated in Japan, the land of cherry blossom, where the **Japanese cherry** (*P. serrulata*) is almost a national emblem. Among the many forms produced by scientific breeding and culture, are standard trees and bush plants blooming at times varying between March and May. The clouds of flowers often make a sight never to be forgotten.

The flowers may be large or small, single or double, and varying in colour from snowy white through the palest of pink to a deep pink. The fact that the flower buds are usually of a deeper shade adds to the general lovely effect. No one should miss seeing the ' flowering ' cherries when they are in full bloom in the Royal Botanic Gardens, Kew, and elsewhere.

> The cherry-trees are seas of bloom and soft perfume and
>   sweet perfume,
> The cherry-trees are seas of bloom (and oh, so near to
>   London!) ;
> And there, they say, when dawn is high and all the
>   world's a blaze of sky,
> The cuckoo, though he's very shy, will sing a song for
>   London.
>
> *The Barrel Organ* : ALFRED NOYES

Cultivated Cherry.   *Eric J. Hosking*

Further interest is added to Noyes's verse by the fact that in mythology the cherry and the cuckoo are associated. Johns quotes the German proverb that " the cuckoo never sings until he has thrice eaten his fill of cherries "; and he also describes an old Yorkshire children's game in which the children danced round a cherry tree singing :

> Cuckoo, cherry tree,
> Come down and tell me
> How many years I have to live.

Then each child shook the tree, and the number of cherries which fell denoted the number of years which that child would live.

OTHER SPECIES OF *PRUNUS*

Among other species of *Prunus* there are some which are not indigenous to Britain and not very often cultivated, yet they are so well-known in Britain as to be worthy of mention. There is, for example, the **apricot** (P. *armeniaca*), the fruit of which is very popular at British tables. This tree is native to temperate Asia, especially China, but it is now cultivated extensively in Armenia and is a staple product of the fruit-growing regions of California. Seldom does the fruit ripen in Britain, though its cultivation here has succeeded on occasions.

The cultivation of **peaches** (*P. persica*) is also not very satisfactory in Britain, except in sunny warm areas where the plants are protected by high walls. But the popularity of this expensive fruit is such that it pays to cultivate it in the larger greenhouses. The actual origin of the peach has never been really settled : one school of thought, formerly headed by Darwin, looks upon it as a modified form of almond ; another considers it a distinct species originally hailing from China.

The **nectarine** is a variety of the peach.

Varieties of apricots and peaches now figure among the ornamental 'flowering' trees in Britain. There are, for example, a Japanese apricot having rose-coloured flowers, and several lovely varieties and forms of peach, for example, *P. persica* var. *magnifica* with bright crimson flowers of partially double structure.

Other species of *Prunus*, too, are grown for garden ornamentation. The most common is the **cherry laurel** (*P. laurocerasus*), which, of course, is no relative of the true laurel (p. 143). There are many varieties and forms of this handsome shrub.

Cultivated Plum.

By courtesy of the Royal Horticultural Society
Young Apple Orchard.

APPLES

The apple in all its varieties and forms is the most widely cultivated of all fruit trees. In Britain alone there are about two thousand different kinds varying considerably in popularity, so it would serve no useful purpose here to consider in any detail the breeding of this fruit. It has been known to be cultivated in this country since the days of the Romans; but there is no doubt that all varieties and forms of this plant are descended from the wild or crab-apple. The cultivated fruit is eaten naturally or in many forms of confection and preserve; from the wild crab delicious jelly is made, and from the same fruit and certain of its cultivated varieties the well-known beverage cider is also brewed. Verjuice, an acid liquor used in cooking, is made from crab-apples as well as other fruit.

The apple tree is cultivated almost solely for its fruit. The wood is little used. In Britain the tree is grown to a considerable extent in orchards, some of which are old-established (p. 169); but so much research has now been carried out on the cultivation of this plant that

M

many new orchards have gradually been developed. The climate of
Scotland handicaps the growth of this tree, though there are extensive
orchards in Perthshire. Ever since Norman times the greatest apple-
growing areas in Britain have been Somerset, Devon, Gloucester, the
Wye Valley and Herefordshire. Abroad, apples are also cultivated in
small orchards and gardens, especially in European countries; but in
warmer countries, such as the United States, certain parts of Canada,
South Africa, Australia and the West Indies, the trees are grown on extensive farms.

The progenitor of all apples is the **wild** or **crab-apple.** This plant
was formerly a member of the genus *Pyrus,* to which the pear belongs,
and then the apple was designated *Pyrus malus*; but recently it has been
relegated to a genus of its own—*Malus pumila.*

The general botany of this tree is given in *Flowers in Britain.* It
is found growing in woods and hedgerows throughout Britain (except
the north of Scotland), and it blooms during April to August. The
general form of the tree is irregular with spreading and slightly drooping
branches. It attains a height of 20 to 50 feet. The leaves are simple
with slightly serrated edges. The twigs are somewhat spiny.

The flowers are white, tinted with pink, and look very lovely as they
are borne in clusters on short shoots.

> The apple blossom's shower of pearl
> Though blent with rosier hue,
> As beautiful as a woman's blush—
> As evanescent too.
> *Apple Blossoms* : LETITIA E. LANDON

To each apple flower there are five boat-shaped sepals, five free
petals which are heart-shaped, many stamens and five carpels joined to
form an ovary embedded in the base of a slightly hollow receptacle
(pp. 160 and 170). There are usually five styles.

The fruit is actually formed from the five joined fertilised carpels
which have horny walls enclosing the seeds or pips (constituting the
core), and the receptacle which has swollen to form the fleshy edible part
of the fruit. This type of fruit is called a pome (p. 170).

> Already now behind the glistening petals,
> Slowly grow round and hard
> The fruit which will, within the sugary pulp,
> Hold the immortal seed.
> *In the Orchard* : EDWARD SHANKS

Lonsdale Ragg

Old Apple Orchard.

Apple Blossom.
Right, a fruit (pome) cut in longitudinal section.

Wild crabs, which may be either yellow or red, are usually too sour to eat because they contain a high percentage of malic acid ; but, as already stated, they make excellent jelly.   In earlier days, crab-apples were used more often than they are now.   They were served in hot drinks and punches (see also p. 167).

> When roasted crabs hiss in the bowl,
> Then nightly sings the staring owl.
> > *Love's Labour Lost* : SHAKESPEARE

> And sometimes lurk I in a gossip's bowl
> In very likeness of a roasted crab.
> > *Midsummer Night's Dream* : SHAKESPEARE

There is a host of popular varieties of ' flowering ' crabs, many of which ornament our gardens and parks not only with their lovely flowers but also in some cases with their bright red, purple or yellow fruit, sometimes growing in dense clusters.   The autumn foliage tints of some forms, too, present a striking effect.

PEARS

The pears again are members of the genus *Pyrus*. All varieties and forms are derived from the **wild pear** (*Pyrus communis*). The cultivation of the pear dates back to antiquity ; but the plant probably originated in southern Europe and western Asia. Pears are not extensively cultivated in Britain because they prefer a warmer climate than does the apple, yet there are some large orchards of pears in Middlesex, Hertfordshire, Kent, Norfolk and Worcestershire. Many gardeners, too, boast a few pear trees.

> Hark, where my blossomed pear-tree in the hedge
> Leans to the field and scatters on the clover
> Blossoms and dew-drops—at the bent spray's edge—
> That's the wise thrush ; he sings each song twice over,
> Lest you should think he never could recapture
> The first fine careless rapture !
> *Home Thoughts, from Abroad* : R. BROWNING

The wood of the pear tree has little commercial value, though it is sometimes used in the making of mathematical instruments, and has been known to be stained black and then passed off as ebony. The fruit is used as an article of diet in many forms, and an alcoholic beverage known as perry is prepared from it. There are about five thousand different forms of pear in Europe and about a thousand in the United States.

The wild pear (*Pyrus communis*) is not common in Britain, and it is confined to the southern counties. It varies in height from 20 to 60 feet, and its branches are somewhat spiny. The flowers, which appear during April and May, are similar in structure to those of the apple ; but they are pure white. The fruit, too, differs in shape from that of the apple and is yellow when it ripens in November. The grittiness of the pear fruit is due to many thousands of groups of microscopic woody cells embedded in the flesh. These are called stone cells. There are no stone cells in the apple fruit.

MEDLARS AND QUINCES

The fruits of medlar and quince are not so popular in Britain today as they were at one time. The former is sometimes found growing in the wild state in the south of England, though it has probably originated as a garden escape ; the latter is never found growing wild, neither is it often cultivated.

Leaves, Flowers and Fruit of Medlar.

Though it is assigned to a different genus from *Pyrus*, the **medlar** is closely similar to members of the latter genus. The botanical name of medlar is now accepted as *Mespilus germanica*. It is a native of continental Europe and western Asia, and was known to the ancient Greeks, Romans and Persians. It was probably introduced into Britain towards the end of the sixteenth century. Though usually of shrubby habit, it sometimes achieves tree-like proportions and reaches a height of 10 to 20 feet. In the wild state it is spiny, but the spines are seldom present on the cultivated forms.

The flowers, which appear in May and June, are not borne in clusters but are solitary. They are comparatively large, frequently attaining a diameter of more than an inch. They are sometimes white and sometimes very pale pink in colour. A diagnostic feature is the exceptionally long and leafy sepals, the prominent remains of which persist in the fruit. The latter becomes brown and more or less spherical with a very deep depression at its apex around the margin of which the remains of the sepals, which are now hard and tough, persist.

After it has become ripe, the fruit is still unfit to eat until it has begun to decay. It then has an acid flavour.

The **quince** belongs to still another genus (*Cydonia vulgaris*). There is still some confusion about its origin, though it is certainly not indigenous to Britain ; in fact, its fruit seldom reach maturity except in sheltered positions in the south of England.

It is native to Persia and other parts of western Asia, though certain varieties were also known to the ancient Japanese, and different varieties were familiar to the ancient Greeks.

> Solon bade the bride eat a quince the first night of marriage, intimating thereby, it seems, that the bridegroom was to expect the first pleasure from the bride's mouth and conversation.
>
> *Morals : Conjugal Precepts* : PLUTARCH

The leaves of the quince have smooth margins. Like those of the medlar, the flowers are large and solitary, pink or white (superficially like dog-roses), and the sepals are extremely long and leafy. But the fruit is more pear-shaped and there is no apical depression. It has a peculiar fragrance and is acid when raw ; but it makes a good preserve and is used for other culinary purposes.

Even more familiar to British garden lovers is the **Chinese quince** (*Cydonia lagenaria*), commonly called **japonica**, which is often cultivated, usually as a wall shrub, but sometimes as a small standard tree, for its handsome flowers. Though it originally hailed from China, this plant was introduced into Britain from Japan in 1796. The fragrant pear-shaped fruit is inedible, though a tasty jelly can be made from it. There are several varieties of this plant with flowers varying in shade from white through rose pink and salmon to rich red.

WHITE BEAM AND WILD SERVICE

To the rosaceous genus *Sorbus* belong several rather important trees, and the first to be considered here is the **white beam** (*Sorbus aria*). It should be noted that this species and other members of the genus *Sorbus* have for a long time been placed in the genus *Pyrus*, but now they are considered better placed in the former genus. Furthermore, it should be pointed out that the word ' beam ' is the Saxon derivative of ' tree ', and it is therefore not correct to speak of the ' white beam tree '.

The white beam is very wide in distribution in Britain, yet in spite of this it is not very common. From the utilitarian point of view, therefore, the tree is of little value in this country. On the most exposed sites it scarcely develops beyond the habit of a bush ; but when sheltered, especially on limy soils, it assumes the proportions of a tree, sometimes reaching as high as 50 feet. The bark is smooth in a young tree, but becomes fissured as the tree ages.

The leaves are rather curious in shape, being broadly elliptical and becoming deeply serrated on the distal half but only slightly so nearest the stalk (p. 174). They are white and fluffy on the lower surface.

The flowers are basically similar to those of the *Pyrus* genus, but are borne in white clusters called cymes (p. 174). They appear during May and June, and the tree then looks very handsome. Each flower is white and rarely exceeds half an inch in diameter. The fruits (p. 174) are bright red and ovoid in shape. Many wild animals eat them raw, either when still on the tree or when fallen to the ground ; but, like the medlar, they are agreeable to the human palate only when they are decaying.

Sorbus aria is distributed chiefly in Ireland and in the south of England, spreading to the Midlands. Some trees are found further north, where they are sometimes called **chess-apples**.

In certain woodlands of the west of England a rare species of white beam, the **Cornish white beam** (*S. latifolia*), may be found. Its leaves are broader than those of the commoner species and are lobed. Then there is an even rarer species, the **Scots white beam** (*S. intermedia*), occurring in the mountains of Wales and Scotland, but more often seen under cultivation. Its leaves are even more deeply lobed and are very broad across the middle. A few varieties of white beam are cultivated for their beauty of form and for the attractiveness of the flowers and fruit. One variety has a distinctive foliage of a greyish colour.

Closely related to the white beam is the **wild service** (*S. torminalis*). This plant may easily be mistaken for a white beam, though closer observation will reveal that the leaves are lobed like the maple and for this reason the tree was at one time called **maple tree**. Furthermore, when young, the leaves are covered with hairs on their under-surfaces, though they become smooth as they mature. They present lovely shades of red in the autumn.

Eric J. Hosking

Flowers and Fruit of White Beam.

The flowers are larger than those of white beam, and the fruit somewhat smaller. The latter are dry; but when they have been subject to frost they decay and then they are quite palatable. In some localities they were at one time sold as a dessert.

The wild service is distributed in the same areas as the white beam though seldom farther north than the north midlands and never in Scotland. It is only a small tree, though specimens 80 feet high have been recorded.

Since this tree is uncommon, its timber is very seldom used commercially, though, according to Elwes and Henry, it has been used for decorative work.

Foliage of Wild Service.

In the white beams and the wild service there seems to be a transition to the rowan (see below). The leaves of the common white beam (*S. aria*) are simple, whereas those of the rowan (*S. aucuparia*) are completely compound. The other species already described then show transitional forms. In fact, the Cornish white beam (*S. latifolia*) is usually looked upon as intermediate between the common white beam and the wild service, whereas the latter is more closely related to the rowan. Thus the transition can be seen best in the leaf-forms.

ROWAN AND TRUE SERVICE

The **mountain ash** (*Sorbus aucuparia*) is a common inhabitant of the mountains, especially of north Britain, so that part of its common name is justified; but it is a pity that the name ' ash ' has been applied to it, for, apart from a close resemblance to the compound leaves, mountain ash is nothing like the true ash (*Fraxinus*, p. 322). The former is frequently also known as **rowan,** a name which is common enough, being much more widely used than such localised names as **white ash, witch-wood, fowler's service, cock-drunks, witchen, wicken, wiggin,** and so forth. This plant has now been assigned to the genus *Sorbus*, though at one time it was a member of the genus *Pyrus*. The specific name *aucuparia* is reminiscent of the days on the Continent when bird-catchers used the fruit as a bait for their traps—

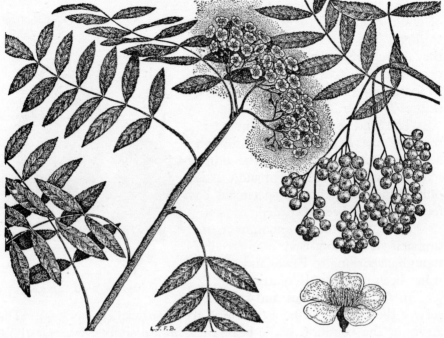

Rowan.
Left, a twig bearing leaves and flowers; above right, fruit; below right, a single flower.

auceps meaning a fowler. The tree has for centuries been associated with witches since it was supposed to counteract their evil intents, hence the vulgar names ' witchen ', ' wicken ' and ' wiggin '. According to Edward Step, the name ' rowan ' may be derived from the old Norse *runa* meaning ' a charm '. On the other hand, the name may be cognate with the Swedish *rönn*, meaning red, referring to the berries. ' Cock-drunks ' is a more localised name given in the belief that the fruit make fowls intoxicated.

At one time the rowan was the object of great veneration. It was planted in churchyards, especially in Wales.

The rowan is native to most of Europe, including Britain, and other parts of the north temperate zone in both Old and New Worlds. It grows to an average height of 40 feet.

The grey bark which surrounds a clean bole is smooth on the branches and on a young trunk, but later it becomes fissured horizontally. Each leaf is compound, having a terminal leaflet and five to eight pairs of lateral leaflets. Each leaflet is lance-shaped and has serrated margins. The upper surface is bright green ; the lower, pale green. The

Rowan.

Eric J. Hosking

small, cream-coloured flowers are borne in dense cymes (p. 176 and Plate 7) and they bloom during June and September. Fundamentally they resemble hawthorn flowers (p. 182), but are much smaller.

In September the fruits begin to ripen. They are not berries but small pomes. After passing through various phases of colour beginning yellow, they finally assume the brilliant scarlet hue so familiar to countrymen and town dwellers. They are eagerly sought by birds, by which the seeds are dispersed. In north European countries the fruits are eaten by man, but they are not very palatable. John Evelyn recorded that " the juice of the berries, which fermenting of itself, if well preserved, makes an excellent drink against the spleen and scurvy. Ale and beer brewed with these berries when ripe, is an incomparable drink, familiar in Wales." There is an old Scottish recipe for making a marmalade from the rowan fruit. It is also used for making birdlime.

The wood of the rowan is not utilised very much these days, though it was frequently used instead of yew for making bows. Later, the wood was at times used in turnery since it is fine-grained and takes a high polish.

The rowan is frequently cultivated for its graceful and attractive leaves and for its striking bunches of red fruit. There are also many different varieties and forms. The autumn tints of the leaves of some varieties are very bright—often a fiery red. One variety, *S. aucuparia* var. *asplenifolia,* has very deeply serrated leaflets which are particularly graceful. Another variety bears fruit which remain yellow all the time ; others bear orange-coloured fruit. Perhaps one of the most striking is *S. aucuparia* var. *hupehensis,* of Chinese origin, which bears white fruit with ' red ' eyes.

Very closely resembling the rowan is the **true service** (*S. domestica*), which is very rare in Britain. It is probably not native to this country. It is cultivated in certain parts of Europe. A very few specimens have occurred in remote districts in the west of England. A single specimen once grew in the Wyre Forest in Worcestershire and was described in the *Philosophical Transactions of the Royal Society* as far back as 1678 ; but this tree was eventually destroyed. It has never been definitely established whether this tree and those in Cornwall (all of which have now probably disappeared) were truly indigenous. It was sometimes called **sorb** and sometimes **chequer tree.**

But sometimes the true service is cultivated in Britain for ornamental effect. It will attain a height of 60 to 80 feet, and, though very like the rowan, can be distinguished from the latter since its bark is rougher and darker. Furthermore, the leaflets are broader than those of the rowan and they are somewhat hairy. This tree is therefore the most massive of all rosaceous trees, and it frequently outlives all its relatives.

The flowers are white, rather larger than that of rowan, and the fruits, instead of being spherical and red, are often pear-shaped and of a speckled reddish-brown colour.   Sometimes they are nearly spherical.

Though there are some handsome specimens of true service in Britain—for example, those in the Botanic Gardens at Oxford and at Cambridge and on certain country estates, the tree is never grown *en masse* in Britain.   But in France and Switzerland it frequently appears in avenues among other related trees.   The lovely autumnal tints of this tree are very effective.   In France, an alcoholic drink is sometimes prepared from the fruits.   They are also preserved in the dry condition.

HAWTHORN OR MAY

It is difficult to decide at what time of the year the park is in its glory. The mayflower on the great hawthorn trees in spring may perhaps claim the pre-eminence, filling the soft breeze with exquisite odour.   These here are trees, not bushes, standing separate, with thick gnarled stems so polished by the constant rubbing of the cattle as almost to shine like varnish.   The may-bloom, pure white in its full splendour, takes a dull, reddish tinge as it fades, when a sudden shake will bring it down in showers.

RICHARD JEFFERIES

The **hawthorn** or **may** scarcely needs introduction.   It has played the most prominent part of all our forest trees for generations in giving pleasure and happiness to millions of people of all ages, especially in our sports and pastimes.   For example, one only has to recall the first verse of the famous nursery rhyme :

Here we come gathering nuts in May,
Nuts in May, nuts in May,
Here we come gathering nuts in May,
This cold and frosty morning.

The rhyme quoted is a Yorkshire version : there are several others. The verses were sung during a folk-game, and the interpretation placed on the words by the well-known folklorist Lady Gomme is of interest. She attributes the origin to parties of young men gathering bunches of may at the May festivals and dances, to decorate not only the may-pole and kissing-bush, but also the doors of houses.   It is certain that neither the version ' Nuts in May ' nor the version ' Nuts and may ' can be transcribed literally, for nuts and may flowers are never available at the same time of the year.   Lady Gomme considered the word ' nuts ' in the rhyme to be a corruption of ' knots ', meaning ' bunches '.   This is supported by the fact that years ago the ' May girls ' in London used to call at the house on May day with garlands singing :

> Knots of may we've brought you,
> Before your door it stands ;
> It is but a sprout, but it's well budded out
> By the work of the Lord's hands.

Since the time of the Greeks, too, this lovely blossom has inspired poets.

> There are the twisted hawthorn trees
> Thick-set with buds, as clear and pale
> As golden water or green hail—
> As if a storm of rain had stood
> Enchanted in the thorny wood,
> And, hearing fairy voices call,
> Hung poised, forgetting how to fall.
>
> *Green Rain* : MARY WEBB

Shakespeare frequently referred to hawthorn and may ; so also did Burns :

> Tho' large the forest's monarch throws
>   His army-shade,
> Yet green the juicy hawthorn grows,
>   Adown the glade.
>
> *The Vision* : BURNS

The term ' hawthorn ' is most probably derived from the Old English for ' hedge-thorn ', for this plant is frequently used for hedge-making. To the Ancient Greeks it was the emblem of hope, and the Romans used it for the torches at wedding processions. In some parts it is believed that the Crown of Thorns was made from this tree, though others believe that holly was used for this purpose (p. 294). In parts of France it was claimed that the hawthorn groans on Good Friday. The famous Glastonbury Thorn (p. 184) has a different tradition.

There is a widespread superstition against bringing may blossom into the house.

The hawthorn belongs to the genus *Crataegus*, and there are two species in Britain, namely, *C. oxyacantha*, having white flowers and one style to the ovary, and *C. oxyacanthoides* which has two styles. Furthermore, the flowers of *C. oxyacanthoides* are smaller and the branches are more thorny. The leaves are also more indented. *C. oxyacantha* is much more common than *C. oxyacanthoides* and is the one most commonly found in hedgerows ; *C. oxyacanthoides* being usually confined to the woods.

Eric J. Hosking

Hawthorn in bloom in Hatfield Park.

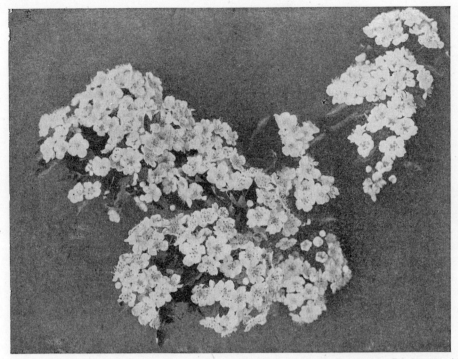

Eric J. Hosking

Hawthorn Flowers.

The botany of the hawthorn is set out in *Flowers in Britain* (p. 134). The thorns are really modified branches, and are sometimes so large that they themselves bear lateral leaves. The leaf is simple, though very deeply indented (Plate 7). The flowers are white and are borne in dense clusters. They make a lovely scene in the hedgerows during May and June. Frequently one comes across a single tree or bush, and this in bloom is a most inspiring sight (p. 181).

Each flower has five sepals, five white petals, many stamens and one or two styles according to species (Plate 7). The fruit is composed of a stony seed surrounded by a swollen receptacle which eventually turns dark red. It is sometimes called a 'haw'. Though edible, these 'haws' are dry eating and not very palatable; yet children sometimes eat them, and in certain parts of the United States they are used in jellies.

It is still believed by many that if the hawthorn haws and rose hips are borne in profusion then a hard winter lies ahead—and this in spite of no meteorological confirmation.

Hawthorn Fruit.

The thorns and briars, vermilion-hue,
Now full of hips and haws are seen;
If village prophecies be true,
They prove that winter will be keen.
Autumn : J. CLARE

As a tree, the hawthorn will attain a height of 40 feet, though it branches so profusely that very often its bole is lost in a tangled mass looking more like a very thick bush; hence the suitability of this plant for hedges. When very old its trunk becomes gnarled and, if in an exposed position, the branches are twisted, giving the whole tree a sinister appearance (p. 185).

Nevertheless, the hawthorn has been the forerunner of numerous ornamental trees which are to be seen frequently in parks and gardens and along the roads, sometimes in very densely built-up areas. Among these varieties we have standard trees and bushes bearing white, rose-pink or scarlet flowers—sometimes single and sometimes double—and fruit of varying size, form and shades from yellow through bright red

N

to deep purple. One variety, *C. oxyacantha* var. *pendula*, is of weeping habit.

The well-known Glastonbury Thorn is a variety (*C. oxyacantha* var. *praecox*) which blooms both in winter and in early summer. According to legend the original Thorn sprang from the staff of Joseph of Arimathea who planted it in the grounds of Glastonbury Abbey when he visited that place with his eleven disciples.

> Glastonbury, where the winter thorn
> Blossoms at Christmas, mindful of our Lord.
> *The Holy Grail* : TENNYSON

It is probable that the Glastonbury Thorn is really a ' sport ' from the common thorn, for though cuttings from the original Thorn still bloom twice a year those plants produced from its seeds revert to the ordinary type and bloom once a year only—in early summer. Similar thorns which bloom twice a year are to be found on the Continent.

The wood is very tough and hard ; but it is seldom used now except sometimes as a substitute for the wood of box (see p. 197) in wood-engraving.

In North America there is another genus of rosaceous shrubs and trees, *Amelanchier* or **june-berry**. There are several species of this which produce edible fruits, sometimes also known as **service-** or **sugar-berries**. Some species are cultivated in Britain for ornamental purposes. Here they bloom early in spring ; then in the autumn they produce glorious foliage. *A. canadensis*, for example, is clouded with white flowers which later produce crimson fruit ; *A. vulgaris* also bears white flowers, but these are followed by purple fruit.

23

TREES OF THE PEA FAMILY

(Leguminosae)

Like the rose family (ROSACEAE), the pea family (LEGUMINOSAE) is a very large one, and it is cosmopolitan in distribution ; in fact, the pea family is more cosmopolitan than the rose family, for there is a higher percentage of tropical members. There are altogether more than five hundred genera and twelve thousand species, with a host of varieties

Thorn.
Merdon Castle
Hursley

os-7-39
LR

Old Thorn in Hampshire.

of many of the latter. Furthermore, the family comprises plants of all sorts of habits—tall herbs, climbers, creepers, small herbs, shrubs and small and large trees.

The flower of the pea family is very characteristic, no matter whether belonging to herb, shrub or tree; reference to *Flowers in Britain* will show the floral similarity between vastly different members of this interesting family.

In all British members of the family there are five united sepals separating into five teeth at their tips. There may be five regularly arranged teeth, or the calyx may be two-lipped, with two teeth at the top and three at the bottom. The petals show the greatest irregularity, having a large standard at the back, two side wings, and two smaller petals forming a keel at the bottom. The keel encloses the other organs of the flower. This floral form gives a butterfly effect, so all very irregular members of the family are sometimes placed in a sub-family called the PAPILIONACEAE. In some members of the family the ten stamens are united along about two-thirds of their length forming a tube around the carpels, as in the broom and the gorse; in other genera nine of the stamens are so joined, but the tenth—the upper one—is free along its entire length, as in the bird's-foot trefoil, the vetches and the laburnum. Some exotic members of the family, for example, the genus *Sophora* (p. 194), have completely free stamens; but such plants are not common taking the pea family as a whole.

The single carpel contains one to several ovules and the fruit formed after fertilisation is the very characteristic pod or legume. The legume splits in varying ways in order to eject its ripe seeds.

Some members of the pea family have quite regular flowers, with many stamens. The most important examples are *Mimosa* and the true *Acacia*; but since neither of these genera contains trees which are to be found in Britain they do not concern us here.

Only a very few trees belonging to the pea family (LEGUMINOSAE) are to be found in Britain, but these are very lovely plants.

LABURNUM

Like the hawthorn, the laburnum is quite as well-known to town-dwellers as to those more used to rural surroundings, for, though it is not found growing in the wild state, it is very widely cultivated, some-times flourishing quite well in the meanest back garden.

The laburnum belongs to the genus *Laburnum*—a small genus

native to Europe and western Asia. The **common laburnum** (*L. anagyroides*) is indigenous to France, Switzerland and parts of Germany and northern Italy, and though it is not found growing wild in Britain it may now be looked upon as being naturalised in this country, though we do not know exactly when it was introduced.

One example is recorded as growing in Gerard's garden in 1597, and in those days it was called not only laburnum but also **anagyris** and **beane trefoyle.** Today it is known in certain localities as **golden chain, golden rain** and **watch-and-chain.**

The laburnum is of a definite arboreal habit, though it is never a very tall tree—usually about 20 feet high. The bark is smooth and of a greenish tint, and the branches are irregular and unshapely.

The attractive leaves, which are delicate and attractive and downy beneath, are obscured during May by the long chains of flowers. They are trifoliate, that is, each leaf is composed of three leaflets, each leaflet being lance-shaped and having smooth margins. The centre, that is the terminal, leaflet is somewhat larger than the two lateral leaflets (Plate **2**). The leaves are deciduous.

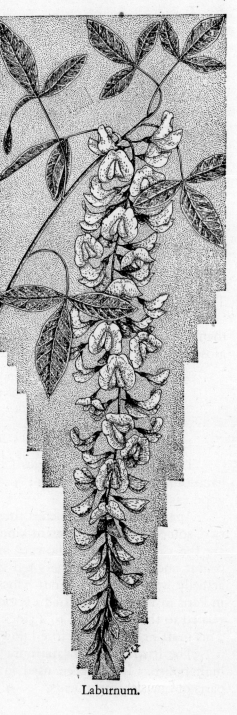

Laburnum.

The lovely yellow flowers are borne in long pendulous racemes.

> Laburnums, dropping-wells of fire.
>
> *In Memoriam* : TENNYSON

The structure of the flower has already been described. It should be noted that the tenth stamen is free. As one might expect, the flowers are insect-pollinated, chiefly by bees. The fruit takes the form of a long pod, so that each raceme produces a bunch of pods, though not all the flowers in any one raceme set seed (Plate 2).

- There is also the **alpine laburnum** (*L. alpinum*), native to France and Central Europe, which blooms later than the common laburnum and bears larger leaves and longer racemes of flowers which stand out conspicuously when the tree is in bloom.

As might be expected, a number of interesting varieties of both laburnums have emerged under cultivation. Of the common laburnum (*L. anagyroides*) there are several forms, boasting a variety of leaves and flowers. The very common variegated form has little to recommend it. The golden-leaved form (*L. anagyroides* var. *aureum*) is attractive ; the ' oak-leaved ' variety (*L. anagyroides* var. *quercifolium*) is more interesting than effective ; *L. anagyroides* var. *alschingeri* blooms later and has very glossy leaves. There is also a variety having pink flowers.

> The pink laburnum lays her cheek
> In married, matchless, lovely bliss,
> Against her golden mate, to seek
> His airy kiss.
>
> *A Benedictine Garden* : ALICE BROWN

The varieties of the species *L. alpinum* have particularly long and handsome racemes of flowers ; *L. alpinum* var. *vossii* is a particularly good example.

Apart from these varieties there is a very curious form. It bears two, sometimes three, different kinds of flowers simultaneously. There are the ordinary yellow flowers borne in racemes, others purple in colour and sometimes others red in colour. This strange example is actually what is called a graft hybrid. It was first produced by Adam in Paris in 1828, who grafted a scion of *Cytisus purpureus* (a plant closely related to the broom) on to a stock of laburnum (*Laburnum anagyroides*). This graft hybrid is therefore known as *Cytisus adami*.

The hard wood of laburnum is dark in colour and takes a very high polish. It has been used in high-class cabinet-making and for parts of musical instruments.

WISTARIA

The genus *Wistaria* contains some of the most beautiful climbing shrubs to be seen in Britain, though it is not indigenous to this country. The genus hails from China and Japan, the most common species being the Chinese, *W. chinensis*, and the Japanese, *W. floribunda*. The flowers are basically similar to those of laburnum, but lovelier in shape and sweetly scented. Thus for beauty climbing over trellis-work or even over the house, and for perfume, it is difficult to imagine anything excelling this lovely ' old-fashioned ' plant.

Then there are species of *Wistaria* bearing white flowers, the most common of which is the **silky wistaria** (*W. venusta*) of China. *W. chinensis* var. *alba* is also white. In the southern United States there is a wild species, *W. frutescens*, having purple flowers, as also have some other Japanese species.

Though *Wistaria* is usually a climber, some varieties can be trained as weeping standard trees.

INDIAN LABURNUM

Sometimes, though not very often, the **Indian laburnum** may be seen growing in a British garden. But this tree belongs to a different genus, *Cassia*—a large genus indigenous to tropical and warm temperate regions. The Indian laburnum (*C. fistula*) is a native of Africa but is cultivated in the East and West Indies. The seeds are surrounded within the pod by a pulp which is used as a laxative.

The same genus, *Cassia*, contains trees which yield the drug senna which is actually the dried pods of these trees. **Alexandrian senna** is *C. acutifolia*; **Italian**, *C. obovata*; and **Arabian**, *C. angustifolia*.

Even rarer in Britain is the **Nepal laburnum** (*Piptanthus nepalensis*), which belongs to another, though very small, genus. The Nepal laburnum is native to the north of India and China. In Britain it thrives only as a well-sheltered wall shrub. It is evergreen and bears racemes of flowers very like those of laburnum though larger.

LOCUST OR FALSE ACACIA

The **locust** or **false acacia** (*Robinia pseudacacia*) is a native of North America which was introduced into Europe during the early part of the seventeenth century. It received its generic name from Linnaeus in honour of Jean Robin, the botanist whose son worked at the Jardin des

Plantes in Paris and was the first to cultivate the tree in Europe. The common name 'locust' was given to this tree by North American missionaries who mistakenly assumed that it was the fruit of this tree which contributed to the 'locusts and wild honey' which comprised John the Baptist's diet in the wilderness. When the tree was introduced into Europe it was mistaken for the true *Acacia* which is native to Africa and Australia. Actually the two plants are distinct though they belong to the same family; but the mistake inspired the common name 'false acacia' and the specific name *pseudacacia*.

The false acacia is not cultivated for commercial purposes in Britain; but it is a handsome tree and so appears very often in parks and gardens where it attains a height of anything from 40 to 80 feet and a girth up to 12 feet. The bark is often spirally fissured.

> A great acacia, with its slender trunk
> And overpoise of multitudinous leaves
> (In which a hundred fields might spill their dew
> And intense verdure, yet find room enough)
> Stood reconciling all the place with green.
> *Aurora Leigh* : E. B. BROWNING

The leaves are particularly interesting. They are very graceful, being compound with a terminal leaflet and seven to ten pairs of lateral leaflets. Each leaflet has a rounded apex. At the base of the leaf-stalk, where it joins the stem, there are two stipules which are modified into a pair of small, sharp spines. The leaflets close upwards if the weather is particularly dry or hot.

The flowers of the false acacia, like those of the laburnum, are borne in racemes, though there are not so many flowers per bunch. They are white, fundamentally similar in structure to those of laburnum, very fragrant and at their best in May. The fruit is a typical pod.

The wood is light brown and durable. It is very tough, but not easily worked. It is not utilised to any great extent in Britain.

Several varieties of this tree are cultivated for ornamental purposes in Britain, and there are also other species of *Robinia*, most of them having pink flowers.

HONEY LOCUST

The **honey locust** (*Gleditschia triacanthos*) is quite different from the locust or false acacia. It is native to temperate North America, and was named by Linnaeus after Johann Gleditsch, his close friend.

Judas Tree
Holloway, Bath

13.5.46

LR

Lonsdale Ragg

Old Judas Tree at Bath, Somerset.

This tree is not common in Britain, though it was first cultivated here by the Bishop of London in his Palace grounds at Fulham in the seventeenth century. Its cultivation has since spread, chiefly throughout the south.

The secondary branches of this tree are covered with long sharp spines which may be simple or forked into three. When young, these spines are bright red, but later they become a dull brown. They are responsible for another common name of this tree—the **three-thorned acacia**. The foliage is compound and very graceful. Sometimes the plant is used for making hedges.

JUDAS TREE

The **judas tree** (*Cercis siliquastrum*) is not particularly common in Britain, though it is plentiful enough in the Mediterranean regions of Europe and in western Asia, especially Palestine. In coastal towns of southern Europe it flourishes in parks and along the streets, and when the pinkish-purple flowers appear on the older branches, before the leaves are open, then the tree is very impressive, for the flowers are like large pea-flowers with their standards and wings well open.

The tree is not very large, but is low with a very spreading crown; in Britain it varies from 15 to 30 feet in height, and young trees bloom more freely than older ones. The leaves are large and simple.

It is a pity that a tree of such handsome form and beautiful flowers should, by tradition, have acted as gallows for Judas Iscariot; but such is the belief and hence its common name.

In some countries the flowers are eaten in fresh salads and are sometimes added to cooked dishes.

There are other species of the genus *Cercis* distributed throughout the north temperate zone. The **American Judas tree** or redbud (*C. canadensis*) is well distributed in North America and is in general of smaller habit than the European species. The **Texas redbud** (*C. reniformis*) is even smaller; and the **California redbud** (*C. occidentalis*) is nothing more than a shrub. The **Chinese Judas tree** (*C. chinensis*) has very large leaves whose margins are practically white.

With the exception of *C. reniformis*, all the species of *Cercis* mentioned are cultivated in Britain for ornamental purposes, though the European species (*C. siliquastrum*) is the most common.

One of the oldest and largest Judas trees in Britain is that at Bath (p. 191). Then there is one 40 feet high at Dulwich. Several other

Sophora Japonica
Kew Gardens

LR
7. X. 35

Lonsdale Ragg

Sophora japonica in the Royal Botanic Gardens, Kew

handsome specimens are to be seen in various London parks and gardens and in other parks of Britain (mainly the south), often looking quite weird when old, and there they seem stranger still when, while bare of leaves, they are in flower. But in Mediterranean regions they are very charming trees.

This tree has been cultivated in Britain for about 350 years. There are a variety with white flowers and another with flowers of a deeper pink than the ordinary species.

SOPHORA

The genus *Sophora* is so uncommon in Britain that it may seem unworthy of notice ; yet the trees belonging to this genus are so fine that we cannot ignore them altogether. The genus is indigenous to the tropics and certain warm areas in the temperate zones. The flowers are interesting in that, although they are papilionaceous, all their stamens are free. The winter buds have no bud-scales, so they are quite naked—an unusual feature.

The only species at all common in Britain is *S. japonica*, or **Japanese pagoda tree** : there is a very fine specimen of this in the Royal Botanic Gardens, Kew (p. 193). This species is one of the most elegant of flowering trees, bearing its white blooms so late as in September. It is a large tree with enormous branches spreading widely. The bark is deeply fissured.

The leaves are like those of the false acacia except that the leaflets are more lance-shaped and there are no spiny stipules. There are several varieties of this tree including a weeping form and another with variegated leaves. *Sophora* can be highly recommended to those interested in trees as a subject of landscape architecture.

Another species sometimes cultivated in Britain is *S. vicifolia*. This blooms copiously with blue and white flowers resembling those of *Wistaria*. According to W. J. Bean in Henrey and Bean's *Trees and Shrubs throughout the Year*, this variety was introduced into Britain from China by Augustine Henry in 1898, and there is still a group of plants obtained from the original near the Cactus House at the Royal Botanic Gardens, Kew.

The large **New Zealand laburnum** (*S. tetraptera*) is grown but seldom in Britain, and then only as a sheltered wall plant, though it is a large tree when growing in its native New Zealand, Chile and Juan Fernandez.

24

LIQUIDAMBAR OR SWEET GUM

(Hamamelidaceae)

To the family HAMAMELIDACEAE belong a number of trees and shrubs all of which are sub-tropical in distribution, though this distribution is very disjointed. There are about eighteen genera and more than fifty species in the family. Since all members of the family thrive best in warmer climates, none is indigenous to Britain; but several genera and species have been introduced to grace our ornamental woods, shrubberies and avenues. One, namely, the North American satin walnut, is being cultivated on an experimental scale with a view to commercial development.

The non-commercial genera and species to be found growing in Britain under cultivation are listed in *Flowers in Britain.*

Parrotia persica, a native of Iran, presents beautiful foliage which turns gold and crimson in the autumn. The flowers appear during February and March. W. J. Bean, in Henrey and Bean's *Trees and Shrubs throughout the Year*, states that, though it has been claimed that this plant attains a height of 50 feet in its native Iran and Caucasus, it will probably never achieve such a height in Britain. There is one on Kew Green near the main gates of the Royal Botanic Gardens, 40 feet in diameter and 30 feet high. *Fothergilla major*, a North American tree, is a slow-growing plant, usually with the habit of a shrub in Britain. It bears fragrant white flowers in close spikes, and its foliage also turns golden in autumn. *Distylium racemosum* is a Japanese evergreen shrub with graceful glossy leaves. *Sycopsis sinensis* is native to China. It also is an evergreen shrub which attains a height of about 10 feet. Like most members of this family, it blooms very early in the year when cultivated in Britain. Several other cultivated species of this genus are of Japanese origin. Certain species of the genus *Corylopsis*, which hails from China and Japan, can now be seen cultivated in British shrubberies. They all bear fragrant yellow flowers. *Hamamelis virginiana*, the **witch hazel,** is an American import, bearing red and yellow flowers which open very early in the year before the leaves develop. Other species and varieties of *Hamamelis* also bear red or yellow flowers during the winter. The **Chinese witch hazel** (*H. mollis*) was brought from China

195

by Charles Maries in 1879. W. J. Bean considers that this is one of our best early-flowering shrubs ; it blooms in January. Though sometimes these species of *Hamamelis* assume the habit of small trees, they are usually of shrubby form.

The genus *Liquidambar* is widely spread, being native to Mediterranean regions, Asia and North America. From some species fragrant balsams are extracted. Perhaps the most useful species of all is *L. styraciflua*, the North American **satin walnut, sweet gum, red gum or bilsted.** Sometimes the wood is referred to as ' satinwood '.

This tree is not common in Britain, though it has already proved itself suitable for growth in towns. There are some good specimens in certain of the London parks, at the Royal Botanic Gardens, Kew, and in the grounds of Syon House, Middlesex.

The first record we have of this tree is in a book by the Spaniard Hernandez, published in 1651. He was struck by the fragrant resin which exuded from it and wrote that it was like " liquid amber " ; hence the name of the tree. John Banister, the missionary, brought back the first specimen to Britain, and Bishop Compton, of London, planted it in the grounds of Fulham Palace in 1681.

Though this tree frequently attains a height of 140 feet and a bole diameter of 5 feet in its native America, it never reaches such dimensions in Britain. In fact it usually averages about 50 feet in height, though taller specimens do exist here.

The fragrant gum is present between the bark and the sap-wood and exudes through fissures in the bark. Unlike some gums, this has no particular medicinal value ; but in France it is used for perfuming gloves. The bark of the tree is deep brown in colour, heavily fissured on old trees, but smooth on young ones. The leaves are serrated and lobed, and are shaped very like those of the maple. They are fragrant. They turn a striking red colour or purple in the autumn before leaf-fall sets in. The flowers are unisexual, but both sexes grow on the same tree. The male flowers are borne in upright spikes and the female in clusters at the ends of long pendulous stalks. The seeds are winged.

The timber of *Liquidambar styraciflua* is used for many purposes, chiefly domestic and for panelling. Since the sap-wood and the heart-wood are sometimes utilised for different purposes, the commercial names vary, and some are very misleading. The British Standards Institution lists the following commercial names : ' satin walnut ' (heart-wood) ; ' hazel pine' (sap-wood); 'bilsted'; 'red gum' (heart-wood); 'sap gum' (sap-wood) ; 'sweet gum '; ' yellow gum '; and there are even more of them.

25

BOX
(*Buxaceae*)

The box is familiar to almost everyone, but mainly as a shrub or in the form of a hedge or even more commonly as a border for walks and flower beds. Even the dweller in the most thickly populated areas must come across it either in window-boxes or in the form of small, clipped trees decorating halls, parterres and balconies. For all these purposes, box is especially suitable since it withstands any amount of clipping, and, above all, it is evergreen. Furthermore, as a decorative shrub it does not soon get out of hand since it grows so slowly.

Yet, in spite of all this, the box is by nature a tree, and thrives as such in the region of the Mediterranean, in Iran and on the slopes of the western Himalayas. In these regions the tree sometimes attains a height of 50 feet. This tree is also mentioned in the Bible.

> I will plant in the wilderness the cedar, the shittah tree, and the myrtle, and the oil tree ; I will set in the desert the fir tree, *and* the pine, and the box tree together ;
>
> *Isaiah*, 41

Today, the box grows throughout Britain, but chiefly under cultivation, though it may possibly be native to the chalk hills of the south, especially in Surrey, Buckinghamshire and Gloucestershire where it now grows wild. Box Hill, Surrey, is famous for its box trees, and there they really are of arboreal habit. But it is certain that the box trees of Box Hill have lost much of their past glory. The diarist and arboriculturist, Evelyn, recorded: " These trees [box] rise naturally at Boxley in Kent, and in the county of Surrey, giving name to that chalky hill [Box Hill] . . . whither the ladies and gentlemen, and other water drinkers from the neighbouring Ebesham Spaw, often resort during the heat of summer to walk, collation, and divert themselves in those antilex alleys and shady recesses among the Box-trees, without taking any offence at the smell which has of late banished it from our groves and gardens." And again : " He that in winter should behold some of our higher hills in Surrey clad with whole woods of these trees, for divers miles in circuit . . . might, without the least violence to his

197

imagination, fancy himself transported into some new or enchanted country ; . . ." The box tree in Britain seldom grows more than 20 feet high.

The box belongs to the family BUXACEAE, a rather small family of half a dozen genera and about thirty species scattered throughout the temperate and tropical zones of the world. All are evergreens, and most, except the box, are shrubs. Box belongs to the genus *Buxus*, and the common box is *B. sempervirens*.

The bark of the box is only slightly fissured. The branches are long and drooping. They bear the familiar small, more or less oblong, thick evergreen leaves in opposite pairs.

The flowers are insignificant since they are so small and have no petals. They sometimes appear as early as January, but are usually in full bloom during April and May. They are unisexual ; but both sexes are borne on the same plant, usually in clusters in the axils of the leaves, each cluster having one large female flower in the centre surrounded by several smaller male flowers. The male flower is composed of four whitish-green sepals, four stamens (inserted opposite the sepals and not alternating with them), and an insignificant sterile ovary. The female flower has the same number or even more of sepals, and a large, three-celled ovary which bears three prominent styles. After fertilisation, the ovary develops into a fruit which takes the form of a dry capsule bearing three prominent tough horns in place of the styles, and enclosing three chambers each of which contains two black seeds.

Box wood is of considerable commercial value ; but today, as might well be expected, most of it is imported, though at one time the supplies in Britain were good and valuable. Confusion might arise owing to the various names applied to this wood. That obtained from the box described above—*Buxus sempervirens*—is often named after the country from which it is imported. The names in common commercial use are, according to the British Standards Institution : ' boxwood', ' Abassian box ', ' European box ', ' Iranian or Persian box ', and ' Turkey box.' The ' Cape box', sometimes called ' East London box ', is obtained from another species, *B. macowanii*, of South Africa. Then there are other commercial forms of box wood which are obtained from totally different trees belonging even to different families.

Box wood is yellow in colour, and its very dense structure renders it heavier than water—the only British wood that is. Its grain is very uniform, so it is suitable for special purposes. It is used for making mathematical instruments (especially rulers), various musical instru-

Harold Bastin

Box Tree.

o

ments, chess-men, etc. In France, the trinkets which used to be made with such art and delicacy were cut from the wood of the roots of box. The blocks of wood-engravers were also made from box since its grain is so uniform; but the art of wood-engraving is now almost completely supplanted by the photographic process. Many years ago, perfumes and quack medicines were prepared from the leaves and the bark; but with the development of medical science and perhaps common sense, these concoctions have now been discarded.

Several species and varieties of *Buxus* are frequently cultivated for ornamental purposes in Britain.

Box.
A male flower and a fruit are also shown.

The **Minorca box** (*B. balearica*) is a much more massive tree which grows to a height of 60 or even 80 feet in Mediterranean regions. It has yellowish-green leaves up to two inches long. It succeeds, however, only on well-sheltered and well-watered sites. *B. japonica* is very similar to the common box, but it is hardier: there is also a golden form of this species, *B. japonica* var. *aurea*. Then there are several forms of the common *Buxus sempervirens*. A particularly pleasing variety is the dwarf *B. sempervirens* var. *elegantissima* with leaves striped with silver. Other variegated forms are not so attractive. Some varieties of *Buxus* are used in edgings. Also, alas, the plant has for many years, like the yew (p. 116) been subjected to the hideous cult of topiary, since it is an evergreen and very tolerant of clipping.

The box is most familiar to British people as a hedge or edging plant, but it might well be considered as an ornamental tree, especially since it is evergreen. Although it grows very slowly, the fact that it can withstand even the densest shade should recommend it to some, especially for cultivation in shrubberies.

26

PLANES
(*Platanaceae*)

To many people who are familiar with the most common of all road-side trees in London, namely, the London plane, it might seem quite incredible that this tree, which of all trees can stand up best to the appalling atmospheric conditions of that great city, is not a native of Britain. Furthermore, it never occurs in the wild state. But such is the case (see p. 204). Yet botanists are able to explain, at any rate partly, this apparent phenomenon. For one thing, everyone must have noticed the curious yellow patches on the trunk and main branches. These are the results of the bark peeling off in large flakes, a process which eliminates certain of the outer layers choked with soot and those lenticels, through which gaseous interchange occurs, which are out of action for the same reason. Furthermore, the winter buds are especially well protected by the leaf-base (see p. 205). There is no doubt that this tree is the most tenacious of our town trees ; it never betrays any adverse effects of the comparatively unfavourable conditions to which it is constantly subjected, for it not only thrives but also grows regularly and evenly—a characteristic of the utmost value in a tree so often used for long road-side planting.

> The chestnut's proud, and the lilac's pretty,
> The poplar's gentle and tall,
> But the plane tree's kind to the poor dull city—
> And I love him best of all.
> *Child's Song in Spring* : EDITH NESBIT

In London itself, it is quite impossible to walk any distance of consequence, in East End, West End, north or south, without coming across some planes, and very frequently one can walk for great distances beneath a practically unbroken shade of plane trees. The long Thames Embankment, especially on the north side, is one example. Then the exceptional evenness of growth is well exemplified by the lovely double avenue of young planes stretching along The Mall from Admiralty Arch to Buckingham Palace. In contrast to this youthful collection, there are the dauntless veterans in Lincoln's Inn Fields, practically in the City

London Plane.

itself. Beautiful though this famous open space is, one could not easily visualise it without its inspiring planes, dotted irregularly over paths and lawns. Yet, in spite of their age, and the irregular yet beautiful nature of their massive boles, in general form of branching and crown these trees are still even and comparatively equal. Further west, the planes of Berkeley, Grosvenor, Portman and Manchester Squares are just as inspiring though not so aged. Those at Ranelagh and Hurlingham are some of the finest specimens in the country.

But these trees have the not inconsiderable advantages of a certain amount of immediate space and of care when young; those in more built-up areas have not been and are not so fortunate; yet they thrive. Some are seen, hemmed in by buildings and subject to almost stifling conditions, but on they go, season after season, growing and producing foliage, flowers and fruit against every possible disadvantage. Many such heroic trees are to be seen in the City and in small courts and even backyards throughout London.

The London plane seems bewitched; for not only do naturally unfavourable conditions seem to have little or no effect on its growth and development, but it has also proved itself equal to the more unnatural conditions, equally as trying, imposed more directly by man. During some of the worst of the air raids on the capital, the planes took their share of destruction, depredation and mutilation; yet any one which had the least shred of vitality left in it burst forth again to life anew. I have seen trees, completely denuded of young foliage by blast from bombs, bring forth fresh leaves in seemingly complete defiance of anything that man might attempt towards their destruction.

There are, apart from the many avenues and groups of planes in London and elsewhere, single specimens which have won the affection of all who are familiar with them; but these individual famous trees are so many and so widespread that it would be invidious to mention even a few; and to describe them all in a reasonable space would be an impossible task.

But there is another side to the story of the London plane; it is believed by many to be an unhealthy plant to live near. The general impression, backed by a certain amount of experimental observation well set out by A. D. Webster in his *London Trees*, is that the small spicules from the fruit (p. 205) which swarm the air surrounding the trees cause bronchial catarrh and pneumonia and certain throat affections.

The plane tree belongs to the family PLATANACEAE, a family comprising one genus only, namely, *Platanus*. This genus is now distributed in the north temperate and sub-tropical zones. There are several species; but the only ones to be found in Britain are the **oriental**

Bole of an Oriental Plane in Wiltshire.

plane (*Platanus orientalis*), the **western plane** (*P. occidentalis*) and the **London plane** (*P. acerifolia*). There is some doubt about the date of introduction of the oriental plane though it is supposed to have been brought from the Levant by Francis Bacon. It is more probable, however, that the tree arrived some time before this, during the first half of the sixteenth century. The western plane (sometimes called the **American** or **occidental plane**) was first introduced from Virginia in 1640. Though the London plane, which is by far the most common species in Britain, is never found growing wild, some confusion about its origin still exists; it is now supposed to have arisen as a hybrid between the oriental and the occidental plane.

Although there are many handsome specimens of the oriental plane in Britain (p. 204), the western plane is not hardy here, and never thrives.

The London plane is a beautiful deciduous tree which attains a height of 70 to 100 feet (p. 202), with a bole up to 12 feet in circumference. It is almost impossible to mistake the tree, for the outer layers of its bark are periodically shed in patches displaying the yellow layers beneath (see p. 201).

The leaf resembles that of the sycamore, but it is usually slightly larger, of a brighter green and quite devoid of hairs (p. 206 and Plate 2). It has three very pronounced lobes and two nearer the base of the blade which are not so pronounced; but apart from this it is deeply indented. The leaf-stalk is long but firm. The leaf of the oriental plane is more definitely five-lobed and its margins are even more indented. They are arranged alternately on the stem. The axillary bud is especially well protected, because the leaf-base is swollen and fits right over it like a helmet. The winter buds which are exposed after leaf-fall are broad at the base but very pointed.

The plane is unisexual, though both sexes are borne on the same tree. They appear during June. They grow in dense spherical heads (one sex only in each head, the male yellowish and the female red), and the heads grow on long pendulous stalks, usually two to four heads to each stalk (Plate 2). The flowers are wind-pollinated. The collections of fruits are very attractive and each takes the form of an even larger ball covered with spicules (p. 206 and Plate 2). The hairy fruits eventually become detached when quite ripe, and are easily disseminated by wind.

Our quite natural enthusiasm for the London plane which seems so nobly to bear the often unhappy vicissitudes of urban life and thus

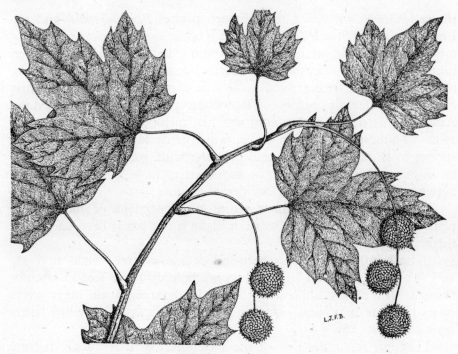

Foliage and Fruit of the London Plane.

brings joy and the advantages of relaxation to man as no other tree does, must not distort our view as students of trees, for in order to obtain a balanced impression of plane trees we must realise that, massive and majestic as the planes in Britain really are, they dwindle almost to insignificance when compared with the offspring of their ancestors in their native habitats.

For example, there are some beautiful examples of the oriental plane (*P. orientalis*) in Britain; but they are as nothing when we consider further examples in the region of the Mediterranean and of western Asia. Referring to the oriental plane, Pliny wrote: "... who would have thought it possible that a tree should have been brought from a remote region of the world, for the sake of its shade only? Yet such was the case: the Plane was first carried across the Ionian Sea to shade the tomb of Diomede, who was buried in one of the small islands off the coast of Apulia; then it was introduced into Sicily; from Sicily it was brought to Rhegium in Italy by the tyrant Dionysius; and has now extended so far, that the Morini (people of Calais) are taxed for its shade. Dionysius held it in high honour, and since his time it has so much increased in estimation, that its roots are nourished with wine instead of water."

When Xerxes was on the way to invade Europe he was so attracted by a plane tree at Lydia in Asia Minor that he decorated it with golden ornaments, and when he moved on he left one of his men behind to tend it. The peoples of the East still hold these noble and massive trees in veneration, even though they do not now go to such extremes in the expression of their care and admiration. A hundred years ago, the Rev. S. Clark, writing to the Rev. C. A. Johns, described an enormous plane at Vostitza on the Gulf of Lepanto. Its bole was 46 feet in circumference and it was 100 feet high. It is of interest that " the symmetry of the tree would else be as remarkable as its size."

A hundred years ago, there stood on the shores of the Bosphorus one of the oldest and largest trees in the world; it was an oriental plane.

The western or occidental plane (*P. occidentalis*) is native to the United States, growing best in the valleys of the Ohio and Mississippi rivers. There it is a massive plant, frequently outgrowing all surrounding trees and having a bole which is quite clean and free from branches for the first 80 feet.

Since the plane has for so long been treasured as an ornamental and shade-giving tree, it has not been much used for timber, for felling is not encouraged. In any event the wood is not very durable. That of the western plane is used for a certain amount of cabinet-making in the United States. But the commercial names for the timber, and sometimes the popular names for the trees, have been, and still are, so confusing that attention should be directed to them. First, the plane tree in Scotland is not the true plane but the sycamore (p. 312). Wood of the London plane is frequently referred to in the timber trade as ' lace wood '. The timber of the western plane is sometimes called ' button wood ' and sometimes ' sycamore ', and the latter name is applied to the trees themselves in America. Then also in the States, there are two smaller species, the Californian ' sycamore ' (*P. racemosa*) and the Arizona ' sycamore ' (*P. wrightii*).

There are two rare varieties of the London plane, namely *P. acerifolia* var. *laciniata*, having very deeply indented leaves, and *P. acerifolia* var. *variegata*, having variegated leaves. But, for avenue and park planting, by far the most popular of planes is the London plane (*P. acerifolia*) itself. The streets, parks and squares of London testify to this. This tree is also used for screening purposes.

27

WILLOWS
(Salicaceae)

Know ye the willow-tree Whose grey leaves quiver,
Whispering gloomily To yon pale river ?
Lady, at even-tide Wander not near it :
They say its branches hide A sad lost spirit.
The Willow-Tree : THACKERAY

In the round hollow of the moonlight meadow
Over the ponds the seven willows shiver,
And in the ghostly misty shine their branches
Rustle and glance and quiver—
The Willows : WILFRID GIBSON

The willows and poplars (Chapter 28) belong to the family SALIC-
ACEAE, a family of many well-known trees and shrubs all of which
are species of either the genus *Salix* (willows) or the genus *Populus*
(poplars), for these are the only two genera it contains. The family
is of almost world-wide distribution, though it is not represented in
Australasia or Malaya and the surrounding Archipelago. It is composed
of trees and shrubs only.

No one living in the country can be oblivious of the willow,
though more urban dwellers can be forgiven if they plead ignorance of
this genus of plants, for, apart from certain cultivated forms, such as the
ever-popular and always lovely weeping willow, few species are grown
or maybe will grow under the atmospheric conditions imposed by our
towns.

Though, as will be seen later, the different species of willows are
sometimes very difficult to distinguish it is not so with the genus
in general. In other words, no one should experience difficulty in
recognising a willow tree or shrub as such, but to identify the species
will often tax the ingenuity of the keenest and most knowledgeable
botanist. Along the river-banks and in marshy areas one cannot miss
the willows which abound there ; and country-folk find certain species
very useful for making many domestic articles. In fact, the willow is
one of the many raw materials of workers in rural arts and crafts ;

so, for this reason alone, it is to be hoped that its growth and cultivation will be encouraged. Furthermore, some species are of more commercial value. But all are particularly attractive plants which have played a large part in the folk-lore and traditions of Britain as well as of other countries.

It is not known whether it was a true willow that inspired the well-known Chinese legend on which the even more familiar willow pattern of pottery, etc. is based; it has been suggested that the original tree (chosen at any rate for the design) was *Koelreuteria paniculata*, a totally different plant belonging to the family SAPINDACEAE (p. 303). *Koelreuteria* is a native of northern China, but it is sometimes cultivated in Britain for ornamental purposes since its yellow flowers and autumnal foliage are so attractive.

For centuries the willow has been associated with gloom, though it is not easy to discover why (see the quotation from Thackeray at the heading of the chapter). A willow garland used to be worn as a sign that the wearer had been disappointed in love.

> I offered him my company to a willow-tree . . . to make him a garland, as being forsaken.
> *Much Ado about Nothing*, Act 2, Sc. 1: SHAKESPEARE

> Tell him, in hope he'll prove a widower shortly,
> I'll wear the willow garland for his sake.
> *III Henry VI*, Act 3, Sc. 3 : SHAKESPEARE

> When once the lover's rose is dead,
> Or laid aside forlorn,
> Then willow-garlands, 'bout the head,
> Bedewed with tears, are worn.
> *To the Willow-Tree* : HERRICK

Yet, so far back as Biblical times, the willow has its place in festivals of rejoicing.

> And ye shall take you on the first day the boughs of goodly trees, branches of palm trees, and the boughs of thick trees, and willows of the brook ; and ye shall rejoice before the Lord your God seven days.
> *Leviticus*, 23, 40

But in the Scriptures the willow was generally an emblem of woe and sadness, and ever since then, folk-lore has attached that significance to it. The gloomy association of the weeping willow with the weeping and wailing of the Israelites is ill-founded (see p. 219).

GENERAL REVIEW OF WILLOWS

Since it is still very difficult to distinguish between many species of willow, it is not surprising that authorities of the past differed considerably in the enumeration of the species belonging to the genus *Salix*. So confused and sometimes vague were they that it seems scarcely worth while to examine their conclusions. Botanists today recognise about a hundred and thirty species, though even now it is sometimes extremely difficult to identify the species or hybrid to which an actual specimen belongs. Some botanists have claimed as many as eighty species indigenous to Britain, while others are more conservative and recognise no more than fifteen as being actually native to this country. In any event, some species now in Britain are certainly not native.

Here we must confine ourselves to those few frequently met with in Britain and a mere mention of just a few others of particular interest. But before considering individual species, it will be worth while to review the genus *Salix* in general.

The willows may be shrubs growing only a few inches in height, such as the arctic species, those growing in the mountainous regions of northern Britain, and the very rare dwarf or least willow (*Salix herbacea*) or they may be trees attaining a height of 140 feet. Many species of willow thrive best in temperate or cold regions, and most of them flourish near a plentiful supply of water.

The bark of the bole of the arboreal species is fissured and of a light brown colour. It is used for tanning leather. The winter buds are ovoid and are protected by one bud-scale only. The leaves are always simple and generally lance-shaped, though some, for example, the goat willow or sallow (*S. caprea*), have much broader leaves. The margins of the leaves are usually faintly toothed, though the leaves of some species, for example, the osier willow (*S. viminalis*) have smooth but wavy margins. At the leaf-base there are usually two stipules which vary with the species. These act as scales for protecting the winter buds before the leaves open. In all cases, the leaves are deciduous.

The flowers of the willow are individually inconspicuous, but since they are borne in catkins each containing a large number of flowers they are collectively very much in evidence; this applies especially to the goat willow or sallow (Plate 3). Each flower is unisexual, and in no species do the two sexes occur on the same tree —so there are male and female willow trees. In all species the catkins appear in spring, though some species are later than others. In some cases the catkins are ripe before the leaves are extended.

Each flower is simple because the normal constituent parts of a flower are here absent. Yet the flowers secrete a goodly supply of nectar, so in spite of the fact that they are not usually scented and not always conspicuous, they are frequently, though not always, pollinated by insects, chiefly bees, which visit the catkins for the nectar and the pollen. Furthermore, in many cases the absence of leaves at the time that the catkins are ripe makes the latter more conspicuous. It is certain that wind-pollination takes place among the more northerly and the arctic species of willow, for when the catkins are ripe there are few insects about, yet these species set much seed.

Flowers of Sallow.
Above left, male catkin; above right, female catkin; below left, male flower; below right, female flower.

The male flower is borne in the axil of a boat-shaped bract which is hairy (Plate 3). There are two to five stamens (sometimes even more) according to species; the most common number among British species is two. A few small nectaries are also present.

The female flower is quite as simple as the male. It is composed of two carpels joined to form a single flask-shaped ovary enclosing a single chamber and topped with a cleft stigma. The ovary is borne on a short stalk inserted in the axil of the bract like that of the male flower (Plate 3). After fertilisation, the fruit develops into a hard capsule containing a large number of hairy seeds.

WHITE WILLOW

The **white** or **Huntingdon willow** (*S. alba*) is very common in Britain, usually seen growing along river banks and very often pollarded. It is a comparatively large species, frequently growing 60 to 80 feet high, and sometimes attaining 100 feet. It is widespread throughout Britain, with the exception of the very north of Scotland, though many have been planted, since they yield a useful timber. The wood was at one time much used for making charcoal and in the manufacture of wood pulp. The wood is elastic and has therefore also been utilised for lining barges, carts and other vessels.

Leaves of Willow Species.
Left to right: white willow, crack willow, sallow, osier willow.

The tree is called 'white' because the hairy nature of the leaves gives it a white appearance. The leaves are two to four inches long, very slightly serrated, and are narrow and pointed at the tips. The catkins appear during May, and the male flowers have two stamens each.

The white willow is frequently cultivated for ornamental purposes, though few people can have missed it growing wild along river banks and in other damp and marshy habitats. There is a weeping form of this tree, *S. alba* var. *argentea*, having very beautiful silvery foliage which recommends it for landscape gardening.

GOLDEN WILLOW

The **golden willow** is considered by authoritative botanists to be a variety of the white willow (*S. alba* var. *vitellina*). This variety, which figures largely in landscape architecture and as an ornamental tree in gardens, has narrower leaves than the white willow ; its main attraction in winter lies in the bright golden twigs (in contradistinction to the dull grey-green twigs of the white willow). The golden willow does not grow quite so high as the white willow.

CRICKET-BAT WILLOW

This very useful form of willow was once looked upon as a variety of the white willow and was assigned the name *S. alba* var. *coerulea*. Later it was considered that it was really a hybrid between the white willow (*S. alba*) and the crack willow (*S. fragilis*), and it has therefore now been given specific status and named *S. coerulea*.

The cricket-bat willow grows very fast, often reaching maturity within the first twenty years of its life. It attains a height of 100 feet. It may be distinguished from the white willow mainly by its leaves which are grey on the under-surface. Also it is by no means so widespread, being more or less confined to eastern England.

This willow yields the best wood for making cricket bats, since it is white, tough and, above all, elastic. Thus the tree has achieved considerable economic importance especially in Britain, the home of this national game. It has been claimed that the wood of the female tree is better for the purpose of making cricket bats than that of the male, which is all to the good since there are many more female trees than male in Britain; in fact, it has been said that male trees do not grow in this country.

Crack Willow in Summer.

Eric J. Hosking

CRACK WILLOW

The **crack willow** (*S. fragilis*) is one of the most common willows in Britain. It is also frequently known as **withy** (see also p. 216). It thrives not only in damp situations but also on the exposed hillsides (p. 213). The branches are brittle and liable to snap off easily at their bases, hence the common name ' crack ' and the specific name. The leaves are long, sometimes reaching a length of six inches ; the margins are slightly toothed ; but unlike those of the white willow their under-surfaces are not hairy. The stipules do not remain long after the leaves have opened out.

The male flowers are borne in catkins about one and a half inches long. Each male flower usually has two stamens, though there may sometimes be more. Both male and female catkins appear from April to June. The crack willow is of little economic value. According to Johns, in his *Forest Trees of Britain*, the roots afford a reddish-purple dye which was used in France and Sweden for colouring Easter eggs.

ALMOND-LEAVED OR FRENCH WILLOW

The **almond-leaved** or **French willow** (*S. triandra*) is not a large tree and seldom exceeds 20 feet in height. Its bark is periodically shed in patches. The leaves are lance-shaped, tending towards oblong, and their under-surfaces are covered with a pale green bloom. The stipules are large and heart-shaped. The catkins are borne on short stalks. The male flower has three stamens (as implied in the specific name).

This tree grows along river banks and is frequently pollarded or coppiced in order to stimulate the growth of straight thin branches, which are used in basket-making and other wicker work—like those of the osier willow.

BAY-LEAVED OR SWEET BAY WILLOW

The **bay-leaved** or **sweet bay willow** (*S. pentandra*) is a tree about the same size as the almond-leaved willow, though it often assumes the habit of a bush. The lance-shaped, almost elliptical leaves emit a fragrance similar to that of the bay tree (p. 143)—hence the common name. This tree is also to be found growing along river banks and in other wet places. The catkins appear sometimes in May and sometimes so late as June, for this species is the last of all the willows to bloom during the year. The male flower has at least five stamens (as implied in the specific name) and frequently more, even up to a dozen.

GOAT WILLOW, SALLOW OR PUSSY WILLOW

The **goat willow or sallow,** sometimes also called the **pussy willow** (*S. caprea*), is very popular, especially when the striking male catkins covered with golden pollen appear during the months of April and May (Plate 3 and p. 211). This is a small tree found growing in drier situations, especially in hedgerows and on the edges of woods. It does not usually reach more than 40 feet, though the average is round about 20 feet.

It is not difficult to identify this species because the leaves are much broader than those of other common willows (p. 212), though they vary considerably within themselves. The margins are slightly serrated and the stipules persist for a considerable time. The leaves are two to four inches long and are downy on the under-surface.

The catkins appear before the leaves. In the case of the male tree, this fact, together with the bright golden colour of the catkins when ripe, explains why they are so conspicuous. The catkins are borne straight on to the branches without an intervening stalk. The branches of this willow, when covered with golden yellow male catkins, are the ' palms ' collected for church decoration on Palm Sunday. The Rev. C. A. Johns has suggested that the association of the sallow with the palm, and therefore the use of the former as a ' palm ' on Palm Sunday, may be traced to the association of the two in Leviticus (Chapter 23) (see p. 209). But this does not seem very reasonable to me, especially since the willows mentioned in Leviticus are those " of the brook " ; the sallow usually grows in much drier situations. In fact, it often grows on sandy slopes and old slag heaps.

The male flower of the sallow has two stamens (p. 211). Both male and female flowers secrete an exceptionally large amount of nectar attracts clouds of bees.

There is a weeping form of the sallow (*S. caprea* var. *pendula*) which is useful in landscape gardening.

ROUND-EARED AND GREY SALLOWS

The **round-eared sallow** (*S. aurita*) is a small bush found growing in moist copses and on damp heaths, attaining a height of 2 to 4 feet.

P

The leaves are small, oblong and very wrinkled, and are about an inch and a half long. They are downy beneath. The stipules are exceptionally large and are shaped like ears, hence the common and the specific names.

The **grey sallow** (*S. cinerea*) is very common. Its leaves, too, are small, and their margins are partially furled.

THE OSIERS

The **common osier** or **withy** (*S. viminalis*) is a small tree thirty feet high which might be seen growing in osier beds and in other wet places. When young, the branches are covered with short hairs, but as they get older these hairs are cast off and the long straight branches are ready for cutting and for use in wicker work. The leaves are long and lance-shaped ; but their margins, though wavy, are not toothed (p. 212). The lower surface is hairy and presents a silvery sheen. The catkins ripen during April to June, and the leaves open out afterwards. The male flower has two stamens.

The **purple osier** (*S. purpurea*) may frequently be seen growing along river banks. It is seldom anything but a large shrub, 6 to 10 feet high. The bark is purple, and the slender branches are very tough. The leaves are long with serrated margins. A diagnostic feature of this species is that the stalks or filaments of the two stamens in the male flower are fused together and covered with hairs.

DWARF AND ALPINE WILLOWS

Quite a number of willows are normally of shrubby or dwarf habit, seldom, if ever, attaining the proportions of even a small tree. Most willows of the far north and the arctic regions are of this type, but several are to be found in Britain—mainly on exposed sites.

Two such shrubby willows which are larger than most other dwarf forms are the dark-leaved willow and the tea-leaved willow. Neither is particularly common; seldom is either found further south than the north of England. The **dark-leaved willow** (*S. nigricans*) is so called because the oval leaves turn black on drying. It is a procumbent shrub, 6 to 10 feet high. The male flower has two stamens. The **tea-leaved willow** (*S. phylicifolia*) is more bushy with light brown twigs, and the oval leaves do not turn black on drying.

The **dwarf** or **least willow** (*S. herbacea*) is more widespread than the two just described ; though it is seldom found anywhere but high up on the slopes of hills. It is very small, never growing more than a few inches in height. It is shrubby in habit and sends out underground stems from which arise erect flowering shoots about two inches high. The leaves are oval and slightly toothed. The catkins appear late, in fact, after the leaves have opened, that is during June and July.

Salix reticulata in Britain is confined to the mountains of northern Scotland. Unlike the dwarf willow's, its leaves have smooth margins, and the shoots which grow up from the underground stems are five or six times taller. Its specific name can be ascribed to the fact that the net venation is very pronounced. Another dwarf confined to the mountains of northern Scotland is *Salix arbuscula*. Its shoots which arise from the underground stems attain a height of two feet. The leaves are serrated. *Salix myrsinites* is confined to the southern parts of the Scottish Highlands. The species averages nine inches in height.

Two other species of dwarf willows are to be found in certain parts of Scotland, but both of them are more robust shrubs than most of those so far described. They are *Salix lanata* and *Salix lapponum*.

Fox Photos

Stripping Withies by the River Avon at Bidford Bridge, Warwickshire.

Harold Bastin

Weeping Willow in Winter.

CREEPING WILLOW

The **creeping** or **dwarf silky willow** (*S. repens*) is a small, straggling bush to be found growing on hill slopes and on heaths and commons. Its branches trail along the ground, but those which bear the catkins grow upright to a height of 1 to 3 feet. The leaf-buds and young leaves are covered with fine silky hairs, and these persist on the under-surfaces of the older leaves. The leaves are oblong, about a half to an inch and a half long, and have recurved margins. The catkins appear during April and May before the leaf-buds have opened out. There are two stamens in the male flower.

WEEPING WILLOW

The **weeping willow** (*S. babylonica*) is without doubt the loveliest of all the willows, and when it is growing near water (as it frequently does), with its branches and branchlets reaching down to touch their own reflections in the water it makes a beautiful picture.

The same tree in Summer.

Harold Bastin

It was Linnaeus who perpetuated the erroneous belief that the tree growing " by the rivers of Babylon " was the weeping willow, for it was he who gave the tree its specific name *babylonica*.

> By the rivers of Babylon, there we sat down, yea, we wept, when we remembered Zion.
>
> We hanged our harps upon the willows in the midst thereof.
>
> For there they that carried us away captive required of us a song ; and they that wasted us *required of us* mirth, *saying*, Sing us *one* of the songs of Zion.
>
> *Psalms,* 137

The tree to which the Psalmist refers was a species of poplar (*Populus euphratica*) (see p. 230).

The weeping willow is not native to Britain. It originated in China, where it is still a popular tree, and was later introduced into the countries of the Levant, eastern Europe and North Africa. In those parts it is frequently grown in cemeteries, " weeping " through sorrow for the dead.

The Rev. C. A. Johns, in his *Forest Trees of Britain*, gives an interesting account of the introduction of this species into Britain, though he is vague about the date " certainly not earlier than the beginning of the last century [eighteenth] or the close of the seventeenth." The first tree may have been planted at Twickenham either by a merchant from Aleppo or by the poet Pope. The poet loved this tree ; but, alas, after his death it became such an object of curiosity that the new owner of the house had it cut down so that he should no longer be annoyed by the sight-seers. So it seems that such pests existed even in those days ; Johns does not record whether they cut twigs of it as souvenirs.

According to another account, Johns points out, the first tree was planted at Kew in 1692.

Perhaps the most famous of all weeping willows was the one which drooped over Napoleon's tomb at St. Helena whence it was originally taken from Britain in 1810. Napoleon was very attracted by this tree ; but it was short-lived, for it succumbed to a violent storm at about the same time that Napoleon died. However, from it several cuttings were saved and planted around Napoleon's grave ; but none flourished, so a fresh lot were planted in 1828. These were successful, and many a cutting has been taken from the resulting trees and replanted in Britain and elsewhere. From then on for a considerable number of years there was a widespread craze for planting weeping willows in this country, and though enthusiasm has abated, even today most readers must know of examples of this very lovely plant.

A particularly attractive variety, useful in landscape gardening, is the **golden weeping willow** (*S. babylonica* var. *ramulis aureis*).

28

POPLARS
(*Salicaceae*)

A veritable passion for poplars is a most intelligible passion. The eyes do gather them, far and near, on a whole day's journey. Not one is unperceived, even though great timber should be passed, and hill-sides dense and deep with trees. The fancy makes a poplar day of it. Immediately the country looks alive with signals ; for the poplars everywhere reply to the glance. The woods may be all various, but the poplars are separate.

All their many kinds (and aspens, their kin, must be counted with them) shake themselves perpetually free of the motionless forest. ... Light and the breezes are as quick as the eyes of the poplar-lover to find the willing tree that dances to be seen ... the poplars are alert enough for a traveller by express ; they have an alarum aloft, and do not sleep. ... They are salient everywhere, and full of replies. They are as fresh as streams.

ALICE MEYNELL

GENERAL REVIEW OF POPLARS

The poplars belong to the second genus (*Populus*) of the family SALICACEAE to which the willows (*Salix*) also belong. The genus *Populus* is distributed throughout the northern hemisphere, chiefly in the temperate regions. It comprises a smaller number of species than does the genus *Salix*—about thirty altogether. Though quite a number of species are to be found in Britain, only the white poplar, black poplar, Lombardy poplar, aspen and black Italian poplar are at all common.

An outstanding difference between willows and poplars lies in the leaf-forms. Those of the willows are mainly long, narrow and lance-shaped, whereas the leaf-blades of the poplars are much broader and robuster, being lobed in some cases and heart-shaped in others. The long leaf-stalks, too, are flattened in the vertical plane in some poplar species, and because of this the leaves tremble in the slightest breeze.

> Hard by, a poplar shook alway,
> All silver-green with gnarled bark.
>
> *Mariana* : TENNYSON

The winter buds of willow and poplar are also different. Those of poplar are covered with several small bud-scales, whereas those of willow are each enclosed in one large outer scale.

Again the catkins differ. The catkins of the poplar are long and pendulous, whereas it has already been seen that both male and female catkins of the willow are comparatively thick-set and upright (compare pp. 211 and 222). As in the case of the willow, the male and female catkins of poplar are borne on separate trees. The male flower of the poplar has a rudimentary perianth, whereas that of the willow has not even a vestige of a perianth. There are usually many stamens in the poplar flower, the number varying from four to about eighty, though in the British poplars the number seldom exceeds thirty. The female poplar flower resembles the female willow flower more closely ; but the stigma of the former may be cleft into as many as five segments.

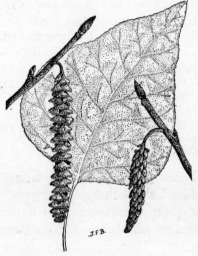

Black Poplar.
Left, male catkin ; right, female catkin.

The presence of so many stamens and the larger number of clefts to the stigma are both useful assets to the poplar, for it is wind-pollinated. This is a wasteful method of pollination, so the large number of stamens ensures the production of much pollen which will allow for wastage, and the larger number of stigma lobes makes the catching of the air-borne pollen more likely.

The fruit of the poplar is a small dry capsule containing two chambers in which there are several seeds when ripe. Each seed has a tuft of long white hairs by means of which it is freely disseminated by the wind.

Most poplars, like most willows, prefer moist habitats, and are therefore frequently seen growing by river-banks and in hedgerows in well-watered areas. Seldom is the poplar found in woods.

WHITE POPLAR

One of the most important poplars in Britain is the ornamental **white poplar** (*P. alba*), sometimes called **abele**. It is doubtful whether this tree is native to Britain, for at one time there was some confusion with it and the grey poplar. It was probably introduced from Holland where it is very common. It is not a very large tree, usually growing to a height of 50 feet, though some specimens have grown considerably higher. It grows very rapidly and achieves perfection within about 50 to 70 years, but given reasonably good conditions it will then last quite as long again, if not longer.

The bark is grey in colour and more or less smooth except at the base of the bole, and for a few feet up where it becomes vertically fissured and almost black in colour.

The leaves vary in shape, though in general they are lobed with indented margins (p. 225 and Plate 3), and the under surface is covered with thick white down which shows up so attractively when the leaves are trembling in the breeze. The leaf-stalk is flattened vertically—a character which allows for this. Country folk at one time believed that when the white poplar was showing the under-surfaces of its leaves then rain was on the way.

Male white poplars are rare in Britain. The catkins are in full bloom during March and April (Plate 3), and the fruit capsules release their hairy seeds in July. The stigma of the female flower is usually only bilobed. This tree seldom, if ever, blooms in Scotland.

The white poplar frequently sends up many leafy suckers from its roots, and these can and do prove themselves a nuisance if the parent tree is growing on or near cultivated ground.

The wood is of little economic value. On the Continent it is used as fuel, and the Ancients of Europe sometimes made their shields from it.

There is a variety of white poplar, *P. alba* var. *argentea*, which has very bright silvery leaves. This form is seen only in ornamental gardens and parks.

Eric J. Hosking

White Poplar in Winter.

GREY POPLAR

The **grey poplar** (*P. canescens*), unlike the white poplar, is considered to be indigenous to Britain. It is very similar to the white poplar, though its trembling leaves are broader and have more rounded margins. The under-surfaces may be covered with greyish hairs, though they are more often smooth. The stigma of the female flower is cleft into four. Some authorities consider the grey poplar to have originated as a hybrid between the white poplar and the aspen.

ASPEN

The **aspen** (*P. tremula*) is another of the so-called trembling poplars, in fact, its leaves rustle more than any others.

> And the wind, full of wantonness, wooes like a lover
> The young aspen-trees till they tremble all over.
>
> *Lalla Rookh* : THOMAS MOORE

> Right as an aspes lefe she 'gan to shake.
>
> *Troilus and Creseide* : CHAUCER

Aspen Trees in Winter.

Eric J. Hosking

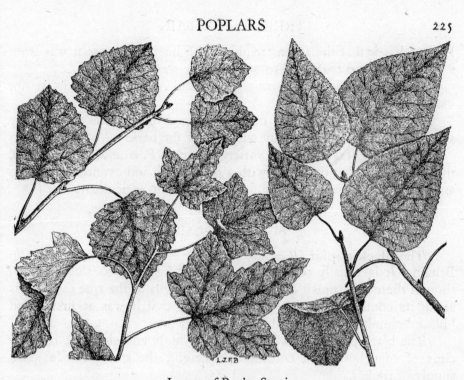

Leaves of Poplar Species.
Above left, aspen ; below left, white poplar ; below right, black poplar ;
above right, Ontario poplar.

The aspen, sometimes called the **asp,** is not so hardy as the white poplar though it is indigenous to Britain and may be found as far north as the north of Scotland. It is also very common on the Continent. As with the white and grey poplars, its roots have a habit of producing many suckers. The tree seldom exceeds a height of 50 feet. Its bole is covered with smooth grey bark.

The trembling leaves of the aspen are quite different from those of the white poplar. They are rather nondescript in shape, tending to be circular with sinuous margins and a blunt apex (Plate 3).

The vertically flattened leaf-stalks are exceptionally long, and this explains why the leaves whisper and rustle so.

How I shake. . . . In very truth do I, an 'twere an aspen leaf.
II Henry IV, Act 2, Sc. 4 : SHAKESPEARE.

In fact, for this very reason the aspen leaf is used figuratively to signify a chattering tongue.

Those aspen leaves of theirs never leave wagging.
THOMAS MOORE

Legend has it that the aspen trembles with horror because it was from some of its wood that the Cross of Calvary was made.

Aspen catkins bloom during March and April. The seeds are not viable in Britain.

Wild animals like eating the leaves borne on any suckers that may surround the tree, and beavers will devour the bark.

There is a very attractive variety of aspen, *P. tremula* var. *purpurea*, the leaves of which open out with a purple hue and eventually turn to an autumnal red—a useful tree for ornamental arboriculture.

BLACK POPLAR

The **black poplar** (*P. nigra*) is the most massive of the poplars in Britain. It is usually regarded as being indigenous to this country, though there is as much doubt about the origin of the tree as there is about its common name. It is quite likely that it was at first called ' black ' simply to distinguish it from the white.

The black poplar grows 50 to 80 feet high, and since the trunk is clear of branches for a considerable height, the tree yields a good supply of timber.

The leaves are of a characteristic heart shape, the apices being rather extended and pointed. The margins are finely serrated, though the teeth are not sharp (p. 225). The under-surfaces are quite smooth. The leaf-stalks are not much compressed so that the leaves do not tremble very much, at any rate, not so much as those of the aspen and white poplar.

The catkins, particularly those of the male, are very conspicuous, especially since they appear during March and April, that is, before the leaves have opened out.

Though the black poplar will produce plenty of clean timber, this is not of very great importance. It is, however, used in turnery. Dutch sabots are made from it, so this tree, like the white poplar, frequently figures in the Dutch scene. The bark is useful for tanning leather.

LOMBARDY POPLAR

The very distinctive shape of the **Lombardy poplar** has made it the most familiar of all poplars in Britain ; yet it is not indigenous to this country. From remote times it has been known in Persia (Iran) and northern India. From there it was probably introduced into

Black Poplar
Coltishall Mead
LR 5-7-38

Lonsdale Ragg

Black Poplar in Norfolk.

southern Europe. It was unknown in Italy during Pliny's time, but it is common enough there now. It derives its name from the fact that it grows in abundance along the river-banks of Lombardy. According to E. Step in *Wayside and Woodland Trees*, this poplar was introduced from Lombardy into Britain by Lord Rochford in 1758, though it has been suggested that the tree arrived here earlier than that. But support is added to Step's statement by the fact that Lord Rochford's tree was a male, and since most Lombardy poplars in Britain today probably originated from this tree by means of vegetative cuttings, they too are all males.

Some botanists consider the Lombardy poplar to be a variety of the black poplar and have given it the botanical name *P. nigra* var. *pyramidalis*. Others accept it as a distinct species and it is then known either as *P. fastigiata* or *P. italica*.

The general shape of the Lombardy poplar is very characteristic— something like that of a cypress. This is due to the fact that all its branches grow practically vertical. The leaves are very like those of the black poplar, that is, heart-shaped with long, pointed apices, though they are of a slightly darker green colour.

The ornamental value of this inspiring tree needs no emphasis, and in this connexion it may be mentioned that the tree is an exceptionally fast grower, often attaining a height of 100 feet, during about the first thirty years of its life. It can scarcely be surpassed for certain purposes in landscape gardening.

OTHER POPLARS

Other poplars are to be seen in Britain, most of which have been introduced from Canada and the United States.

The **Carolina black poplar** (*P. angulata*) is one example. It resembles the black poplar, though it has ridged twigs, large buds and larger leaves, the last-named having very long and pointed tips. This, and certain varieties, make handsome trees for purposes of landscape gardening.

The **Ontario poplar** (*P. candicans*), sometimes called **balm-of-Gilead poplar,** like other American balsam poplars, bears buds covered with a resin exuding a smell of balsam. The young leaves are also fragrant. The mature leaves are shaped like those of the black poplar, though they are larger and the marginal teeth are sharp (p. 225). This tree hails from North America, though it is supposed to have

Eric J. Hosking

Lombardy Poplars in Summer.

originated from Europe and then acquired certain stock from the New World. In Britain it is often cultivated.

The **Oregon balsam poplar** (*P. trichocarpa*) is a fast-growing tree which is proving very successful in British plantations. In its native habitat, that is along the Pacific coastal regions of North America, it is the largest of the broad-leaved trees, frequently attaining a height of 200 feet and a bole diameter of 8 feet. There it is known as the **black cotton-wood**, and its timber is used for making various domestic wooden articles and for wood-pulp. The tree is very handsome, as exemplified by many specimens in Britain, and its cultivation should be encouraged. According to H. L. Edlin, in his *British Woodland Trees*, the fastest growing of all poplars in Britain is *P. generosa*, a hybrid between the Carolina black poplar (*P. angulata*) and the Oregon balsam poplar (*P. trichocarpa*). This hybrid, like other poplar hybrids, indicates, as Edlin says, the great possibilities of the application of scientific plant breeding to trees.

The **balsam poplar** or **tacamahac** (*P. balsamifera*) is another balsam poplar of the United States and Canada. It has now been introduced into Britain, but is not cultivated here to any great extent. Its leaves are very fragrant.

The **black Italian poplar** (*P. serotina*) is a hybrid between the black poplar (*P. nigra*) and the American **eastern cotton-wood** (*P. deltoides*). It is a useful tree for screening purposes, for it is of very rapid growth. Only male trees are seen in this country, though even these are not very common.

The species *Populus euphratica* is the ‘weeping willow’ of the Bible (see p. 219). It is native to Asia and Africa, though seldom seen in Britain.

A species very recently introduced from western China and sometimes seen growing in parks and pleasure grounds is *P. lasiocarpa*. The heart-shaped leaves of this species are enormous and they have conspicuous red veins.

> Willows whiten, aspens quiver,
> Little breezes dusk and shiver
> Tho’ the wave that runs for ever
> By the island in the river
>   Flowing down to Camelot.
>   *The Lady of Shallot* : TENNYSON

29

BIRCHES AND ALDERS

(*Betulaceae*)

To the family BETULACEAE belong two trees commonly seen in Britain, namely, birch and alder, though the birch is much the more familiar since it is such a conspicuously beautiful tree (see *Frontispiece*). The family is distributed throughout the north temperate zone, and some representatives are indigenous to South America.

A general review of the family will serve to bring out the main points of difference between birch and alder.

The family BETULACEAE is composed of trees and shrubs, and in this scheme of classification it contains two genera only, namely, *Betula* (birches) and *Alnus* (alders).

All the leaves of the family are simple, and most of them have serrated margins. The stipules to each leaf are formed from the outer scales of the winter bud, but these soon fall off. The birch leaf has a pronounced apex whereas that of the alder is flattened at the tip. All British species in this family are deciduous.

The flowers are unisexual and are borne in male and female catkins, though both sexes are produced on the same tree. Pollen is distributed by wind. The stamens of the birch are curious in that the anther heads are cleft almost in half. The fruit of both genera takes the form of a nut enclosed in a thin skin ; but whereas that of the birch is winged (p. 235), that of the alder is not.

BIRCHES

Birches, frail whispering company, are these ?
Or lovely women rooted into trees ?
Daughters of Norsemen, on a foreign shore
Left hostage, while the galley draws away,
Beating the rise and fall of manifold oar,
Beating a pathway to the broken coasts,
Forgetful of its ghosts.

V. SACKVILLE-WEST

This "most shy and ladylike of trees" as J. R. Lowell called it, this "Lady of the Woods" as Coleridge named it, though as graceful as any woman, is no sensitive plant, for it is one of the hardiest of trees, thriving best in northern climes and often doing well on sites which would defy even the sturdiest of oaks. Furthermore it is very widespread, which is not surprising since it can cope with the most exacting conditions which a tree could be reasonably expected to withstand. So the various species of birch occur as forest trees or in solitude in most parts of the north temperate zone—in Asia, Europe and America —and one even invades the arctic zone.

Birch belongs to the genus *Betulus* which comprises about forty species.

The **common birch,** so frequently seen in Britain, often called the **silver** or **white birch,** was originally named *Betulus alba* by Linnaeus, and indeed, this specific name is still retained by many botanists. But there is another species, often found growing with the common birch (though it tends towards a more northerly habitat), which is sufficiently different to warrant specific distinction. It is called *B. pubescens.* A. K. and A. B. Jackson, in their revision of Step's *Wayside and Woodland Trees,* have therefore proposed that in order to make the distinction between these two species more complete (because it is certain that in the past both species have been described as *B. alba*), *B. alba* should now be called *B. pendula* as distinct from *B. pubescens.*

Though one must agree that any species, such as *B. pubescens,* which is specifically different from *B. alba* should receive a different specific name, it is difficult to see why that of *B. alba* should also be changed. In fact, since some botanists still retain that name, it is proposed to do so here. Specialist botanists, especially taxonomists, should bear in mind that the changing of specific and generic names, though sometimes essential, sometimes desirable, but perhaps sometimes hair-splitting, always causes confusion among others with an economic, academic, cultural or merely a lay interest in plants. So when considering nomenclature, and especially proposed changes in nomenclature, a sense of proportion should be brought to bear. The question : is it logical ? is not enough. Other points of view should be taken into consideration, and after a thorough weighing of pros and cons the deciding question should be : is it desirable ? With the case in point, we should say : no. Although a new species (*pubescens*) is now recognised, and though certain intermediate forms are yet to be investigated and described, there seems no valid reason why the name for the first-named, *B. alba,*

Silver Birch in Sussex.

Lonsdale Ragg

should be altered. The fact that this name was given by Linnaeus and has been used ever since for well-nigh two hundred years should also be weighed in the balance, for it is important. And this fact, and also its corollary, that the name *B. alba* has been utilised by many authorities and authors ever since, would seem to be the most valid reason why the silver or white birch should still be designated *B. alba*.

The main points of difference between *B. alba* and *B. pubescens* are : the winter twigs of the former bear prominent warty outgrowths, whereas those of the latter do not ; the twigs of the former are smooth, those of the latter are covered with down ; the terminal branches of the former are more pendulous, and its bark is not so white. As might be expected, since the two species often grow together, intermediate hybrids are common.

The silver birch, since it can withstand extremes of climate, is common throughout the whole of Europe and is also to be seen in many parts of western Asia and Siberia. It is as much at home in the exposed Scottish Highlands (it is one of the few trees to be seen growing among heather) as it is in the protection of the back garden in a built-up area.

Eric J Hosking

Silver Birch.

Winter.　　　　　　　　　　　　　　　　Summer.

The average height of the tree in Britain is 50 feet, though trees much taller than this sometimes occur. The tree is not very long-lived, usually reaching a ripe old age at fifty years, though sometimes living for eighty years. The tree is conspicuous by virtue of its silvery bark (pp. 234 and 237) which periodically peels off in layers; but as the tree gets older the silvery sheen of the trunk disappears and is replaced by a drab dullness caused by the formation of fissures which make the whole surface rough and uneven.

The leaves begin to open out in March and are at their best towards the end of April (Plate 5). They vary in shape from more or less triangular with a prominent apex to nearly oval. The margins are un-

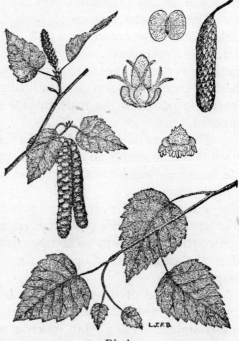

Birch.

Above left, male catkins; below right, spray of foliage; above right, female catkin, winged seed, scale bearing female flowers, scale bearing male flowers.

evenly serrated. The leaves are grey-green in colour, and being small with thin stalks they flutter easily in the breeze. In autumn they turn a bright yellow.

> Lo ! in the middle of the wood
> The folded leaf is woo'd from out the bud
> With winds upon the branch, and there
> Grows green and broad, and takes no care,
> Sun-steep'd at noon, and in the yellow moon
> Nightly dew-fed ; and turning yellow
> Falls, and floats adown the air.
>
> *The Lotos-Eaters* : TENNYSON

As the leaves begin to open, so do the flowers which have already been formed in catkins as early as the previous autumn. In their earlier stages, the female catkins are shorter than the male. The male catkins are more or less pendulous and dark red in colour (p. 235 and Plate 5). They become still more pendulous as they ripen. The female catkins are more erect (p 235). The male catkin is composed of bracts, and each bract subtends male flowers—usually three in number. Each flower is composed of a single sepal and two stamens, the anther head of each being cleft longitudinally into two equal halves. During April the bracts of the male catkins move apart and the stamens are exposed.

The bracts of the female catkin each subtend two or three flowers. Each flower is simply an ovary with two fine styles. After pollination, the female flower becomes fertilised and then the female catkins grow longer (Plate 5).

The fruit of the birch, which is a very small nut surrounded by a thin layer of tissue, has two wings (p. 235) by means of which the fruit is carried through the air. The ripe fruits are released during September after the catkins have opened right out and shed their protective bracts.

The wood of the silver birch is brownish-yellow in colour. In Britain the trunk seldom grows straight enough to render the tree of any commercial value ; but much is imported, and is used for making all sorts of domestic articles.

So it seems that this very lovely tree, even in its wild state, is most valuable as a decorative plant—and that it certainly is. But it has other uses. For example, where our larger towns have stretched their tentacles into the surrounding birch woods (as in the outskirts of London), those who value their gardens would be well advised to make composts of fallen birch leaves, for they make excellent humus. It is gratifying to note that on some of these housing estates, birches have been allowed to remain in the pleasure-grounds and even in some of the small gardens. Then again, the twigs tied together make good brooms, and where heath-fires are prevalent they are useful for making beaters. The twigs of birch were used for making the lictors' rods with which the way was swept for the magistrates in Ancient Rome. Brooms and besoms are made from birch twigs, especially in the U.S.S.R. The Finns use bunches of birch twigs with which to chafe their bodies and thus restore circulation after taking an icy cold bath or rolling in the snow.

In the U.S.S.R., the birch is a highly important forest tree. It is particularly widespread there. The wood is used for making all manner of things and for the production of charcoal. Shoes are made from the

Boles of a Silver Birch.

Eric J. Hosking

very durable bark, and an oil which is used for treating leather is extracted from the bark. An alcoholic toddy is sometimes also distilled from the unopened leaf-buds.

But many small boys in the past have had no cause for showing any particular appreciation of the birch, for with its twigs the ' birch ' for punishing at any rate the culprits who were discovered was made. And even today the ' birch ', more in a metaphorical sense, figures in school-room discipline.

The third species of birch in Britain is more distinctive since it never assumes the habit of a tree, in fact, it is a small shrub seldom growing more than three feet in height and of creeping habit. It is therefore called **dwarf birch** (B. *nana*). It occurs mainly in Scotland and is possibly a remnant of the Ice Age, for it occurs even further north (in Greenland, for example)—that is, at the world's northern limit for trees. Its leaves are rounder and the leaf-stalks shorter.

The silver birch is often cultivated for its beauty of form. There are also other species and varieties to be seen under cultivation in Britain. For example, a variety of the silver birch, B. *alba* var. *purpurea*, has particularly beautiful purple foliage. Another variety, of an even more pronounced weeping habit than B. *alba*, is B. *alba* var. *youngii*.

Some birches, not to be seen in Britain, are of sufficient interest to warrant mentioning. The **paper** or **canoe birch** (B. *papyrifera*) is common in North America and Canada, where it grows chiefly in the coastal areas but seldom further south than New York and Washington States. The bark of this species separates easily into layers from which North American Indians construct their canoes and many domestic utensils because the bark is waterproof. The wood of this species is also used for many purposes.

The **yellow birch** (B. *lutea*) of North America is an important lumber tree and is one of the largest deciduous trees, especially in the north-east of the American continent.

> Touched with beauty, I stand still and gaze
> In the autumn twilight. Yellow leaves and brown
> The grass enriching, gleam, or waver down
> From lime and elm : far-glimmering through the haze
> The quiet lamps in order twinkle ; dumb
> And fair the park lies ; faint the city's hum.
> And I regret not June's impassioned prime,

When her deep lilies banqueted the air,
And this now ruined, then so fragrant lime
Cooled with clear green the heavy noon's high glare ;
Nor flushed carnations, breathing hot July ;
Nor April's thrush in the blithest songs of the year,
With brown bloom on the elms and dazzling sky ;
So strange a charm there lingers in this austere
Resigning month, yielding to what must be.
Yet most, O delicate birch, I envy thee,
Child among trees ! with silvery slender limbs
And purple sprays of drooping hair. Night dims
The grass ; the great elms darken ; no birds sing.
At last I sigh for the warmth and the fragrance flown.
But thou in the leafless twilight shinest alone.,
Awaiting in ignorant trust the certain spring.

The Birch Tree : LAURENCE BINYON

ALDERS

The alder belongs to the other genus of the family BETULACEAE, namely, *Alnus* ; the **common alder** is *A. glutinosa* (p. 240). It is known in some parts as **aller**. Though this species is confined to the Old World, there are others to be found in many parts of the north temperate regions of the Old and the New Worlds.

The common alder flourishes in moist situations ; that is why it is so frequent along river and canal banks and among copses covering marshy ground. The tree is not a tall one even when growing in the best conditions. It averages 30 to 40 feet at maturity, though it is sometimes known to exceed this height considerably. The black trunk develops a girth of anything from 2 to 6 feet. In boggy areas it is very prone to sending up root suckers, and for this reason it is frequently coppiced. If, on the other hand, it is planted or grows naturally in dry sandy soil where its ramifying roots find it impossible to retain plenty of moisture, then it does not develop an arboreal habit but grows only as a bush. But in spite of all this, alder flourishes best where its main root system is above the usual water-table.

Although the timber is of little use today, it has proved itself resistant to the ravages of continuous immersion in water. Virgil claimed that the first boats were made of alder :

Tunc Alnos primum fluvii sensere cavatos.
Nec non et torrentum undam levis innatat Alnus.

A. H. Bastin

Winter.   Summer.

Alder.

Vitruvius, the celebrated Roman architect and engineer favoured alder for piles on which buildings were erected, giving the town of Ravenna as an example. The piles supporting the Rialto at Venice and many other structures in towns such as Amsterdam, where the presence of water has to be taken into consideration, are of alder wood.

The bark of the alder is black in colour and very uneven. It is sometimes used for tanning leather, and at one time a dye was extracted from it. The rather large, ovoid and pointed winter buds are borne on short stalks. They are very deep red in colour and adpressed to the surface of the twig.

The glossy leaves are on an average about three inches long. They are rounder than those of the birch and are flattened at the top with a slightly re-entrant curve at the end of the mid-rib (p. 241 and Plate 5). The margins are wavy and serrated unevenly. Although the alder is deciduous, the leaves remain on the tree much longer than do those of most other deciduous trees. This is due, no doubt, to the close proximity of a plentiful supply of water. When young, the leaves are sticky, hence the specific name.

The male catkins are erect when young, but after a spurt of growth during March and April (before the leaves open out) they droop. They are conspicuous since their scales are bright red. Each scale subtends three male flowers, and each flower bears four stamens cupped in a perianth of four segments. The anther heads are not cleft as they are in the birch. The female catkins are smaller and erect. They are made up of reddish scales, each subtending two flowers. Each female flower is very like that of the birch. The stigmas are bright red. After fertilisation, the female catkins grow larger; but, whereas the scales of the female birch catkin are deciduous, those of the alder are not. In fact, they become woody and black, so that the old catkins persist on the tree long after the seeds have been

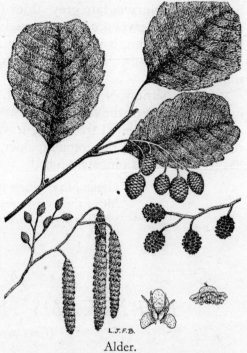

Alder.
Above, twig bearing foliage and ripe female cones; below left, twig bearing female cones and pendulous male cones; middle right, old female cones; below right, scale from female catkin bearing two flowers, and scale from male catkin bearing three flowers.

dispersed. Though the fruits, unlike those of the birch, are not winged, they contain air bubbles which assist in water distribution.

Like the birch, the alder seldom sets seed until it is about twenty years of age.

Alder wood is at first white, but turns reddish on exposure, finally settling to a pink shade. Though occasionally used in the making of furniture and clogs (which are so often subject to immersion in water), the value of the wood as timber has declined. It does, however, make excellent charcoal; but even in this connexion it is not so valuable as it was years ago. In the days when gunpowder was in great demand, alder charcoal was considered the best form of charcoal to use in making it.

A rather rare species of alder in Britain, not seen growing wild here, is the **Norwegian grey alder** (*A. incana*). Its bark is grey in colour and the leaves are more pointed than the common alder. According to H. L. Edlin, it is useful as a nurse tree for other young trees on dry limestone soils. In northern Europe this species yields a valuable timber.

A rare variety of this species, *A. incana* var. *incisa*, is perhaps the most handsome of the several cut-leaved alders, and it was at one time used as an ornamental tree. The leaves are very deeply lobed. Then there is a variety of the common alder, *A. glutinosa* var. *laciniata*, which has slender leaves pinnately lobed.

> Green-hoary alders near the wheat
> Move their crisp glister:
> *The Royal Aspects of the Earth* : LORD DE TABLEY

30
HORNBEAMS AND HAZELS
(*Corylaceae*)

The family CORYLACEAE is closely related to BETULACEAE, considered in Chapter 29, and both families are distributed throughout the north temperate zone. CORYLACEAE is a family of herbs and shrubs ; though there are others, only two genera are of interest so far as trees in Britain are concerned ; they are *Corylus*, which includes the hazel, and *Carpinus*, including the hornbeam.

HORNBEAM

The genus *Carpinus* comprises a large number of species, most of which are indigenous and confined to eastern Asia, though there are some in the New World. The **hornbeam** (*Carpinus betulus*) is the only representative of the genus in Britain, where it is distributed erratically. In some localities it is called **yoke-elm.** Hornbeam is considered to be indigenous to the Midlands and south of England ; even there it flourished in greater numbers in by-gone days than it does now, often being an important member of those forests, including Epping, which surrounded London.

Several theories have been propounded to explain the common name, ' hornbeam '. One is that the wood of this tree is so tough that

Hornbeam
Knole

Lonsdale Ragg

Old Hornbeam in Knole Park, Sevenoaks, Kent.

Hornbeam in Hatfield Park in Winter.   *Eric J. Hosking*

beams made from it are as strong as horn. Another is that the yokes made for bullocks, used as beasts of burden, and attached to their horns were constructed from this wood. This theory might account for the other name, ' yoke-elm.'

The tree is not very large, seldom growing more than about 45 feet, though exceptional specimens have been known to attain a height of about 70 feet.

The trunk is curious in that it is somewhat vertically flattened so that a cross-section of it would be not circular but elliptical. The grey bark is rather smooth though sometimes slightly fissured ; old trees often become gnarled with a very rough surface (p. 243). The trunk gives off many branches, so the main trunk usually disappears above the first main branches. The crown is massive and irregular.

The winter buds are fairly long and pointed and they are curiously bent.

The leaves are arranged alternately on the stem. Each leaf is one to three inches long, something like that of the elm, though more wedge-shaped towards the base of the blade, more pointed at the tip, and with

Eric J. Hosking

The same tree in Summer.

double-toothed margins (p. 246 and Plate 5). The under-surface is hairy. There are two small stipules which act as protective scales to the axillary winter bud and then fall off as the young, bright green leaf begins to open. The leaves assume a yellow or golden hue in the autumn. In France the young foliage is used as fodder for cattle; but in Britain it is relished only by rabbits and hares and other wild animals.

The flowers are unisexual, and are borne in male and female catkins; but both sexes grow on the same tree. The catkins open out during April and May concurrently with the leaves. The male catkins range from one to two inches in length (p. 246 and Plate 5). The bracts subtend three to twelve stamens, the anther heads of which are deeply cleft and hairy at the top. The female catkins are very loosely constructed. The bracts are small and lance-shaped, each subtending two flowers. At the base of each flower there is a curious small three-lobed bract known as a bracteole. Early in the season the lance-shaped bracts are shed, and as the flowers develop, the bracteoles enlarge until their centre lobes are about an inch and a half long. Thus each bracteole subtends one flower, and this is composed of a two-chambered ovary

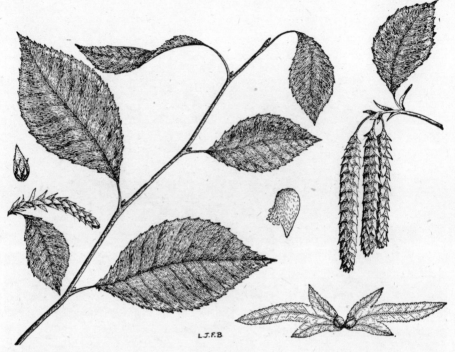

Hornbeam.
A twig bearing foliage; left of twig, female catkin and a single scale bearing two
female flowers; right of twig, male catkins, a single scale bearing stamens and
two ripe fruit each subtended by a tri-lobed bracteole.

and two styles. Pollination is by wind. After fertilisation, the fruit
becomes woody and is then subtended by a large, three-lobed bracteole
which acts as a wing for its dispersal.

The uses of the timber of hornbeam are now very limited. It is
very tough and therefore does not take kindly to the carpenter's tools.
It does make an excellent fuel, however, and in the past charcoal produced from it was used for making gunpowder. Hornbeam will
coppice well, and since it branches profusely it makes a good hedge. In
time past it figured in the absurd cult of constructing labyrinths and
mazes (see p. 117). No wonder John Evelyn warmly commended this
tree, for he lived in the days of 'formal' gardens, clipped hedges and
trees, and topiary. During the eighteenth century, hornbeam was very
popular for hedge-making, in Britain and on the Continent.

There is a variety of hornbeam, *C. betulus* var. *pyramidalis*, which is
regular in general habit and pyramidal in form. It is therefore useful
in landscape architecture.

HAZEL

Today I saw the catkins blow
Altho' the hills are white with snow ;

While throstles sang, " The sun is good ",
They waved their banners in the wood.

They came to greet the lurking Spring
As messengers from Winter's King.

February : DOROTHY UNA RATCLIFFE

The hazel is a member of the genus *Corylus*, which comprises about eight species of the north temperate regions of both Old and New Worlds. The **common hazel** in Britain is *Corylus avellana*. Very rarely, however, does the plant achieve the proportions of a tree, for it produces so many suckers from its roots that the entire plant looks like a very large shrub. Furthermore, for various agricultural purposes it is frequently coppiced.

The common hazel occurs in all parts of Europe, Asia (except the more northerly regions), and North Africa. It is most commonly seen growing in hedges and copses, where it is usually of the shrubby habit ; but it does sometimes assume the habit of a tree about 12 feet high ; indeed on rare occasions it is known to grow more than twice that height.

The bark of the older branches and stems is brown with patches of grey, though on the younger twigs it is grey and covered with short hairs. The winter buds are almost spherical.

The leaves, alternately arranged on the stem, are between two and four inches long, and closely resemble those of the hornbeam in shape (Plate 5). When young, they are often tinged with purple.

The flowers are unisexual ; but both sexes are borne on the one plant. The male flowers are grouped in the form of the characteristic ' lamb's tail ' catkins, tightly packed and firm when young during the previous autumn (p. 248), but more open, bright yellow and pendulous when mature in January or February, that is, before the leaves open out. These catkins usually occur in groups of two to four, and each is about two inches long (p. 249 and Plate 5). Each male flower is composed of a bract with a pair of large bracteoles subtending four deeply cleft stamens (p. 249).

The female flowers are vastly different. They are clustered, not into drooping catkins, but very close, erect structures which superficially resemble fat winter buds. At the tips, the red styles protrude. The

R

Harold Bastin

Hazel.
Left, foliage, young catkins and fruit of cob-nut; right, section of ' filbert.'

bract of each female flower is boat-shaped and subtends two flowers. Each flower is composed of a two-chambered ovary cupped in a collection of small bracts called the involucre. Each ovary has two long red styles (p. 249 and Plate 5).

The male flowers produce a large amount of pollen, and when this is ripe and dry, yellow clouds of it may be seen being blown away from the plant—for it is wind-pollinated. After fertilisation, the fruit develops into the familiar nut. The kernel inside is the seed produced by the fertilised ovule, and the woody shell has developed from the ovary wall. The involucre also grows considerably and forms the well-known leafy cupule in which the nut is cupped.

The hazel nut is distributed by birds and small mammals such as squirrels.

The different forms of hazel nut, for example, **Barcelona nut, cob** and **filbert** (cultivated extensively in south-east England), are merely varieties of the common hazel. All varieties of hazel demand a good, moist soil, but they are intolerant of a badly drained soil. Today, the hazel is appreciated chiefly for its palatable and nutritious fruits, and in this connexion the wild form finds just as much favour as the cultivated varieties. The fruit has a very high oil or fat content; this accounts for the considerable food value of the fruit. Sometimes, but not very often, the oil is extracted.

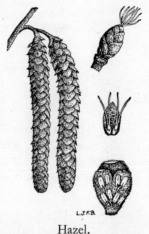

Hazel.
Left, male catkins; above right, bunch of female flowers; middle right, scale bearing two female flowers; below right, male bract bearing two bracteoles each subtending four stamens.

The wood of the hazel is seldom used commercially, since it is not easily available in planks; but it has been used in cabinet- and toy-making and in turnery. The long branches, especially those produced from the suckers, are very tough yet particularly pliable, and for this reason they are used for many agricultural purposes (such as hurdle-making), for whip handles, driving and walking sticks, and so forth. Hazel twigs frequently also constitute the paraphernalia of the water-diviner. In order to obtain good pliant staves, the plant is frequently coppiced in Britain and elsewhere. The hazel is frequently associated with the oak in British woodlands; furthermore it is often cultivated in small copses to form coverts for game.

Since the leaves of the hazel turn a striking yellow during autumn, the common form is sometimes cultivated for ornamental purposes. But there are varieties which serve this purpose better; for example, the variety *C. avellana* var. *aurea* presents a beautiful golden foliage in the autumn. Then there is the attractive *C. avellana* var. *purpurea*, whose large, shining leaves are purple throughout the season. There are a few other varieties.

> . . . but the hazels rose
> Tall and erect, with tempting clusters hung,
> A virgin scene !—A little while I stood,
> Breathing with such suppression of the heart
> As joy delights in ; and, with wise restraint
> Voluptuous, fearless of a rival, eyed
> The banquet.
>
> *Nutting* : WORDSWORTH

31
OAKS
(Fagaceae)

The oak grows silently in the forest a thousand years ; only in the thousandth year, when the axeman arrives with his axe, is there heard an echoing through the solitudes ; and the oak announces itself when, with far-sounding crash, it *falls*.

The French Revolution, Vol. I : CARLYLE

Those green-robed senators of mighty woods,
Tall oaks, branch-charmèd by the earnest stars,
Dream, and so dream all night without a stir.

Hyperion, Book I : KEATS

Though before the age of steel and teak the ships that ruled the waves were built of oak, and though this tough tree may be found throughout the length and breadth of Britain, we must not make the mistake of claiming it as an exclusively national emblem, for other nations have claims just as equal. In many parts of Europe, especially the lands of the Teutonic and Norse peoples, in France and in Britain, the oak has been venerated since times prehistoric.

In our own land and elsewhere, the Druids held the oak as sacred, and for that reason they also treated the mistletoe with care and respect ; so whenever this semi-parasite was gathered from its host oak it was cut with due solemnity and ritual, for the Druids and the people over whom they ruled believed that the mistletoe took care of the spirit of the great oak on which it was growing during the long hard winter when, as they believed, the host was temporarily dead.[1]

It seems idolatry with some excuse
When our forefather Druids in their oaks
Imagined sanctity.

W. COWPER

But the oak has been sacred to many others ; even in the Scriptures we find it treated with reverence, though the oaks in those lands and of those days were not the same species as the oaks most commonly seen in Britain today.

[1] See *Flowers in Britain*, p. 174.

Oaks in May
Llandrindod
19.5.43

Young Oaks in May.

Lonsdale Ragg

And they gave unto Jacob all the strange gods that *were* in their hands, and *all their* earrings which *were* in their ears ; and Jacob hid them under the oak which *was* by Shechem.

Genesis, 35

According to the Rev. C. A. Johns, the oak "which *was* by Shechem", like the oaks at Mamre beneath which, according to Jewish tradition, the father of the faithful reared his tabernacle, was the ever-green, holm or holly oak or something akin to it. This species is not native to, nor particularly common in, Britain (see p. 262). As Johns points out, the Israelites, on their restoration to the land of Canaan, regarded with particular respect the oak " which *was* by Shechem ", for it had a peculiar connexion with their history. The Scriptures offer other evidence of the particular reverence with which the Ancients of the Levant regarded the oak. Then, too, the Saxons venerated this tree, for they held their national assemblies beneath it, and their conferences with the Britons were held under the oaks of Dartmoor.

John Evelyn, who looked upon the oak with such special respect that he gave it pride of place in his *Sylva*, wrote : " It is natural for man to feel an awful and religious terror when placed in the centre of a thick wood; on which account, in all ages, such places have been chosen for the celebration of religious ceremonies." But, as Johns retorts, it must be left to the historian to trace by what degrees this pious feeling degenerated into dangerous superstition. In any event, we must admit that, forgetting all superstitious or religious background, most of us experience a feeling of awe or of subdued respect when entering a wood, whether it be of oaks or of pines. Yet such has been the privilege of the oak through many centuries. Even the grove of oaks at Dodona in Epirus was the meeting-place of all the inhabitants of Ancient Greece when they wished to know the will of the god Jupiter.

The ancient Prussians believed that the majestic oaks were the homes of their gods. Perpetual fires were made of oak in the worship of the Aryan gods, and similar sacred fires of oak were burned by the old Norsemen before their god Thor, by the Lithuanians before their god Perkunas, and by the Greeks before Jupiter. It is of interest that all three of these gods were the gods of thunder. So the oak has figured largely in the tree-cults of pagan worship ; no wonder therefore that with the advent of Christianity which ousted paganism, the oak still had a part to play. The great Oak of Jupiter at Geismar in Germany was felled by Bonifacius who built a chapel from its wood. On the

The Knightwood Oak

R 26/7/39

Lonsdale Ragg

The Knightwood Oak in the New Forest.

Heinzenberg mountains in Switzerland stands a chapel on the site where once flourished the old oak which groaned in protest when it was cut down. At Kildare, a church was built beneath an oak—the name means ' church of the oak.' Several monasteries also were founded in the oak groves of Ireland.

In Ancient Rome, a wreath of oak leaves was awarded for life-saving ; in Nazi Germany a decoration of oak leaves was awarded for much less worthy accomplishments.

In more recent British history the oak has played a greater part than any other tree.

> See you our stilly woods of oak,
> And the dread ditch beside ?
> O that was where the Saxons broke,
> On the day that Harold died.
>
> *Puck's Song* : KIPLING

Royal Oak Day is on May 29, for it was on that day in 1630 that Charles II was born. We have all heard how, after his defeat by Cromwell at Worcester on September 3, 1651, and before his escape to France, was that when he hid from Cromwell's men in an oak tree at Whiteladies, a short distance from Boscobel House. He returned from France on his birthday when his Royalist supporters bedecked themselves with oak to celebrate the event. Usually, those who celebrate this day now (and the number has perceptibly declined during the past two or three decades) wear twigs bearing conspicuous ' oak-apple ' galls (see p. 264).

So, despite the very widespread respect which the oak has enjoyed for many centuries and in many lands, we must agree with Johns who, like Evelyn in his *Sylva*, gives pride of place to the oak in his *Forest Trees of Britain*, that : " As long as the Lion holds his place as king of beasts, and the Eagle as king of birds, the sovereignty of British Trees must remain to the Oak. . . ." In truth it is a kingly tree, the emblem of majesty, strength, and durability.

For many centuries, the oak was used in ship-building—long before the Elizabethan era. Old vessels, dating back to the beginning of the Christian era at least, have been excavated in various parts of Britain, and some were of oak. The same wood was frequently used by the Ancient Greeks and Romans and also by the Vikings. But the greatest age for the building of ships of oak was during the reign of Elizabeth.

The Hawkhurst Oak &
Famous already in XIth Cent^y
LR 21-7-32

Lonsdale Ragg

The Hawkhurst Oak in Kent.

The oak, when living, monarch of the wood ;
The English oak, which, dead, commands the flood.
Gotham : C. CHURCHILL

Before the reign of Elizabeth and for some time after it, the oak was protected by law against wanton felling, for the tree was an absolute necessity to such a maritime nation as Britain. In many parks, both in London and elsewhere, and on large country estates, oaks were reserved solely for naval requirements. Those in Greenwich Park left that open space always to be associated with our Navy ; Regent's Park (then known as Marylebone Park Fields) yielded nearly a thousand oaks during the reign of Charles II ; now there are scarcely any left. Even so recently as 1812, it was reported to the House of Commons that two thousand oak trees were required to build a seventy-four gun ship.

Oak wood was used for other purposes in the past apart from building the Royal and the Merchant Navies. The doors of the inner chapels of Westminster Abbey are made of oak ; so also is the shrine of Edward the Confessor. At Winchester one may still see Arthur's Round Table : certainly ancient and of oak, but not genuine. In fact, oak was used for all kinds of outdoor and indoor construction.

The length of life of the oak is still a matter of some controversy, though there seems little doubt that it is a long-lived tree. It is quite likely that we still have with us oaks dating back to Saxon times, for without doubt many examples have lived for one thousand to fifteen hundred years and more. But the tree yields its best timber when it is about two hundred years old, though as a plant it will flourish for several hundred years before it shows signs of decline.

Still the unmoving winter trees
Hold up the pure curves of their boughs,
Forms clothing calm immortal life
No change of time or state can rouse.
Winter Trees : EDWARD SHANKS

There are still many well-known veterans which are preserved for sentimental reasons throughout Britain, though, alas, such well-known trees as Honor Oak and Parliament Oak formerly in London are no longer with us. The Knightwood Oak still grows in the New Forest (p. 253) ; but the Hawkhurst Oak in Kent (p. 255), though its remains are preserved, is now dead. Other single veterans have captured the imagination of local people so that they were preserved at

Gospel Oak
Polstead Park.
LR
26.6.31

Lonsdale Ragg

The Gospel Oak, Polstead Park.

any rate for a time. Some are still with us, others have disappeared, but for many years they have stood, emblems of British history and the inspiration of poets. At the risk of causing him who finds his favourite omitted to raise his eye-brows, a few more examples might be cited. The Abbot's Oak, near Woburn Abbey, received its name from the fact that on the orders of Henry VIII the Abbot was hanged on it in 1537. The Ellerslie Oak, near Paisley, was used as shelter by Wallace and three hundred of his men. The Cowthorpe Oak, in the village of Cowthorpe, near Wetherby, Yorkshire, is nearly two thousand years old. This specimen is beautifully figured by Strutt in his *Sylva Britannica*. Dr. Hunter, in a note to his edition of Evelyn's *Sylva*, gives this rustic giant its best testimonial when he says : " When compared to this, all other trees are but children of the Forest." Sir Philip Sidney's Oak, another veteran figured by Strutt, was planted on the Penshurst Estate (the seat of the Sidney family) on Sir Philip's birthday in 1554. Ben Jonson refers to this tree as :

> That taller tree which of a nut was set
> At his great birth where all the Muses met.

And Waller has these elegant lines :

> Go, boy, and carve this passion on the bark
> Of yonder tree, which stands the sacred mark
> Of noble SIDNEY's birth ; when such benign,
> Such more than mortal-making stars did shine,
> That there they cannot but for ever prove
> The monuments and pledge of humble love :
> His humble love whose hope shall ne'er rise higher,
> Than for a pardon that he dares admire.

It would be impossible to do justice in short space to the many uses of oak wood today, and no such attempt will be made save perhaps to say that its considerable strength renders it of inestimable value ; also in the natural state, polished, stained or fumed, it is, and for centuries has been, an ideal medium for indoor construction, furniture and decorative work. It is therefore gratifying to note that the Forestry Commission is now planting oaks again in Britain.

GENERAL STRUCTURE OF OAK TREES

The oak is a member of the family FAGACEAE, a family of noble trees which includes also the beech and the sweet chestnut. The family

Oak Leaves.
Above left, American willow oak (*Q. phellos*); below left, common oak (*Q. pedunculata*); above middle, American red oak (*Q. coccinea*); below middle, holm oak (*Q. ilex*); above right, American red oak (*Q. rubra*); below right, Turkey oak (*Q. cerris*).

is distributed throughout temperate and tropical regions, though it is absent from tropical and South Africa with the exception of some cultivated representatives.

Oaks belong to the genus *Quercus* which is very widely distributed throughout the north temperate parts of the Old and New Worlds, and in the mountainous regions of the tropics. It is difficult to estimate the actual number of species ; in fact, it is quite likely that not all of them are yet known to science ; but we do know that there are at least three hundred species, and probably many more.

Before considering some of the most important and interesting species in more detail, a general description of the tree, based chiefly on the common oak, will be given.

The **common oak** is indigenous to Britain, and this is the oak which has largely figured in history and mythology. At one time it was

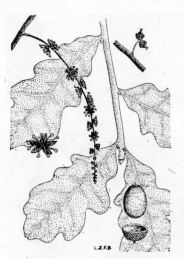

Common Oak
(*Q. pedunculata*).
Above left, male catkin;
middle left, male flower;
above right, female flowers;
below right, acorn removed
from its cupule.

designated *Quercus robur*; but today, two distinct species (to be distinguished later) are recognised, namely, *Q. pedunculata* and *Q. sessiliflora* or **durmast** oak.

The common oak is a large, robust tree, the older specimens being more remarkable for their girth than their height. The trees vary considerably in height (from 60 to 150 feet), according to their position and surroundings.

The bark on the trunk and larger branches is grey in colour and very thick and rough (p. 251). Even in winter, this tree can be recognised by the tortuous nature of its branches (p. 251 and Plate 4). The stout winter buds are light brown, and are enclosed in many bud-scales.

The leaves are more or less oval in shape, though their general outline varies with the species. Those of the common oak (*Q. pedunculata* and *Q. sessiliflora*) are deeply lobed, and each lobe is rounded at the tip; those of the Turkey oak (*Q. cerris*) (p. 262) are more deeply lobed; the lobes of the leaves of the American red oak (*Q. coccinea*) (p. 263) have very pointed, almost spiny lobes; the lobes of the other American red oak (*Q. rubra*) (p. 263) are square in outline; on the other hand, the leaves of the American willow oak (*Q. phellos*) (p. 263) have long, lance-shaped leaves very like those of the crack willow, with here and there a pronounced lateral lobe. In all species, the leaves are arranged alternately on the stem. In the common species, the foliage presents a rather dull brown autumnal tint; but some of the exotic species have fiery red foliage in autumn. Some species of oak are deciduous, others are semi-evergreen and others are quite evergreen (p. 259).

The flowers appear during April and May. They are unisexual, but both sexes are borne on the same tree. The male flowers are clustered in very loose catkins two or three inches long, and since they are green and do not appear before the leaves, they are rather inconspicuous (Plate 5). Each flower is made up of five to seven sepals and about the same number of stamens, though sometimes there may be as many as a dozen. The female flowers are even more inconspicuous. They may or may not be borne on short stalks (according to species) and they occur in groups of two to five (p. 260). Each female flower is composed of a three-chambered ovary with three crimson styles. The ovary is enveloped in a cupule of scales.

The oak is wind-pollinated. After fertilisation, the fruit develops into the familiar acorn. This takes the form of an ovoid fruit cupped in a cupule which has been formed from the bracts of the flower. The shape and structure of the acorn varies according to species (see below and Plate 5). Acorns were at one time used for human food, especially in Italy and Greece and Ancient Britain.

> Acorns were good until bread was found.
> *Colours of Good and Evil* : BACON

In some countries today they are used for various substitutes in human diet. They are relished by pigs and many wild animals.

COMMON OAKS

There are many examples of the **common oaks** (*Q. pedunculata* and *Q. sessiliflora*) in Britain today. *Q. pedunculata* is more widespread in the south, and though *Q. sessiliflora* (**durmast oak**) grows in the west and north of Britain it is not very common anywhere. (The etymology of the word ' durmast ' is doubtful, though the term ' mast ' is applied to the fruit of several forest trees such as oak and beech.) It is of interest

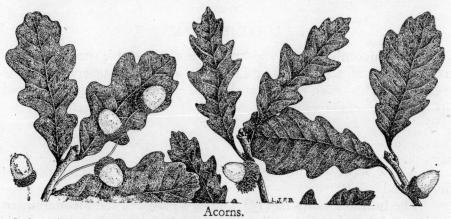

Acorns.
Left to right : common oak (*Q. pedunculata*), Turkey oak (*Q. cerris*) and common oak (*Q. sessiliflora*).

to note that much of the wood in old buildings in the west of England, Wales and Ireland, formerly believed to be chestnut, is now known to be durmast oak ; the same can be said of the carved roof in Westminster Hall.

The leaves of both species have stalks, but those of the latter are longer. Another important point of difference is (as the specific names imply) that the flowers of *pedunculata* are borne on stalks or peduncles whereas the flowers of *sessiliflora* have no stalks ; that is, they are sessile. Furthermore, the acorns of *sessiliflora* taper much more than do those of *pedunculata* (p. 261).

Since both these species of oaks have reigned in Britain for many centuries, it should not be surprising that many hybrids (not yet described in detail) have arisen.

TURKEY OAK

The **Turkey oak** (*Q. cerris*) (p. 7) is a native of Balkan countries. It was introduced into Britain some time during the first half of the eighteenth century, though the exact date is not known. Now this handsome tree flourishes here, especially in the south.

This tree is of a more pyramidal form than the common oaks, and the bark is thicker and of a greyish colour. The leaves, as described on p. 260 (see also p. 259), are more deeply lobed. The acorns have no stalks ; the cupules are very attractive, being covered with green scales (p. 261). The acorns do not ripen until the second year.

The timber is not very good from the utilitarian point of view.

LUCOMBE OAK

The **Lucombe oak** (*Q. lucombeana*) is a remarkable species. It was raised first of all about 1760 by Lucombe, an Exeter nurseryman. It is very pyramidal—even pointed at the top. It has a very thick bark, and its leaves are semi-evergreen.

OTHER OAKS

A few more of the less common oaks in Britain may now be mentioned.

The **holm** or **holly oak** (*Q. ilex*) is a native of the Mediterranean regions. It was introduced into Britain in the sixteenth century and is now cultivated in ornamental parks and gardens. It is sometimes called

OAK IN WINTER

PLATE 4

the **evergreen oak** : its leaves last for two years, so this densely shaded tree is always green. The distinguishing feature is the shape of the leaves. These are oval and pointed at the tip ; but the margins may either be smooth or, more usually, spiny (p. 259). This characteristic explains the common and the specific names, for the leaves resemble those of the holly (*Ilex aquifolium*). Seldom does this tree grow more than about 35 feet high. The bark is very black.

The **cork oak** (*Q. suber*) is another evergreen oak of the Mediterranean regions, chiefly Spain and Morocco. It is the commonest source of commercial cork. On occasion this species may be seen growing in Britain.

Other exotic oaks are cultivated for their ornamental beauty. Many of these hail from America. For example, the **willow oak** (*Q. phellos*), which is a valuable timber tree in the United States, has long, wavy, lance-shaped leaves with here and there a marginal lobe on some of them (p. 259). Of the **American red oaks,** there are *Q. rubra,* having enormous leaves reaching as much as eight inches in length and having less-pronounced lobes (p. 259), and *Q. coccinea,* whose leaf lobes are pointed, almost spiny (p. 259). There is a handsome variety of this species, namely, *Q. coccinea* var. *splendens.* The red oaks present most striking red tints in autumn. Other American species may be seen in Britain, but only rarely.

OAKS AND INSECTS

Oak seems to have a peculiar attraction for insects, for it is attacked by more of these pests than any other tree. In fact, the oak can count several hundred different species of insects among its natural enemies.

During the summer it is almost impossible to overlook the stag-beetle (*Lucanas cervus*) with its formidable horn-like antennae. This insect thrives among the foliage of the oak. Its larvae live in any wood which might be, or is on the point of, decaying, and sometimes they eat the roots of the tree.

Other beetles of the family *Scolytidae* feed on the wood and the bark of oak and other trees.

Then among the leaf-eating insects the caterpillars of which frequently attack oak are many moths, butterflies, leaf-rollers, and the common cockchafer.

But perhaps the most interesting are the gall-wasps belonging to several genera of insects, the larvae of which live in various parts of the

S

oak (among other plants) and stimulate the growth of the galls to be seen on leaves, stems and roots. One of the most common oak galls is the so-called ' oak-apple '. The almost spherical gall itself is the result of the abnormal development of plant tissue among and around the eggs which the insect has deposited there by piercing the plant. As the larvae hatches from the eggs and develop they feed on this tissue which gradually becomes powdery in consequence. When mature, the young insect makes a perforation in the tissue of the gall and thus escapes.

> While thus through all the ages thou hast push'd
> Of treeship—first a seedling hid in grass ;
> Then twig ; then sapling ; and, as century roll'd
> Slow after century, a giant bulk
> Of girth enormous, with moss-cushioned root
> Upheav'd above the soil, and sides emboss'd
> With prominent wens globose—till at the last
> The rottenness, which time is charg'd t' inflict
> On other mighty ones, found also thee . . .
>
> *Yardley Oak* : W. COWPER

32
SWEET OR SPANISH CHESTNUT
(*Fagaceae*)

The **sweet or Spanish chestnut** is another member of the family FAGACAEA (p. 250). It belongs to the genus *Castanea*—a genus very widely distributed. The sweet chestnut (*Castanea sativa*) is so called to distinguish it from the horse-chestnut—a totally different tree (p. 301). The sweet chestnut, being indigenous to Mediterranean regions, is sometimes also called **Italian, Spanish, French** or just **European chestnut.** Some doubt has been felt whether this tree is indigenous to Britain ; but in view of certain investigations more recently made, it seems likely that it was introduced here by the Romans for the sake of its edible fruit. It is supposed that the tree was called *Castanea* by the Romans after Castanum, an old Italian town, around which it grew in considerable numbers ; though it has been suggested that the town might have been named after the tree.

Though one cannot say that the sweet chestnut has been a successful producer of edible fruit in Britain throughout its centuries of residence (owing to climatic conditions), yet it has succeeded as a tree, for many noble specimens are to be found growing in these Islands. Furthermore, they live to a great age.

A sweet chestnut tree grows anything from 60 to 80 feet high, sometimes even higher (specimens up to 110 feet are known) ; but it seldom presents a tall, clean bole, for within about a dozen feet from the ground the first main branches emerge. A very characteristic feature is the spirally twisted bark (p. 266). Though this phenomenon is frequent in other species of tree, it is particularly evident in the sweet chestnut. The twigs are ribbed, and the winter buds are ovoid and pointed.

The very handsome leaves, which open out during April, are as much as ten inches long. They are simple, lance-shaped and deeply indented, with large and even very pronounced marginal teeth (Plate 2). They are arranged alternately on the stem. They are deciduous, and present the most striking tints in autumn. It is impossible to confuse them with the compound leaves of the horse-chestnut.

The sweet chestnut is unisexual, but both male and female flowers are borne on the same tree, as they all are in the members of this family (Chapters 31 and 33). Each year, the sweet chestnut is about the last of the trees in Britain to bloom, for the flowers never appear until towards the end of July, and frequently not before well into August. Then the groups of flowers are very conspicuous, for they are inserted on pendulous stems which are anything from six to eight inches long (Plate 2). These long, pale yellow catkins are borne in the axils of the leaves ; those growing from the lower leaf-axils bearing male flowers only, those growing from the upper leaf-axils bearing both male and female flowers, the male at the distal ends of the catkins and the female nearest the axils.

Each male flower consists of about ten stamens surrounded by five or six sepals. The female flowers are borne in groups of two or three, each group being surrounded by a scaly cupule. Each flower is very simple, being composed of a single ovary with several styles. The female flowers may be pollinated either by wind or by insects. After fertilisation has taken place, each ovary develops to form a nut. The cupule also enlarges to form a strong, green, very spiny covering to the two or three developing nuts (Plate 2).

Since the flowers bloom so late in the year, there is little time left for the fruit to develop before conditions make this impossible. That

Twisted Chestnut
Kew

LR. 2.4.38

Lonsdale Ragg

Spanish or Sweet Chestnut in the Royal Botanic Gardens, Kew.
Note the twisted nature of the bark.

is why the sweet chestnuts much further north than the Midlands in Britain seldom bear fruit.

When ripe, the cupule splits and the brown edible seeds are exposed (Plate 2). In Nature, these nuts are distributed by animals. The edible nut is treated as an article of diet in Mediterranean countries, especially in Italy, Spain and the more eastern parts of the Mediterranean. In those countries, the nut has been relished for many centuries; according to Alcaeus, the Arcadians were chestnut eaters. According to R. St. Barbe Baker, 400,000 acres of chestnuts have been planted in Italy for their fruit. The nut is not very popular in Britain, though it was eaten more often in days of old. Then it was dished up raw, roasted or chopped up in seasonings. Sometimes, the Christmas turkey is stuffed with chestnuts, though in Britain this method of stuffing is not now so frequent.

In the New World and in Japan, other species of *Castanea* yield edible fruit, and the timber of an American chestnut, *C. dentata*, is imported into Britain.

The timber of the sweet chestnut is light brown in colour and it is very durable. Since it is somewhat like oak in appearance, it is sometimes used as a substitute for the latter. Sweet chestnut and oak have often been confused in the identification of old timber (p. 262). The tree is often coppiced for the production of posts, piles, poles, and fences, and the copses make excellent coverts for game.

The chestnut raises the interesting question of the origin of the same term as applied to a stale joke. It is difficult to decide whether this term is derived from the sweet chestnut or the horse-chestnut. Anyhow, 'chestnut' as meaning a stale joke originated in an old play, *The Broken Sword*, by William Dillon. There, the character Captain Xavier persistently recounted variations on old jokes. In this play, he tells a tale to another character, Pablo, and in the story refers to a cork tree.

> Pablo : A chestnut-tree you mean, Captain.
> Captain : Bah ! I say a cork-tree.
> Pablo (insisting) : A chestnut-tree.
> Captain : I must know better than you ; it was a cork-tree, I say.
> Pablo (persisting) : A chestnut. I have heard you tell the joke twenty-seven times, and I am sure it was a chestnut.

Perhaps the enduring qualities of the sweet chestnut tree or its timber also had something to do with inspiring the connexion with stale, enduring jokes.

33
BEECHES
(Fagaceae)

Unflinching I have borne the brunt of spears—
Yet, under these dark boughs that writhe and twist,
My heart is as a wren's heart when she hears
The litch-owl calling through the evening mist,
And falters cowed, a thing of fluttering fears,
Before some shadow-plumed antagonist.

Quaking I ride, yet know not what I dread :
Naught stirs the boding silence but the sound
Of beechmast crackling 'neath my horse's tread,
Or some last leaf that flutters to the ground ;
And long it seems since, roofless and blood-red,
The sun in seas of night-black boughs was drowned.

In the Forest : WILFRID GIBSON

The beech is one of our most beautiful forest trees : in winter when the tall massive trunk covered with its characteristically smooth grey-green bark is displaying to advantage its enormous branches coming off obliquely or almost horizontally to produce a gigantic crown ; in spring and summer when the dense foliage casts a shade deeper than that of any other broad-leaved tree ; and above all in autumn when that foliage has turned to a blazing red or golden brown (Plate 5).

The beech is usually gregarious in habit and may be seen growing in small groups or forming large woodlands or forests. Frequently it dominates the scene, for it appears to thrive anywhere, even on the poorest of soil (though then it grows more slowly) ; this dominance may be ascribed to the fact that it competes very successfully with other trees, mainly because its roots take quickly to the upper layers of soil. In fact, as Evelyn has stated, woods which begin as mixtures of beech and oak usually end up by being pure beech. Since the beech has a very strong vitality it is able to withstand bad weather and even much soil erosion.

Furthermore, the very dense shade which it casts prevents the growth of smaller plants such as shrubs and herbs ; and the constant

Lonsdale Ragg

Beech Grove at Abberley Hall, Worcestershire.

drip from the leaves kills most herbs which get an initial footing. On the other hand, plant saprophytes, such as the yellow bird's nest (*Monotropa hypopithys*)[1] and the bird's nest orchis (*Neottia nidus-avis*)[1] and many fungi, none of which needs sunlight, thrive on the thick leaf-mould of the beechwood. Apart from such plants, however, which only grow either singly or in small groups, the carpet of the beechwood is almost barren.

> Oh, leave this barren spot to me !
> Spare, woodman, spare the beechen tree !
> Though bush or floweret never grow
> My dark unwarming shade below ;
> *The Beech Tree's Petition* : T. CAMPBELL

Since the beech sends out strong roots very near the surface of the soil, it is able to cope with physiographical conditions as few other large trees can. That is why it is no uncommon experience to meet an enormous beech growing on the side of a practically vertical embankment and thus exposing to view many strong and sturdy roots.

The beech belongs to the genus *Fagus*—another genus of the family FAGACEAE. This genus is but a small one, containing a few species distributed over north temperate regions. The common beech is *Fagus sylvatica*.

The tree often grows to a height of 100 feet and develops a girth of 20 feet. The smooth-barked bole is usually clean, though tillering is common among woodland specimens.

The winter buds are very distinctive—in fact, there can be no mistaking them. The twigs are covered with a very smooth, light brown bark in which the lenticels are very pronounced. On the twig, the lateral buds are borne alternately, and there is a terminal bud also. Each bud is long and pointed and is enclosed in a series of overlapping, lance-shaped, very pointed brown scales. Two of these usually remain as stipules at the base of each leaf after it has opened.

The beech leaf is particularly beautiful, especially when young. In fact, young beech twigs are very much in demand for household decoration. As it opens out, the bud presents a very delicate leaf-blade of pale green edged with fine white, downy hairs. Later on in the year, the white down is shed, and the leaf becomes thicker and of a deeper shade of green and displays very pronounced veins (p. 271 and Plate 5). Each leaf has a short leaf-stalk, and the blade is oval with serrated margins and terminating in a sharp point. The leaves are all arranged

[1] See *Flowers in Britain*, pp. 193 and 362

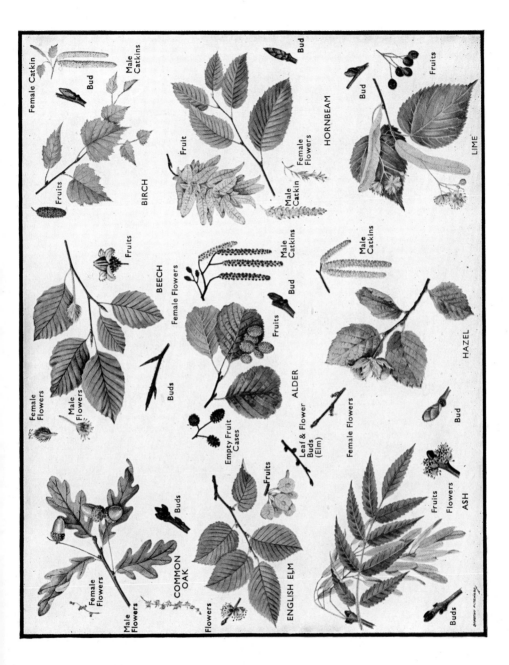

Female Catkin

Bud

Male Catkins

Fruits

BIRCH

Fruit

BEECH

Female Flowers

Female Flowers

Male Flowers

Fruits

Buds

COMMON OAK

Female Flowers

Male Flowers

Flowers

HORNBEAM

Female Flowers

Male Catkin

Male Catkins

Bud

Fruits

Empty Fruit Cases

ALDER

Leaf & Flower Buds (Elm)

Fruits

ENGLISH ELM

Flowers

Bud

Fruits

LIME

Male Catkins

HAZEL

Female Flowers

Bud

Fruits

Flowers

ASH

Buds

PLATE 5

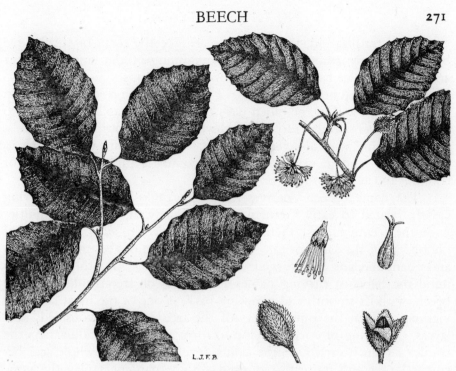

L.J.F.B.

Beech.

Left, twig bearing foliage ; above right, twig bearing clusters of male flowers
and two female flowers enclosed in a cupule ; middle right, single male and
female flowers ; below right, ripe cupule closed and one opened exposing seeds.

alternately on the stem, thus giving the whole leafy twig a flattened
mosaic. Though the beech is deciduous, the shrivelled leaves often
remain on the tree during the winter months, and there they stay until
they are pushed off by the developing leaves of the following spring.

The beech is unisexual, but both male and female flowers are borne
on the same tree. The tree does not invariably bloom each year. The
flowers appear during April and May, and are more conspicuous than
those of several other trees, such as the oak. The male flowers are
crowded in clusters borne at the ends of long pendulous stalks. Each
flower is brownish-purple with long, golden-headed stamens. There
are no petals, but there are four to six united sepals which separate towards their tips. They are hairy. There are twice as many stamens as
sepals. The female flowers are borne usually in pairs, though sometimes
there may be three or even four in a group. Each group is surrounded
by a collection of overlapping, prickly scales forming a cupule. Each
female flower contains three joined carpels with three styles (see above
and Plate 5).

After fertilisation, the fruits, which take the form of three-sided brown nuts, are embedded in the hairy lining of the cupule (p. 271 and Plate 5). The latter eventually opens at the tips which breaks into four backwardly curling segments. Like acorns, the ripe nuts are often called ' mast ', and in the olden days they were valuable for feeding to pigs which were driven into the beechwoods for that purpose. Squirrels, mice and some birds also feed on them. The ripe fruit yields 17 to 20 per cent oil, and in certain European countries this is extracted for cooking and as a substitute for butter.

The name ' beech ' derives from the Anglo-Saxon, which, being closely related to early German and Scandinavian, has close affinities with their equivalents (German, *Buche* ; Swedish, *bok*). The word ' book ' is of the same origin since the literature of the early Germans and Scandinavians was carved on beech wood. And this brings to mind the habit of carving names and initials on tree trunks ; for the beech, with its smooth and tempting bark, is one of the most common victims. When the outer layers of the tree are thus wounded, new layers, consisting of cork, develop to form a protective callus. As the trunk or branch grows, so the callus develops, and the whole scar becomes larger and more pronounced. Some gardeners play the same stupid trick on vegetable marrows. It is an age-old custom, and in at any rate one place—the lovely Botanical Gardens in Buitenzorg, Java— it is even encouraged, for a cactus grows there and on it visitors are allowed to carve their initials. This form of mutilation seems to be as unnecessary and as childish as the custom of clipping trees into shapes of animals which Nature never intended they should represent. Perhaps the element of romance is being ignored ; but it is difficult to visualise anyone being interested in the initials of a couple of people but the people themselves, and there is no doubt that very few of those ever return to the scene of their crime to recapture the spirit of the past.

> Fond lovers, cruel as their flame,
> Cut in these trees their mistress' name :
> Little, alas, they know or heed
> How far these beauties hers exceed !
> Fair trees ! wheres'e'er your barks I wound,
> No name shall but your own be found.
>
> *Thoughts in a Garden* : A. MARVELL

There is little doubt now that the beech is indigenous to England, though probably not to Scotland or Ireland. At one time, authorities

1932 LR

Beeches:
Beauport
10. 8. 33.

Beech Bole.

Lonsdale Ragg

were not sure about this point, probably having been misled by Caesar's report of his invasion of Britain when he wrote: " timber of every kind which is found in Gaul also grows in Britain, except the Beech and Silver Fir." But then, as Johns points out, in his *Forest Trees of Britain*, Caesar did not penetrate very far into Britain. It also surprises me that any botanical authority should have been misled by a botanical statement made by such a man as Caesar—military and political genius though he was. Elwes and Henry, in their *Trees of Great Britain and Ireland*, are quite emphatic that the beech is indigenous to at any rate England, especially since remains of it have been found in neolithic and pre-glacial deposits of this country.

Beech woods and forests occur in most parts of northern, western and central Europe. The tree does not extend far into the U.S.S.R.; in the northern parts of that country, where it exists, and in Finland, it assumes the habit of a bush only. In Germany there are many beech forests, though, according to R. St. Barbe Baker, they are losing ground in favour of pine and spruce. In France, especially the north, the beech thrives. At Domrémy in Lorraine a beech once grew beneath which Joan of Arc saw her vision of St. Margaret and St. Catharine.

There are many fine beech trees in Britain too. Some particularly handsome specimens are to be seen in the New Forest, Knole Park, Sevenoaks, Ashridge Park, Buckinghamshire, Windsor Great Park, and in various parts of Yorkshire, the Midland counties and the south-west of England. Then there are also many fine beech woods, especially those in Hampshire, Burnham Beeches in Buckinghamshire (' Buckingham ' means ' home of beeches '), Purley Beeches and certain parts of the downs of Surrey, Sussex and Kent.

Though, as already stated, the beech in its adult phase is no friend of other nearby trees, it is, when young, of inestimable value as a nurse to other broad-leaved trees. The wood is not rated very highly, for it is not durable out of doors. It is used, however, for furniture-making and for all sorts of small articles. It is useful since it is easily bent after treatment with steam. But the living tree, apart from its value in forestry as a nursing tree, is of considerable value to the community by the very essence of its beauty and shade-giving form. It is a matter of congratulation, therefore, that the Forestry Commission is paying attention to this tree in its programmes of afforestation, especially since so many have been felled for war needs.

North American beech (F. *grandifolia*) yields a valuable timber which is imported into Britain.

BEECH IN AUTUMN

PLATE 6

COPPER BEECH

The **copper beech** is not a separate species. This ornamental tree, so popular in Britain today, is believed to have arisen suddenly from the purple variety (*F. sylvatica* var. *purpurea*) which also arose very suddenly in the Hanleiter forest near Sondershausen, Germany, in the eighteenth century. There are also purple beeches growing wild in the Vosges Mountains. All copper beeches in Britain probably originated from the German purple beeches.

It might be wondered how the copper beech manages to manufacture its food, since food manufacture (photosynthesis) can only take place through the agency of the green colouring matter, chlorophyll (p. 27). Actually there is plenty of green chlorophyll in copper beech leaves, so photosynthesis takes place apparently quite normally ; but the greenness is masked by the presence of a purple colouring matter dissolved in the cell-sap of the outer layers (epidermis) of the leaves.

OTHER VARIETIES OF BEECH

As might be expected, horticulturists have produced some very charming varieties of beech. There are, for example, the **green weeping beech** (*F. sylvatica* var. *pendula*) (p. 276) and the **weeping copper beech** (*F. sylvatica* var. *purpurea pendula*). These are not common, yet they make a lovely sight when growing in an appropriate setting. Another attractive variety is the **cut-leaved** or **fern-leaved beech** (*F. sylvatica* var. *heterophylla* or *asplenifolia*). The leaves are deeply cut ; but sometimes both cut and normal leaves are borne on the same twig or on different twigs of the same tree. The first of the alternative names to designate this variety seems, therefore, more appropriate. There are many other varieties of beech, but they are very rare.

How do I love you, beech-trees, in the autumn,
Your stone-grey columns a cathedral nave
Processional above the earth's brown glory.

I was a child, and loved the knurly tangle
Of roots that coiled above a scarp like serpents,
Where I might hide my treasure with the squirrels.

I was a child, and splashed my way in laughter
Through drifts of leaves, where underfoot the beechnuts
Split with crisp crackle to my great rejoicing.

Beechwoods at Knole : v. SACKVILLE-WEST

Weeping Beech
Busbridge

Weeping Beech.

Lonsdale Ragg

NOTOFAGUS

Another genus of the family FAGACEAE is *Notofagus* (or *Nothofagus*) —a genus of south temperate regions, chiefly South Australia and Tasmania and Chile. *N. cunninghami*, the **myrtle tree** of Tasmania and Australia, is a valuable timber tree, and so are other species, some of which are being cultivated under experimental conditions in Britain. Other species, the timber of which is imported into Britain, include the **hard** or **clinker beech** (*N. truncata*) and the **red beech** or **tawhai** (*N. fusca*), both of New Zealand.

34
ELMS
(Ulmaceae)

Not unbeloved is this serious tree, with its leaf sitting close, un-thrilled. Its stature gives it a dark gold head when it looks alone in the summer.

ALICE MEYNELL

And the great elms o'erhead
Dark shadows wove on their aërial looms
Shot through with golden thread.

Hawthorne : LONGFELLOW

At any rate one species of elm, the so-called common elm, occurs so often in the countryside, not so much in forests as in smaller wood-lands and particularly as a hedgerow tree, that it is quite a part of the normal rural English scene, though it is not so common north of the Border. It figures frequently in our town parks, too ; but as a roadside tree it is not to be recommended, because its twigs and branches (even large ones) are very brittle and tend to break off, sometimes even in the quietest of atmospheres. It can be well imagined, therefore, what a nuisance such a tree could be growing in streets unless its boughs were periodically lopped off ; but then we should be assailing the whole *raison d'être* of such a tree. Better not to grow it in towns.

Ellum she hateth mankind, and waiteth
Till every gust be laid,
To drop a limb on the head of him
That anyway trusts her shade.

A Tree Song : KIPLING

And for long
At night he could not bear to see
An elm against the stars.
'Twas wrong,
He knew, to blame the innocent tree—
Though some folk hated elms and thought
Them evil, for their great boughs fell
So suddenly . . .

The Elm : WILFRID GIBSON

For other reasons, too, this tree, beautiful though it is, is not a desirable guest to invite into our urban areas ; it is best left to beautify the countryside. It is very subject to disease. Many of us must remember the epidemics of Dutch elm disease which have killed off thousands of these trees and left others standing only to be condemned. It seemed a real tragedy when the elms in Windsor Great Park were condemned for this reason. Then again insects are attracted by the elm, especially the vapourer-moth and large tortoise-shell butterfly ; and their eggs and certainly their caterpillars are a frequent source of annoyance to visitors to the parks. Furthermore, the elm is shallow-rooted, and fallen specimens all over the country sometimes bear witness to the passing of a gale which has left other trees unharmed. I have seen in my father's grounds in the west country a dozen elms fall in about the same number of seconds during a strong wind ; and further away an exceptionally beautiful avenue of elms leading up to a country mansion was, in a matter of minutes, almost completely destroyed.

Elms belong to the genus *Ulmus* of the family ULMACEAE—a family of trees and shrubs distributed chiefly in the north temperate zone. Several genera, apart from *Ulmus*, contain valuable timber-producing trees, for example, *Celtis* (one species of which is used for fodder in India and another of which yields edible fruit ; yet another species, in Australia, yields a useful timber), and *Zelkova*, specimens of which may be found in British parks and gardens (p. 284).

There are well-nigh two dozen species of *Ulmus*, but not all occur in Britain, and only two, the common elm and the wych elm, are to be met with at all frequently. Other elms in Britain include the Cornish elm, the smooth-leaved elm, the Plot elm, the Dutch elm, the Huntingdon elm, and so forth. Hybrids of elm, too, are to be found in many parts of the country. Most species of elm grow in north temperate regions and in the mountainous areas of tropical Asia.

Lonsdale Ragg

Elm in Victoria Park, Bath.

GENERAL STRUCTURE OF ELM

The elm is a tall tree with a pronounced cylindrical trunk bearing a massive crown. The bark is deeply fissured in a vertical direction. The winter buds are conspicuous though blunt, and they are protected by a number of overlapping scales.

T

Common Elm.
Above, twig bearing foliage ; middle, twig bearing flowers, and a single flower ; below, foliage and fruit.

The leaves are arranged alternately on the stem. Each leaf is oval but fairly pointed, and the margins are serrated with large and small teeth. In most species, each half of the leaf-blade joins the leaf-stalk at a different level, thus making the two halves about the midrib asymmetrical. The leaves open very early in the year, that is, during March, and they do not fall until November, which is comparatively late. On the Continent the leaves are used as a fodder, just as those of other closely related species in different parts of the world are.

There is a very close resemblance between all species and even genera of this family so far as leaf-form is concerned.

Though some members of the family ULM-ACEAE are unisexual, the genus *Ulmus* is hermaphrodite, that is, each flower contains both male and female organs (stamens and carpels). The flowers of the elm are produced in tufts before the leaves appear, so that, since the flowers are dark red, the bare trees begin to assume their familiar reddish tinge during February and March. Each flower comprises a calyx of about five sepals forming a cup. This encloses the same number of stamens and an ovary with two styles. The fruit is characteristic; it takes the form of a seed surrounded by a very thin membrane which is flattened out all round the seed in one plane to form a wing; by this means the seed is distributed far and wide by the wind. The fruit sometimes ripens as early as June; this is very early for a tree (Plate 5). But elm seeds are seldom viable in Britain, so seedlings are rare.

COMMON AND WYCH ELM[1]

The common or **English elm** (*U. procera*) and the **wych elm** (*U. glabra*) are the two elms most frequently seen throughout Britain. The origin of the term 'wych' is obscure: Dr. R. C. A. Prior suggested that the term is derived from the chests or 'wyches' of old writers, since such chests were made from this wood; but it has also been suggested that the term simply means 'pliant' or 'weak'. The common elm is the elm of the hedgerows, whereas the wych elm is usually found growing in more open spaces.

It is difficult to decide whether either of these elms is really indigenous to Britain. Some authors considered that the Romans introduced the tree since it was the custom to plant it on funeral mounds. There is such a Roman mound in Somerset (near Bath), and I well remember an old elm on the top of it, but this elm has now disappeared. (In any event it could not have dated back to the Romans.) The fact that coffins are frequently made from elm wood might lend support to this theory of a Roman introduction. John Evelyn, too, did not consider the elm indigenous to Britain; but Dr. Hunter, his editor, did; and Johns, who seemed a bit doubtful, favoured Hunter's view after carefully considering all arguments. Others did likewise, so there we must leave the matter. It is certain that the common elm and the wych elm are quite at home in Britain now, whereas on the Continent at any rate, the common elm is never found growing wild.

From the roots of the common elm, many suckers usually grow, and these produce a dense array of branches which sometimes completely hide the base of the trunk. Many small branches also arise from the bole. The wych elm does not produce suckers.

[1] For a brief review of the elm flora of Britain, see a communication by Dr. R. Melville, of the Royal Botanic Gardens, Kew, in *Nature* of February 12, 1944, p. 108.

Eric J. Hosking

Winter.   Summer.

Common Elm in Hertfordshire.

> . . . the lowest boughs and the brushwood sheaf
> Round the elm-tree bole are in tiny leaf.
>
> *Home Thoughts from Abroad* : R. BROWNING

The **wych elm** (*U. glabra*) is not usually as tall as the common elm, but it is more robust. The former attains a height of 80 to well over 100 feet. Both trees frequently live for five hundred years.

The leaves of the common elm are about an inch long, whereas those of the wych elm reach a length of three inches or more. Furthermore, the foliage of the former presents yellow autumnal tints whereas that of the latter does not. The flowers and the fruit, too, of the latter, are more robust. *U. glabra* var. *pendula* is a weeping variety.

SMOOTH-LEAVED ELM

Whether the **smooth-leaved elm** (*U. carpinifolia* or *nitens*) is indigenous to Britain is doubtful ; but examples of it occur in southern England. It resembles more closely the common elm than the wych elm, though its long-stalked leaves may reach a length of three inches. The upper-surfaces of the leaves, however, are smooth. Like the common elm, the smooth-leaved elm produces dense suckers from its roots.

EAST ANGLIAN ELM

The **East Anglian elm** (*U. diversifolia*) is one of several forms of the elm confined to eastern England. It is curious in that, interspersed with shoots bearing the normal asymmetrical leaves, are shoots bearing leaves which are quite symmetrical about their midribs.

DUTCH ELM

The **Dutch elm** (*U. hollandica*) probably originated as a hybrid between the smooth-leaved elm and the wych elm. It has been suggested that it was introduced from Holland; but at one time folk were too prone to call anything 'Dutch' that appeared at all foreign. It grows to a great extent in the hedgerows of the south of England, and, since it produces many suckers, makes its own contribution to the hedge proper. Many single specimens may be seen on estates and in parks, and sometimes they are used for making avenues.

CORNISH ELM

The **Cornish elm** (*U. stricta*), as its name implies, is fairly common in Cornwall and in Devon where it is probably indigenous. It is not difficult to identify since it is very pyramidal in habit. The leaves are folded along the mid-rib, and are smooth on the upper-surface. Since it is so often subject to lopping—it frequently grows in hedgerows— the tall pyramidal habit and the trunk extending almost to the very top of the tree are seldom seen.

PLOT ELM

Plot elm (*U. plotii*) is rare in most parts of Britain, though it occurs in the valleys of England in a line stretching from the Wash to the Severn.

USES OF ELM

All species of elm yield excellent fire-wood. Since two of the species are so common, it is not surprising that the wood should also be used for many and various purposes. Reference has already been made to its use for making coffins. Since the common elm is easily available, its wood is not appreciated as much as it should be; only cheap types of furniture are made from it. Though elm cannot withstand alternating dry and wet conditions, it is durable when permanently under water and is therefore valuable for under-water construction of various types, such as piles in docks and harbours, for wooden boats and ships' keels, etc.

For commercial purposes, the various elms have various alternative names : the common elm is ' English elm ', ' red elm ' or ' nave elm ' ; the Dutch elm is ' cork bark elm ' ; and wych elm is ' mountain elm ', ' Scotch elm ', ' white elm ' and ' wych hazel '.

The timber of foreign elms is also imported into Britain, for example, the **rock elm** (*U. thomasi*) of eastern Canada and the United States, and the **white elm** (*U. americana*) of the same areas ; other species come from Japan.

On the Continent, elms are frequently used as vine-props, and for this purpose they have to be carefully pruned. The vine is said to be ' married ' to the elm.

> They led the Vine
> To wed her Elm ; she, spoused, about him twines
> Her marriageable arms, and with her brings
> Her dower, the adopted clusters, to adorn
> His barren leaves.
>
> *Paradise Lost* : MILTON

Elm is frequently planted for purely ornamental purposes, and in this connexion some very handsome varieties—weeping, variegated and golden—have emerged.

> Huge elm, with rifted trunk all notched and scarred,
> Like to a warrior's destiny ! I love
> To stretch me often on thy shadowed sward,
> And hear the laugh of summer leaves above ;
> Or on thy buttressed roots to sit, and lean
> In careless attitude, and there reflect
> On times, and deeds, and darings that have been
> Old castaways, now swallowed in neglect.
>
> *The Shepherd's Tree* : JOHN CLARE

Among other genera of ULMACEAE sometimes cultivated in Britain, either for academic reasons or for ornamental purposes, is the genus *Zelkova*. The leaf of this genus is particularly beautiful, being quite symmetrical and having very regular marginal teeth.

35

MULBERRIES AND FIGS

(Moraceae)

To the family MORACEAE—a family mainly of trees and shrubs—belong a large number of trees of considerable commercial importance, such as mulberries, figs and bread-fruit. The family is mainly tropical, though some of them have achieved such world-wide economic importance that they have been cultivated for centuries in other parts. The fig and mulberry thrive even in Britain, provided they are sheltered and looked after. There are about sixty genera in the family and more than eight hundred species ; so it is a large family.

MULBERRIES

Mulberry trees belong to the genus *Morus* which comprises mainly trees together with a few shrubs.

Mulberry trees may sometimes be seen in old gardens and grounds, for they are very handsome ; but in spite of this they are no longer cultivated in Britain, because the timber is of little use, and the silk-worm—that valuable animal which feeds almost exclusively on mulberry—does not thrive here. Yet mulberry trees are cultivated extensively in such countries as China, Italy and France simply as food for the silkworm. It would therefore be of interest to see how the silkworm has made the mulberry tree of such considerable economic importance, even in this age of artificial silks and other dainty fabrics.

———————

Silk is produced by many insects, spiders and other animals, but the true silk of commerce is obtained from the cocoons of the Chinese silkmoth (*Bombyx mori*) and other related insects.

China was the original home of the silkmoth. It is the larvae or caterpillars of this moth which feed on the leaves of the mulberry tree, and it is said that the cultivation of these trees for feeding the silkworm began in China about 4,600 years ago. The Chinese of those days guarded closely the secret of the origin and manufacture of the silk, and it was probably many centuries before the art of silk-making became known in any other country. About three thousand years afterwards, the secret reached Japan, and then the industry developed there.

Shortly after reaching Japan, the industry spread westwards and reached India. Later it developed in the more westerly Asiatic countries, such as Iran, and eventually reached the Mediterranean countries of Europe, where it is still a thriving industry, especially in the south of France, Italy, Turkey and certain parts of Switzerland. There have been repeated attempts to establish the cultivation of the silkworm and the manufacture of silk on a commercial scale in Britain; but all have so far failed. At the present time private individuals are attempting to establish the industry here; but it is proving too costly to compete successfully with those countries where the industry has become firmly established through centuries.

The silkmoth begins its individual life as a fertilised egg which is laid by the female moth. The egg is about the size of a pin's head, and since the young silkworms which hatch out start feeding immediately on the leaves of the mulberry, the moth lays its eggs by the hundred directly on the leaves. To prevent the eggs from falling off, the moth covers them with a glutinous material. It is easy to tell when the young silkworm is mature inside the egg and thus ready for hatching because the egg itself changes from whitish-brown to a darker brown.

The silkworm which is hatched is actually not a worm but the larva or caterpillar of the silkmoth. It starts at once to feed voraciously on the mulberry leaves; so it grows very quickly. When hatched, the silkworm is about a quarter of an inch long. The body is divided into very pronounced segments. The whole body is greyish or cream in colour. After about four days, the silkworm stops eating and becomes listless. Eventually its skin bursts and the worm emerges with a new skin. Then it begins eating and growing again. After about a week the same thing happens again, and so on four times. By the time that it has reached maturity the silkworm is about three inches long. Running along the sides of the body, just inside, are two sacs or bags. These are the silk glands. As the larva attains its mature size—that is, just before the fifth moult—these glands become filled with a sticky substance. This substance will harden to a solid if exposed to the air.

Before the fifth change, the silkworm goes without food for a long time and usually hides itself in some out-of-the-way place. Then the sticky fluid is forced out of the two silk glands through a common pore called the spinneret which is situated on the under-lip of the caterpillar. As the fluid is forced into the air it forms a long, solid thin strand of silk. One silkworm can eject about a thousand yards of silk thread in this fashion. While it is ejecting the fluid, the caterpillar moves its head from side to side ; this goes on for about three days. By moving its head thus, the silk thread is woven around the body to form a covering called the cocoon, and in this cocoon the animal eventually settles down to sleep. This is called the pupa stage.

> So spins the silk-worm small its slender store,
> And labours till it clouds itself all o'er.
>
> *The Dunciad,* Book 4 : POPE

During the first ten to fifteen days after the pupa has been become completely enclosed in its cocoon it undergoes very important changes. It first becomes converted into a brownish tubular organism called a chrysalis. This finally changes into a baby insect or imago. Once the imago is formed it is ready to escape from the surrounding cocoon of silk. This it does by moistening one end and forcing its way out through the softened silk. Thus the complete silkmoth emerges.

Almost immediately after they emerge, the male and female moths couple, and so fertilisation of the next generation of eggs takes place. After about four days, the female lays about five hundred fertilised eggs, and then the next life-cycle begins.

Commercial silk is obtained by taking the completed cocoons and placing them in hot ovens, thus killing the pupae. Then the silk is unwound ; but such single threads are far too fine to be of any use to the manufacturer, so several are twisted together.

———————

Mulberry trees are slow-growing with thick, ponderous-looking, rough trunks which give off twisting and turning heavy branches very near the ground.

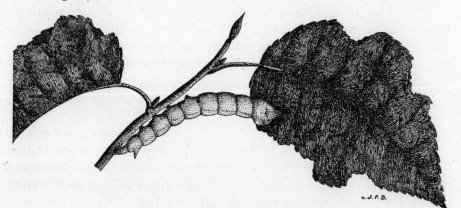

Silkworm feeding on Mulberry Leaf.

Mulberry.

Above, twig bearing foliage and cluster of fruit; below, male catkin, single male flowers, female catkin and single female flowers.

The leaves are large and are arranged alternately on the stem. They are usually heart-shaped (though sometimes three-lobed) and have serrated margins. The flowers are uni-sexual, and each sex is borne in very close catkins. In some species male and female catkins are borne on different trees, but in the more common species, both sexes are borne on the same tree. The male flower is composed of four perianth segments subtending four stamens. The female flower is made up of an ovary closely surrounded by four perianth segments and topped by two stigmas. After fertili-sation, the crowded ovaries of the female catkin become fleshy, as also does the axis on which the flowers are borne, so that the resulting succulent mass is really a multiple fruit. This is edible, though the fruit of some species are more palatable than those of others.

There are about a dozen species of mulberry (*Morus*), though not all of them are represented in Britain.

Most of the handsome mulberry trees extant in Britain today are **black mulberries** (*Morus nigra*). This species is cultivated in other countries more for its delicious fruit than as a diet for the silkworm, for the white mulberry has now largely superseded it in this connexion.

> Ille salubris Æstates peraget, qui nigris prandia moris Finiet. (A man will pass his summers in health, who will finish his luncheon with black mulberries.)
>
> *Satires*, Book 2 : HORACE

The black mulberry is indigenous to eastern Asia, but soon began invading Europe. By the tenth century it had reached the Mediterranean regions and even northern Europe. In Italy it was utilised for silkworm culture from then until the fifteenth century ; but it was not until after then that it was introduced into Britain.

The Sion Cottage
Mulberry
Girth 7 ft 4 ins

Lonsdale Ragg

Bole of Black Mulberry.

In this country it was widely cultivated, but only in the south as a standard tree ; further north it was cultivated as a sheltered wall tree, and it was even grown in greenhouses for the sake of its fruit. James I commanded the making of mulberry gardens in 1609, selecting St. James's Park and Greenwich Park as the sites. Today only single specimens are to be seen there. And now nowhere is the tree encouraged ; but there are some handsome specimens still to be seen in various parts of the country, including many of the London parks, and even places in the City, though some of these suffered grievously during the air raids. There are also some good examples at Cambridge and in the grounds of the University of Reading.

The rich yellow timber has a beautiful grain and is used on the Continent for making furniture and fancy articles. The fruit is still relished as a dessert, and is imported for this purpose.

The largest of the genus *Morus* is the **red mulberry** (*M. rubra*) of North America. This tree frequently attains a height of 70 feet. Its fruit are dark red in colour ; but they are not so palatable as those of the black mulberry. The tree is not cultivated in Britain.

The **white mulberry** (*M. alba*) bears fruit which are almost white in colour. This tree is indigenous to China ; but, since it is now the most favoured species in the culture of the silkworm, it also flourishes in Mediterranean regions. It is very rare in Britain, even under cultivation.

Other species of *Morus* are cultivated in different parts of the world, either for the sake of the silk industry or for the edible fruit, or both.

The **paper-mulberry** of eastern Asia and Polynesia belongs to a different genus of the same family (*Broussonetia papyrifera*). From its bark the ' tapa ' cloth of the South Sea Islands is made. This plant is only a small tree or more often a bush, and is a favourite ornamental plant in the United States.

FIGS

The genus *Ficus*, also of the family MORACEAE, contains about seven hundred species of trees and shrubs, most of them indigenous to the tropics, and among them a very large number of valuable plants of varying habits.

The famous **banyans** of the tropics comprise chiefly the two species *Ficus indica* and *F. benghalensis*. Aerial roots arise adventitiously from the branches of these trees. First of all they hang loosely ; but,

Lonsdale Ragg

Pocock's Fig Tree at Christ Church, Oxford.
Planted in 1636 by Prof. Edward Pocock, professor of Hebrew.

growing all the time, they eventually reach the soil where they become firmly established. Then they thicken and thus form supporting pillars to the large branches above. There may be hundreds of such supporting pillars to one actual tree. It is obvious that Milton knew of these banyans (which are sacred in parts of India) ; but his botany was at fault when he implied that the supporting pillars were branches from the main shoot—for they are roots.

> So counsel'd he, and both together went
> Into the thickest wood ; there soon they chose
> The fig-tree. Not that kind for fruit renown'd,
> But such as at this day to Indians known
> In Malabar or Decan spreads her arms
> Branching so broad and long, that in the ground
> The bended twigs take root, and daughters grow
> About the mother-tree, a pillar'd shade
> High overarched, and echoing walks between.
>
> *Paradise Lost* : MILTON

The **india-rubber tree** (*F. elastica*) is a large tree having outstanding buttress roots, and the latex from the trunk supplies one form of natural rubber. Then there is the **bo-tree** (*F. religiosa*), sacred to Buddhists, for it was beneath one of these trees that the prince, Buddha, first attained enlightenment and supreme knowledge.

The **mulberry** or **sycomore fig** (*F. sycomorus*) is also a very large tree, used for roadside planting in Egypt and Syria (p. 312).

The only member of the genus *Ficus* which will grow in the open in Britain is the **common fig** (*F. carica*). This plant is indigenous to the eastern Mediterranean countries ; but the tree has become so well established further west in Mediterranean regions that it now grows wild over a much wider area. In the north of Britain, and sometimes also in the south, this plant will succeed only if trained against a wall (p. 291). But also in the south there are many fine standard trees, especially in the parks and gardens of our large towns. There are some excellent specimens in both the East and the West Ends of London ; but some of those in the East End have, like the mulberries, suffered from air raids. There are still many fine specimens in various parts of the City and in St. James's Park, and those trained against the walls of the National Gallery facing Trafalgar Square have now become almost a part of the building. There are fig trees, too, in Lambeth Palace gardens ; which is interesting, for it is believed that the first fig trees in Britain were planted there in 1548.

The fig tree is rather small, seldom growing more than about 25 feet high. The bark is very smooth and the winter buds long and pointed. The smaller branches curve upwards abruptly. The leaves are very large, and in the wild state they may be comparatively simple, but when cultivated they are usually so deeply lobed as to be almost compound.

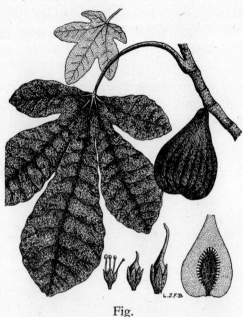

The inflorescence is most curious. It is very short-stalked and borne in a leaf-axil. The whole receptacle is fleshy, pear-shaped and hollow. Lining this hollow are the unisexual flowers, the males nearer the opening. Each male flower is composed of four perianth segments and four stamens. There are two forms of female

Fig.
Foliage and Fruit. Above, a leaf less deeply lobed (reduced). Below, left to right, male flower, gall-flower (sterile), female flower (fertile), inflorescence in longitudinal section.

flowers—the long-styled fertile flowers and the short-styled, so-called gall-flowers. Pollination is rather special, depending on a certain insect, the gall-wasp (*Blastophaga*)—a case of pollination resembling that of *Yucca*.[1] In each gall-flower, the wasp lays an egg, and while on its way to do so some pollen from the male flowers near the entrance to the receptacle adheres to it and then becomes deposited on the stigmas of the fertile female flowers. After fertilisation, the receptacle enlarges considerably and practically encloses the many single-seeded fruits. As it ripens, the complete pear-shaped receptacle becomes more juicy.

This ripe inflorescence of the fig, which is really a collection of fruits enclosed in a more or less succulent receptacle, has been an article of diet since time immemorial; this is the fig so often referred to in the Scriptures.

Make *an agreement* with one *by* a present, and come out to me; and eat ye every one of his vine, and every one of his fig tree, and drink ye every one of the waters of his own cistern.

Isaiah, Chap. 37

[1] See *Flowers in Britain*, p. 352.

In those days, too, it was used for medicinal purposes.

> For Isaiah had said, Let them take a lump of figs, and lay *it* for a plaister upon the boil, and he shall recover.
>
> *Isaiah*, Chap. 38

The fig as a valuable and nutritious form of food was also very well-known to, and favoured by, the Ancient Greeks and Romans ; the Spartans were particularly fond of it.

Today the fig tree is cultivated in Asia and Europe (in the Mediterranean areas) and in certain parts of the United States, in all cases for its delicious ' fruit '. The timber of this tree is of little value.

36
HOLLY
(*Aquifoliaceae*)

'Tis a brave tree. While round its boughs in vain
The warring wind of January bites and girds,
It holds the clusters of its crimson grain,
A winter pasture for the shivering birds.
Oh, patient holly, that the children love,
No need for thee of smooth blue skies above :
Oh, green strong holly, shine amid the frost ;
Thou dost not lose one leaf for sunshine lost.

The Holly : AUGUSTA WEBSTER

No-one can mistake the holly, for everyone must be familiar with it, though perhaps many have never seen it growing. In company with the mistletoe, it is the most favoured of all evergreens for Christmas decorations ; but in the past its significance went even deeper. Holly as the ' holy tree ' is considered fully in *Flowers in Britain* (p. 172).

Holly belongs to the family AQUIFOLIACEAE, a family of trees and shrubs, most of which (including the holly) are evergreen. The family is widespread throughout the world, though rarely are its members to be seen in either Africa or Australia.

The holly is a member of the genus *Ilex*—a very large genus of plants comprising nearly two hundred species distributed in all five main continents, though not common in Australia or Africa. Holly itself (*Ilex aquifolium*) is native to most parts of Europe, though, given the chance (it is a very slow grower), it will grow to be a taller tree in

Holly.
Spray of spined holly bearing flowers, and spray of comparatively smooth-leaved holly
bearing fruit.   Below left, single flower;   below right, leaf of a variegated form.

Britain than in most other parts, sometimes attaining a height of 40
to 60 feet.   It has for years been known in certain localities as **holm** or
hulver.   'Holm' is a corruption of the Old English 'holen', meaning
holly.   Though it is claimed that some of the many place-names in
Britain with the prefix 'Holen' or 'Holme' derived it from the close
proximity of much holly, it should not be assumed that they all do, for
'holm' and 'holme' also signify a meadow or a small island.

The botany of the holly is given in *Flowers in Britain*, from which
the following is quoted: "The leaf ... is leathery and shiny, and the
margins and the tip have some strong spines.   All this is necessary,
because the plant is an evergreen and requires protection against in-
clement winter weather and browsing animals (Plate 3).   In some
trees, the uppermost leaves have no spines except perhaps at their
tips.   It has been suggested that only the lower ones need the spines,
for they are the only ones that animals can reach; but this does not
explain why in many cases the uppermost leaves are spiny, and in
others the lower ones bear no spines.

U

" The flowers appear during May to August, and they may be unisexual or, more rarely, hermaphrodite. Frequently the female flower can be mistaken for a hermaphrodite one, for it often has four large stamens, but these are sterile. The flowers are borne in loose inflorescences growing from the axils of the leaves.

" In each flower there are four united sepals and four white petals slightly united at the base. The male flower has four white stamens (p. 295 and Plate 3), and the female flower four to six carpels joined to form a four- to six-chambered ovary (Plate 3). There are no styles, but the stigmas are fixed direct on the top of the ovary. The fruit is a fleshy drupe containing one to six stones (p. 295 and Plate 3). It is usually red in colour, but there are some varieties of holly which bear yellow or even black fruits. Birds eat the fruit, but since the stones are indigestible they are excreted, and in this way the holly is distributed."

The holly seems to withstand all sorts and conditions of soil and climate. Since it grows so slowly, its timber has never been very much used, though it has been utilised (sometimes dyed as a substitute for ebony) in the making of small articles. It is useless for outdoor constructions, for it is not durable. The bark is used for making birdlime.

For hedge-making, holly has proved particularly valuable in the past, and it is still to be recommended for this purpose provided one is prepared to wait patiently. It makes a desirable, if formidable, hedge because it is evergreen and is tolerant of constant clipping, though under such conditions it seldom bears flowers or fruit. There are many fine specimens of holly hedges in Britain. There was one in Evelyn's garden at Deptford, 400 feet long, 9 feet high and 5 feet wide;[1] and today there are others larger than that.

For centuries, the holly has been a great favourite for home and garden ornamentation, so it should be no cause for wonder that a very large number of hybrids have been produced. They are too many to warrant description ; but there are large- and small-leaved hollies, variegated hollies (p. 295), golden hollies, weeping hollies, and so on. Some of these hybrids are particularly beautiful.

The timber of the **American holly** (*I. opaca*) is now imported into Britain for commercial purposes.

Another species of *Ilex*—*I. paraguensis*—yields **Paraguay tea** or **yerba maté** which is largely consumed in South America. The leaves are dried and then broken up, and the tea is brewed from the broken leaves, just as we brew our tea.

[1] See *Flowers in Britain*, p. 172.

37

MISCELLANY

At this stage in the scheme of classification adopted here, there are several families to which certain trees belong which, though not very important as such, are worthy of some mention.

SPINDLE TREE
(*Celastraceae*)

The **spindle tree** occurs more often as a bush than a tree, though it may sometimes assume arboreal habit.

The spindle tree belongs to the family CELASTRACEAE, a family comprising about forty genera distributed in tropical and temperate lands. The spindle tree is included in the genus *Euonymus* (*E. europaeus*) ; other genera of this family can sometimes be seen under cultivation in Britain.

The bark is smooth and of a greyish colour. The younger twigs are easy to diagnose, for they are strongly ribbed with corky tissue giving a four-angled effect. The very young twigs are particularly bright green during the growing season.

The leaves are simple, pale green, long and lance-shaped, and they have toothed edges (Plate 3) They assume the most vivid autumnal tints—red, yellow and even mauve. They and the bark are acrid and poisonous, and the same is true of both flowers and fruit.

The flowers appear during May and June, borne in small loose clusters in the axils of the leaves. They are greenish-white (Plate 3). and rather insignificant. A flower may be hermaphrodite or unisexual. There are usually four sepals, though sometimes as many as six may occur. In any event, the petals and stamens correspond in numbers. The ovary is usually four-chambered with the same number of styles ; but sometimes there may be only two chambers or as many as six, with the corresponding number of styles.

It is when the fruits are ripe that the spindle tree is most attractive, for they ripen during October and November when the leaves are beginning to assume their brilliant autumn tints, and the fruits are brilliant in colour, too. They are pink, and are divided into four lobes

(Plate 7); when the seeds are ripe, these lobes open out disclosing a corresponding number of seeds each of which is surrounded by an orange-coloured aril.

At one time the wood was used for making spindles, skewers and clothes pegs; it was also found good for charcoal-production. It is seldom utilised now, though there is an Indian variety, *E. europaeus* var. *hamiltonianus*, which yields a useful timber known as 'paiche wood'. But this is not often met with in Britain.

The spindle tree is sometimes called **dogwood**, which is unfortunate, for this name is also applied to another plant which is in no way related to it (see p. 320). It is also known as **pegwood, prickwood** and **skewerwood.**

As one might expect, the spindle tree and other related species and varieties are popular among gardeners more especially for their brightly coloured fruit and autumnal foliage. Among the species and varieties to be seen growing in shrubberies are : the **broad-leaved spindle** (*E. latifolius*); *E. yedoensis*, a species having cream flowers with purple stamens and producing carmine fruit; *E. europaeus* var. *fructo rubra*, a variety bearing fruit of a more vivid colour than that of its progenitor; the **evergreen spindle** (*E. japonicus*); a golden and green variegated variety of the last-named (*E. japonicus* var. *aurea picta*); and so on.

Closely related to *Euonymus* is the genus *Celastrus*, a tropical and sub-tropical genus which provides some interesting climbing shrubs for our gardens. *C. scandens*, for example, produces very showy scarlet fruit.

BUCKTHORNS
(*Rhamnaceae*)

The buckthorns belong to the family RHAMNACEAE, a comparatively large cosmopolitan family of trees and shrubs (with a few herbs) and containing many notable climbers. Few plants of this family, however, are of any economic value.

The buckthorns are included in the genus *Rhamnus*, and there are two species in Britain, namely, the alder and the purging buckthorns.

The **alder buckthorn** (*R. frangula*) is so called because it frequently occurs with alders (p. 239); but its fruit are black drupes, superficially resembling berries, and to get over this difficulty some people call it **berry-bearing alder.** This tree does not thrive in limy soils. It is very small. The bark is practically black, though if the superficial layers are scraped away, bright red layers are disclosed beneath.

The leaves are lance-shaped though broad at the base. They have smooth margins and are arranged alternately on the stem. They are deciduous.

The yellowish-green flowers are borne in small axillary clusters. Each flower has five sepals, five petals, five stamens, and an ovary with five stigmas. The fruit is a drupe containing several stones. When ripe (in September), it is black; but it first goes through a sequence of green followed by red; at the green stage this fruit yields a dye which at one time was used in calico-printing.

The wood of the alder buckthorn is not much used today; but at one time the charcoal produced from it was valued since it was excellent for the making of gunpowder. The tree has certain uses, however, even today. For example, it is easily coppiced; and the resulting straight branches provide walking-sticks, pea and bean sticks.

Purging buckthorn (R. *catharticus*) is a slightly larger tree which will attain a height of ten feet on the limy soils on which it thrives best. Its leaves, unlike those of the alternately arranged leaves of alder buckthorn, are grouped in clusters at the end of small branches, and they are slightly serrated (Plate 7). The small branches, too, are often modified into spines (Plate 7).

The yellowish-green flowers, which appear during May to June (Plate 7), are quite different from those of the alder buckthorn. They are almost always unisexual, and the two sexes are segregated on different plants; furthermore, the constituent organs—sepals, petals, stamens and styles—occur in fours. The fruit, too, is larger, and contains four stones. It is black when ripe in September (Plate 7), but green when first formed, at this stage yielding a green dye.

The ripe fruit of the purging buckthorn was at one time used in the preparation of purgatives (hence the common adjectival name); but these proved to be very strong. The less violent purgative, cascara sagrada, is prepared from the bark of an American buckthorn (R. *purshiana*) which is common in parts of North America, especially in the Pacific coastal regions.

We may here mention the rare **sea buckthorn** which may be found on the sandy shores of the east or south-east coasts of Britain. But this plant does not belong to the same family as the two buckthorns already described. It belongs to the family ELAEAGNACEAE, which, however, follows RHAMNACEAE in our scheme. The sea buckthorn

(*Hippophae rhamnoides*) is a small shrub growing anything from one to eight feet high and resembling a dwarf willow in habit and foliage. Its flowers are unisexual and they appear before the leaves. The fruit is yellow.

A VALUABLE TROPICAL FAMILY
(*Anacardiaceae*)

The family ANACARDIACEAE is mainly tropical, and comprises about fifty genera many of which have a resinous bark. Though a few members of this family are cultivated, but rarely, in Britain, the family is more notable for the very large number of products of economic value that it yields. The following are examples. The cashew nut is the edible nut of the tropical American *Anacardium occidentale* ; the axis beneath the nut becomes fleshy, and this also is edible ; the stem yields a useful gum. Pistachio nuts are the fruit of the Mediterranean *Pistacia vera* ; whereas another species from the same genus, *P. terebinthus*, yields Chian turpentine. The flavouring gum, mastic, is obtained from still another Mediterranean genus, *P. lentiscus*. The favourite tropical mango is the fruit of *Mangifera indica*. The tropical hog-plum is the fruit of *Spondias mangifera*. Another genus, *Harpephyllum*, produces the South African Kaffir nut (*H. caffrum*). The genus *Rhus* supplies several useful products. For example, Japan lacquer is obtained from the Japanese and Chinese *Rhus vernicifera* ; the berries of R. *succedanea* of the same areas yield a wax ; and sumach, used in tanning and dyeing, is obtained from the Mediterranean R. *coriaria*. On the other hand, the notorious climbing **poison-ivy** of North America is R. *toxicodendron*.

Quite a number of species of *Rhus* are cultivated in Britain for their curious flowers and their lovely foliage effects. The **Venetian sumach** or **wig plant** (R. *cotinus*) has reddish flowers which look like masses of fluff. The '**burning bush**' (R. *cotinus* var. *folius purpureus*) has purple stems and leaves throughout the growing season. The **Japanese wax tree** (R. *succedanea*) is also cultivated for its handsome scarlet autumn foliage. And there are others.

TREE OF HEAVEN
(*Simarubaceae*)

The **tree of heaven** or **tree of the gods** (*Ailanthus glandulosa*), a tree prominent in many parks in Britain, belongs to the family SIMARU-

Tree of Heaven in St. James's Square, Bath, Somerset.

BACEAE which, like ANACARDIACEAE, is mainly tropical and is rich in products useful to man.

The tree of heaven hails from China and Japan and is sometimes called the **Chinese sumach.** It is a quick-growing, lofty, very handsome, deciduous tree (p. 301), attaining a height of sometimes 70 feet (sometimes, but rarely, even 100 feet), with gracefully curving branches. It seems to withstand sooty atmospheres quite well, and this, coupled with its quick growth, might explain why it has been so successful in British towns (though it is confined mainly to the south) since its introduction in 1751. It is quite a favourite in parks and gardens, and is particularly common in London parks and some streets. It is also popular in the thickly populated areas of the United States, especially on the eastern seaboard.

The bark is smooth with vertical fissures. The winter buds are very small, but the leaf-scars are particularly prominent. The leaves are very handsome—very like large ash leaves. At the base of each leaflet are several glandular teeth. As the autumn approaches, the leaflets usually fall first, so that eventually the ground surrounding the tree is strewn with bare leaf-stalks, sometimes 2 feet long.

The flowers are unisexual and grow on different trees. Both male and female flowers appear during July and August. They are greenish and are borne in branched panicles near the ends of the branches of the tree. The male flowers emit a most disagreeable odour. The reddish fruit is like that of the ash (p. 322), that is, it is a samara—a fruit with the internal tough membrane drawn out to form a twisted wing; but in the case of the tree of heaven the wing is drawn out in both directions thus leaving the seed in the middle. By means of the twisted wing, the fruit is distributed far and wide.

In China, the tree of heaven is used as a feeding-ground for the caterpillars of another silk-spinning moth (*Philosamia cynthia*); but the silk produced in this case is very inferior to that produced by the caterpillars of the mulberry silkmoth (*Bombyx mori*) (p. 286), by far the more efficient from the commercial point of view.

There are some rare varieties of the tree of heaven; perhaps the only one at all worthy of mention being the slightly weeping variety, *A. glandulosa* var. *pendula.* Elwes and Henry in their *Trees of Great Britain and Ireland* mention several other varieties but do not consider them sufficiently distinct to deserve recognition.

Other species of *Ailanthus* are the timber-producing *A. imberiflora* and *A. punctata* of Australia.

38

HORSE-CHESTNUTS

(*Sapindaceae*)

Chestnut Sunday is the Sunday before Ascension Day, but we do not recognise it so much as our forefathers did when they flocked to see the horse-chestnuts in their full glory in Kew Gardens and in Bushey Park and elsewhere. But perhaps this is just an indication of a general change of fashion these days and may not indicate a declining appreciation of this glorious plant ; for it would be incredible that any horse-chestnut when fully displaying its thousands of floral candles—its " flambeaux ", as Housman calls them—could be passed by unnoticed (p. 308). Furthermore, is there any child who has not delighted in gathering the twigs of sticky buds during late winter and carefully tending them until they burst out into leaf and young flower-bud ? Surely only the unfortunate who lives too far away from an available tree !

The **horse-chestnut** belongs to the family SAPINDACEAE, which is a large family comprising trees, shrubs and climbers, most of which are native to the tropics. To it also belongs the genus *Koelreuteria* containing the north Chinese species, *K. paniculata*, which is reputed to have inspired the willow pattern (p. 209). This tree, by the way, is cultivated in Britain, though rarely, for it is delicate in our climate. It bears yellow flowers in terminal racemes, and presents strikingly handsome autumn foliage.

SAPINDACEAE contains more than a hundred and twenty genera and well over a thousand species. Among them are some of those large woody climbers or lianes which so often dominate a tropical scene.

The horse-chestnut belongs to the genus *Aesculus*, a genus comprising nearly two dozen species, among which is the well-known American **buckeye**. (In some schemes of classification, the genus *Aesculus* is placed in a family by itself—HIPPOCASTANACEAE.) The genus is distributed over the temperate regions of both Old and New Worlds and in South America. The horse-chestnut is *A. hippocastanum*.

This tree must not be confused with the sweet chestnut (p. 264), for the plants are not at all alike except in their fruit, and even here there is an important distinction because the seeds of the sweet chestnut are edible whereas those of the horse-chestnut are not. In fact, it is quite possible that the term ' horse ' was applied to the horse-chestnut in order to imply coarseness or inferiority in this respect. There seems to be no foundation for the suggestion made by John Evelyn, who was clearly repeating what others had said, that the term was applied to a fruit which cured horses of broken wind, for horses will not eat horse-chestnuts. In order to meet the difficulties of live-stock feeding during the Second World War, investigations were carried out at the University of Reading to test the palatability of horse-chestnuts to pigs. But in spite of exhaustive experiment, dried horse-chestnut meals were found to have no nutritive value, and no matter how the meal was presented to the animals they rejected it. The name *Aesculus* was first applied to a species of oak which bore edible acorns (*esca*, food); but it is not certain how or when the name was transferred to the horse-chestnut. It is said that sheep and deer will eat horse-chestnuts.

The horse-chestnut is indigenous to western Asia and south-eastern Europe (chiefly Iran, Greece and Bulgaria); but it has now spread far and wide. It was introduced into Britain some time during the sixteenth century though the exact date is not known. It was raised from seed in France some decades later in the early seventeenth century.

The tree thrives best on a moist sandy loam. It is a light-loving tree, so it seldom, if ever, grows in woods.

The tree attains a height of 80 to 100 feet and a girth of up to 16 feet; but it does not live long. The large, heavy branches are given off obliquely, then they dip gracefully. The bark is in general smooth, but on the older parts of the trunk it tends to become scaly. The trunk often exhibits a twisted form, which is like that of the sweet chestnut, though not so pronounced as in the latter.

The twig of the horse-chestnut cannot be mistaken during the winter (p. 27). The smooth, light brown bark displays very con-spicuous, lighter brown lenticels. The large sticky buds are arranged in opposite pairs, adjacent pairs being in planes at right angles to each other. The terminal buds are usually much larger than the lateral buds. Beneath the buds (which were borne in the axils of the leaves of the previous season) are to be seen the scars of those leaves. Each leaf-scar stands out well, and bears the conspicuous cork plugs of the former veins to the leaf. Each bud is covered with overlapping bud-scales which are protected by a resinous substance. The bud-scales, as pointed

Horse-chestnut at Bath, Somerset, in Winter.

Lonsdale Ragg

out on p. 27, gradually merge into foliage leaves, the most perfect of which are towards the middle of the bud.

As the bud opens, the leaves emerge covered with white down and their leaflets drooping. The adult leaf is very characteristic of the horse-chestnut. It is one of the first of any species of tree to open out, being fully expanded in April (p. 308 and Plate 2). Each leaf is broken up into five or seven leaflets. Each leaflet is long, getting broader and broader towards the tip and then more suddenly narrowing down to a point. The margins are unevenly serrated. The palmate collection of leaflets are joined at the same point, that is, the distal end of a long leaf-stalk which is very broad at the base where it is inserted on the twig. The leaves turn brown or dull gold before they fall in the autumn.

The familiar large, upright inflorescences bloom from late May to early June, and then the tree looks like a huge Christmas tree smothered in candles or like an enormous candelabrum (the tree is sometimes called the ' candle tree '). The whole inflorescence is a complicated raceme. The lowest flowers are borne on longer stalks so that an excellent mosaic of flowers results (Plate 2). The uppermost flowers are usually male only since their ovaries are sterile.

The calyx of each flower is composed of five joined sepals. There are four or five petals of unequal size ; they are white but spotted with yellow patches which later turn pink. These act as honey-guides, for the flower is pollinated by insects, mainly bees. There are usually seven stamens and these are very pronounced, for they have long fila-ments. The ovary is three-chambered and ends in a long style. In each chamber there are two ovules, but not all of them ripen. Usually only one seed is produced in each fruit, which takes the form of a leathery capsule. The seed is very large and dark red in colour. Sur-rounding the seed is the tough green fruit wall which is white and pulpy on the inside and spiny on the outside. The seeds of the horse-chestnut are the much-sought-after ' conkers ' of the school-boy. The tree does not usually bear fruit until at least its twentieth year.

The **red horse-chestnut** (*A. carnea*) is not such a large or robust tree as the white. It is considered to be a hybrid of the white and is reproduced by grafting, though there is some doubt about its origin.

Neither the white nor the red horse-chestnut thrives in built-up areas, especially if the atmosphere is polluted. Since they are quick-growing trees, the timber which they yield is not durable and is there-fore no use for outdoor purposes. It is sometimes used for making

Foliage, Flowers and Fruit of Horse-chestnut.

Eric J. Hosking

Horse-chestnut in Hertfordshire, in Summer.

small articles of furniture. The glycoside aesculin, used in veterinary medicine, is extracted from the bark.

A certain amount of the timber of the **Japanese horse-chestnut** (*A. turbinata*) is imported into Britain.

In the United States there are several species of horse-chestnut or buckeye having white, yellow or red flowers borne in erect racemes. The most common is *A. ohioensis*. Others are of shrubby habit only. The seeds of *A. californica*, like those of the Japanese *A. turbinata*, are edible.

Horse-chestnuts are handsome trees, and it is little wonder that they are often used for ornamental purposes. For this object, there are not only the white and red horse-chestnuts (*A. hippocastanum* and *A. carnea*) but also : *A. indica*, perhaps the finest of all, with white flowers flushed with pink and having yellow honey-guides ; *A. parviflora* having white flowers ; *A. carnea* var. *briotii* with flowers of a deeper shade of red than its progenitor, the common red chestnut ; and others.

39
MAPLES AND SYCAMORE
(*Aceraceae*)

Considerable confusion has been caused through the use of inapt Latin and common names for the maples, and the application of several different names for the one plant ; and confusion has been made worse confounded by the use of the terms usually applied to maples for plants which are in no way related to them. The term ' sycamore ' for example, has more than one totally different application in the United States, and this has been still further confused with the term ' sycomore ', which really applies to a fig tree (see pp. 292 and 312).

Here an attempt will be made to give the names in current use, with corrections where necessary.

Maples belong to the family ACERACEAE, a small family of trees and shrubs indigenous only to the north temperate areas of both Old and New Worlds. All maples belong to the genus *Acer*.

COMMON OR FIELD MAPLE

Most authors, when describing the maple, have in mind the **common** or **field maple,** sometimes also called the **English** or **small-leaved maple** (*Acer campestre*). It is the only maple actually indigenous to Britain and probably only to England, having gradually become naturalised further north in Scotland. In spite of its name, this species is not common, at any rate as a tree : the great maple or sycamore (p. 312) is much more common.

The field maple occurs more often as a shrubby plant in hedgerows than as a tree. Yet it does sometimes occur in the form of the latter—anything from 20 to 50 feet high, sometimes higher. The bark is sometimes smooth and sometimes rather rough ; it is light brown in colour. The older twigs display ridges of cork, and the rather small but pointed buds are enclosed in hairy bud-scales.

The leaves are of a very glossy light green in spring ; but they eventually turn darker and often are then tinged with purple. As autumn approaches they turn a bright yellow, and remain thus until quite late in the season. Though they are smaller than the leaves of other maples commonly found in Britain (p. 315), they vary in size among themselves, those growing on trees being much larger than those growing in hedgerows. They are arranged on the stem in opposite pairs and the adjacent pairs are in planes at right angles to each other. Each leaf-blade is borne on a long graceful stalk. The leaf-blade is divided into five lobes, and each lobe may or may not have one or more large marginal teeth (pp. 311 and 315).

Eric J. Hosking

Winter.   Summer.

Field Maple in Suffolk.

Field Maple.
Left, twig bearing foliage and flowers ; above right, twig bearing fruit ; below
right, male flower and hermaphrodite flower.

The dark patches, which sometimes occur on the leaf-blades of most maples (but especially those of the field maple), are due to attack by a fungus (*Rhytisma acerinum*).

The flowers are borne in erect racemes. In some cases the flowers are hermaphrodite ; but in others they are male only. But all possible cases occur among the trees, that is, a tree may be completely hermaphrodite or it may bear male flowers only or a mixture of both hermaphrodite and male. The flowers appear during May and June. Where the field maple takes the form of a hedge which is frequently clipped, it seldom blooms.

Each flower is greenish yellow, and a perfect example is composed of five boat-shaped sepals, five narrow petals, eight stamens and two carpels joined to form an ovary with two stigmas. After fertilisation, the ovary develops to form the fruit which, like the ash (p. 327), is a samara. But in the case of the maple there are two carpels, so that since the membrane surrounding each of the two seeds is flattened and extended out in one direction only to form a wing ; in the field maple there are two wings to the fruit which may be called a double samara. Sometimes a flower (usually the one at the top of the raceme) has three carpels, and then the fruit has three wings. These fruits are commonly

x

called ' keys ', or in the West country ' hooks and hachets ', and very attractive they are—pale green first, then a pretty red and finally a darkish brown.

Since the field maple occurs mainly in hedges, some of which are constantly clipped, little timber is obtained from it. Yet the wood is very attractive and takes a high polish ; so it is used in turnery and in the making of fancy articles such as trinket-boxes and so forth. In the past it was used for such purposes much more than it is today ; the ancient peoples of the Mediterranean prized it very much, especially since to them more trees, and therefore more timber, were available. Pliny praised its fine grain and attractive veinings. Heavily knotted wood was much sought after, for the knots were usually so beautifully arranged. From it spotted tables were made, and many of these became famous, such as the maple table of Cicero.

SYCAMORE OR GREAT MAPLE

The **sycamore** (*Acer pseudoplatanus*) is a particularly handsome tree, and though it thrives in most parts of Britain, sometimes under the most trying conditions, it is not a native. It occurs naturally in Europe (chiefly the central areas) whence it was introduced into Britain during the fifteenth century.

The term ' sycamore ' is unfortunate, since it is so easily confused with ' sycomore '. The latter is the name for the wild Egyptian fig (*Ficus sycomorus*) (p. 292). It should therefore be emphasised here that the frequent assumption in literature that Zacchaeus climbed into a sycamore or maple tree to see Christ pass by is incorrect, for the Bible is quite explicit on the point.

> And he ran before, and climbed up into a sycomore tree to see him ; for he was to pass that *way*.
>
> *St. Luke*, Chap. 19

In the past the sycamore was called ' plane ' in Scotland owing to the similarity of the form of leaves and the scaly nature of the bark. Though this error of identity is now recognised, the tree is still called ' false plane ' a name which is perpetuated in its specific name.

However, the sycamore is sometimes also called **great maple,** which seems an altogether less confusing and therefore more desirable name. It is also called **large-leaved maple.**

This tree is very robust, even when growing on very exposed sites. It grows very quickly, frequently attaining a height of about 70

Winter. Summer.

Sycamore.

feet within half a century. Altogether it lives for about a hundred and fifty years. The stout trunk bears many robust twisting branches which go to make up a handsome ovoid crown.

The winter twigs and buds are more robust than those of the field maple. The buds are arranged in opposite pairs and are enclosed in prominent yellowish-green bud-scales which are not so hairy.

The leaves are much larger than those of the field maple (p. 315 and Plate 3) and are divided into five lobes which are unevenly toothed. This great maple, like all other maples (but none to such an extent as the sugar maple, p. 315), contains a high percentage of sugar in its sap. This is often exuded by the leaves, and that explains why they are sticky. Evelyn condemned the sycamore for this reason, saying: " The Sycamore is much more in reputation for its shade than it deserves; for the honey-dew leaves, which fall early, like those of the Ash, turn to mucilage and noxious insects, and putrefy with the first moisture of the season; and are therefore, by my consent, to be banished from all curious gardens and avenues."

The flowers appear at the same time as those of the field maple; but whereas those of the latter are borne in erect racemes those of the sycamore form handsome drooping racemes (Plate 3). The fruit takes the form of the usual double samara (sometimes triple or even quadruple), and this too is larger than that of the field maple.

The wood is just as beautiful as that of the field maple and it takes an exceedingly high polish. Furthermore, by varying modes of treatment, a wide range of colours can be produced. The well-known ' bird's-eye maple ' is the result of a collection of small knots around each of which is a circular grain. This is much in demand, especially for veneer. According to Johns, in his *Forest Trees of Britain*, this peculiar form of maple was obtained by cabinet-makers from the sugar or rock maple (p. 315) ; but today it is also obtained from the sycamore.

Sycamore or great maple wood is also utilised for coarser purposes, especially in its unstained, white natural state. Then it is used for mangle rollers, kitchen tables and benches, and so on ; for it does not stain other articles and is easily washed. It is also frequently employed for constructing floors, especially in dance halls.

NORWAY MAPLE

The rapidly growing **Norway maple** (*A. platanoides*) is indigenous to northern Europe and was introduced into Britain in 1683. It is not such a large tree as the sycamore. Its specific name is more justified than that of the sycamore, however, because its leaves are very like those of the plane (p. 315), being five-lobed with large pointed teeth.

The flowers are of a brighter yellow hue and they appear before the leaves.

ORNAMENTAL MAPLES

Among other maples which, though not indigenous to Britain, are frequently cultivated mainly for ornamental purposes, may be mentioned the **ash-leaved maple** or **box-elder** (*A. negundo*) which has compound leaves composed of three or five leaflets. It is quite a small tree.

Then there are the many different maples of Europe, Western and Eastern Asia (especially Japan) and also of North America which have found their way into British gardens and parks. Many of these are familiar because of the brilliant tones of colour which their leaves display. In fact, no family can compete with ACERACEAE for such a wide range of leaf colour. Most of these ornamental maples hail from Japan ; others are hybrids. Some of them are so small that

Harold Bastin

Leaves of Maples.
Above left, great maple; below left, field maple; below right, box-elder;
above right, Norway maple.

they are eminently suitable for the rock garden. *A. japonicum* var. *aureum* presents yellow foliage in spring; this then turns to the most lovely shades of gold, orange and scarlet in the autumn. *A. palmatum* var. *atropurpureum* has very deep bronze foliage, whereas the leaves of the variety *dissectum* are so deeply cleft as to be fern-like. *A. palmatum* var. *reticulatum* has dark green leaves with yellow and white variegations. And so one could go on naming a large number of species and varieties of maple which look exceptionally beautiful in open garden, shrubbery or rockery.

Other maples imported into Britain as timber include the **Pacific maple** (*A. macrophyllum*), **rock maple** (see below) and **soft maple** (*A. rubrum*)—all from Canada and the United States.

The **sugar maple** (*A. saccharum*), often called **rock maple** in the timber trade, is native to North America. In both the United States and Canada it is valued not only as a timber and ornamental tree but also as a source of maple sugar. The trunks are tapped and the sap collected and evaporated.

40

WALNUTS
(*Juglandaceae*)

The family JUGLANDACEAE is a rather small one containing half a dozen genera; yet it is very important. The whole family is confined to the temperate and mountainous tropical areas of the northern hemisphere. All its constituent members are trees, many of them yielding particularly handsome timbers and delicious edible fruit—all known as 'nuts', but none of them true nuts.

The walnut belongs to the genus *Juglans*, and there are several species of economic importance. The most common form of walnut in Britain is *J. regia*, sometimes called the **English walnut,** though outside Britain it is more usually known as the **European** or **Persian walnut,** for, though it is not indigenous to Britain, it is to Yugoslavia and Greece in Europe, and to Iran, northern India and China in Asia. This walnut was probably introduced into Britain by the Romans, for remains of the 'nuts' have been found around their villas in this country. Their authors referred to this fruit as 'Jovis glans', or 'nut of Jupiter', hence the generic name *Juglans*. Serious cultivation of the tree did not begin, however, in Britain until about the middle of the seventeenth century. The name means 'foreign nut'. Then the cultivation of the walnut seemed to capture the imagination of people, especially in the south of England, and extensive planting occurred. Though such enthusiasm no longer exists, there is still much evidence of the plantings of the past. Though avenues are not common, single trees and groups of trees are to be seen in many parts of the south country, from east to west. The trees figure largely in paddocks and on the lawns of farms and other country houses.

But the walnut is more common in certain parts of south and Central Europe than in Britain; it has been so for many centuries. After a wedding ceremony in Ancient Rome, it was the custom of the bridegroom to throw walnuts among the children to indicate that he himself was no longer a child. During John Evelyn's time it was held in high esteem in France, Germany and Switzerland. He wrote: " Whenever they fell a tree [in Burgundy], which is only the old and

Winter.
Summer.
Eric J. Hosking
Walnut in Hertfordshire.

decayed, they always plant a young one near him ; and in several places betwixt Hanaw and Frankfort, in Germany, no young farmer whatsoever is permitted to marry a wife, till he brings proof that he hath planted, and is a father of such a stated number of Walnut-trees, and the law is inviolably observed to this day, for the extraordinary benefit which this tree affords the inhabitants. They render most graceful avenues to our country dwellings, and do excellently near hedgerows. . . . The Bergstras (which extends from Heidelberg to Darmstadt), is all planted with Walnuts ; for so, by another ancient law, the Bordurers were obliged to nurse up and take care of them, and that chiefly for their ornament and shade, so as a man may ride for many miles about that country under a continued arbor or close walk, the traveller both refreshed with the fruit and the shade." Even today walnut trees are cultivated in orchards in Germany and France, whereas in parts of Switzerland and Czechoslovakia they are grown along the highways and are the property of the village communities.

During Evelyn's time, plantations of walnuts were also cultivated in the southern parts of Britain ; but these have now largely disappeared.

The European walnut frequently attains a height of 100 feet

(though the average is much less) and a girth of anything from 10 to 20 feet. The bark is of a characteristic grey colour, beautifully fissured in a longitudinal direction. The huge branches curve obliquely upwards. The winter twigs are very diagnostic. The leaf-scars are particularly prominent, one each below the large hairy winter buds which are inserted on the stem in a spiral arrangement.

The leaves, too, are not easy to confuse with anything else, for they have a pleasant aromatic odour (like the young fruit), and the leaf base is very swollen. The leaf is compound, having two, three or even four pairs of lateral leaflets and a terminal one. All leaflets are oval and pointed with entire but wavy margins (Plate 2).

The walnut is unisexual, both male and female flowers being borne in segregated clusters on the same tree. The male clusters take the form of long, pendulous catkins (Plate 2) which appear before the leaves open out in May. These catkins strew the ground around the trees after they have shed their pollen. Each male flower has usually five perianth segments surrounding numerous stamens, this large number being an advantage, for the tree is wind-pollinated. The female flowers are borne in smaller clusters at the ends of the young twigs. Each flower is stalkless and is composed of two carpels joined to form a flask-shaped ovary topped by a cleft stigma. The ovary is cupped in a very insignificant perianth of four or five segments.

The fruit is not a nut but a drupe, like that of the plum. The fruit-wall surrounding the seed is made up of two main layers—an outer thick, fleshy and green layer and an inner, very woody and corrugated layer. Within this woody 'stone' is the large seed which has two, thick, white lobed cotyledons separated by a thin septum across the cavity of the 'nut'. Sometimes cross walls are also present. When mature, the outer fleshy layer begins to blacken and then split longitudinally thus exposing the wooden 'shell' containing the seed.

Towards the end of June, that is, before the fruit is anywhere near ripe, it is often collected for pickling. This is only possible, of course, before the woody inner layer has formed. If the drupe can be pierced right through with a needle, then it is not too ripe for the purpose. At this stage, the fruit has a high vitamin C content, but this is destroyed, as it always is, by pickling. The kernel (that is, the cotyledons) of the ripe 'nut' contains about 18 per cent protein, 16 per cent carbohydrate and a very high percentage of fat or oil. It therefore has considerable food value. The oil is extracted, especially in France, for the manufacture of paints. At one time, though not so much today, the walnut

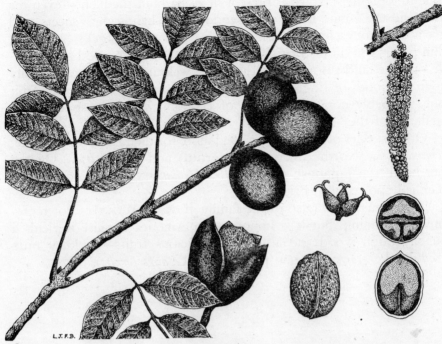

Walnut.

Twig bearing foliage and fruit. Above right, catkin of male flowers; middle, group of female flowers; below, left to right, ripe fruit opening to expose 'nut', complete 'nut', 'nut' in longitudinal and transverse section.

was a popular constituent of the 'nuts and wine' course at the end of dinner.

> In after-dinner talk,
> Across the walnuts and the wine.
> *The Miller's Daughter* : TENNYSON

It is an old belief that the walnut tree thrives best if the fruit is beaten off the tree and not hand-picked.

> A woman, a spaniel, and a walnut tree,
> The more you beat them the better they be.

The **black walnut** (*J. nigra*) is the most successful species in the United States, and its fruit is imported into Britain. This species is altogether larger than *J. regia*, frequently growing 150 feet high.

Both European and black walnuts furnish the very beautifully marked wood which is so valued for furniture-making. Its dark colour is due to a pigment which is present in all parts of the plant—even the leaves and the young fruit. The wood makes handsome veneers, and since it does not easily warp it is used for the best gun-stocks. As H. L. Edlin points out, in his *British Woodland Trees*, walnut wood is so valuable that the cultivation of the European walnut in plantations, at any rate in the south of England, should be encouraged ; though the fruit would probably not make a crop of economic value in spite of the popularity of the ' nut '.

Other species of walnut are valued more for their fruit, for example, *J. cinerea* (the North American **butternut**) and *J. rupestris*. On the other hand, the **Japanese walnut** (*J. sieboldiana*) yields a good timber which is imported into Britain.

The genus *Carya* (also of the family JUGLANDACEAE) is not represented in Britain ; but it is important in America because it yields a valuable tough wood and also some delicious fruits—**hickory nuts** (*C. alba* and *C. tomentosa*) and **pecan nuts** (*C. olivaeformis*).

41

DOGWOODS
(*Cornaceae*)

To the family CORNACEAE belongs a large number of ornamental garden trees and shrubs (especially the latter) including the very familiar Japanese laurel (*Aucuba japonica*) which, however, is not a true laurel (p. 143).

The family is fairly widely scattered in the world ; in Britain it is represented in the wild flora by the dogwoods. Many exotic shrubs belonging to the family are also to be seen in this country.

Dogwoods belong to the genus *Cornus*, a north temperate genus, of which there are two British species, namely, the **dogwood** or **cornel** (*C. sanguinea*) and the **dwarf dogwood** (*C. suecica*). The latter is a perennial shrub confined to the mountainous regions of the north of England and the highlands of Scotland. Annual stems arise vertically from the perennial stems of the dwarf dogwood which is of a creeping habit.

The dogwood seldom, if ever, exists as a tree in the wild state. It is a shrub growing 8 to 10 feet high, and is particularly common in hedgerows. It is recognised by several diagnostic features, but at all times of the year by its reddish or orange-coloured stems (Plate 7). In winter the twigs are of a darker hue—more or less crimson, and the buds, surrounded by distinct hairy bud-scales, are long and narrow.

The leaves are borne in pairs; each leaf is oval in shape with a pointed tip and wavy, though entire, margins (Plate 7). The foliage turns to beautiful shades of red and orange during the autumn, and then the whole tree or bush stands out prominently in the hedge or on the borders of a wood.

The white flowers are borne in dense umbels which are in full bloom during June and July (Plate 7). Very often the flowers open before the leaves are fully expanded. Each flower is composed of four white petals surrounded by a mere suggestion of a whorl of four sepals and surrounding four stamens. In the centre is an ovary composed of two fused carpels. The ovary is embedded in the receptacle and the upper surface takes the form of a nectary. Frequently the whorls of the central flower of an umbel are in fives. The flower is insect-pollinated. The fruit takes the form of a black drupe (Plate 7), containing usually one seed only. This fruit is bitter to the taste.

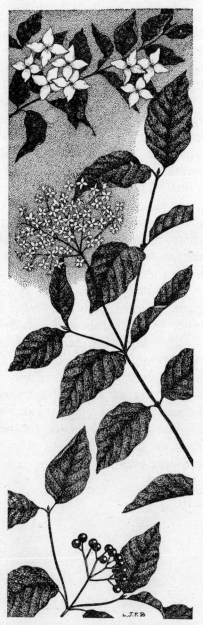

Dogwood.
Foliage, flowers and (below) fruit; above, *Cornus kousa*, a cultivated species.

The wood of the dogwood is little used now ; but at one time it was used for making goads, that is, instruments used for urging on beasts, skewers and dags or daggers—hence the common name. In certain rural areas the fruits are known as **dog-berries** ; and according to Dr. R. C. A. Prior they were at one time called **dog-cherries.**

Among the species of *Cornus* not indigenous to Britain, but cultivated in parks and gardens is the **Cornelian cherry** (*C. mas*). This plant is native to western Asia and south-eastern Europe. Its fruits are edible and are sometimes used for making preserves. The clusters of flowers are yellow in colour and make a handsome sight when in full bloom. Then there are *C. sanguinea* var. *elegantissima* which has green leaves variegated with white ; *C. sanguinea* var. *spathii* with golden foliage, and *C. kousa* with particularly large flowers (p. 321). A variety of the North American red osier dogwood, namely, *C. stolonifera* var. *flaviramea*, has bright yellow bark which stands out conspicuously during the winter.

In North America, the species *C. florida* thrives. This is one of America's most beautiful flowering trees, and it also yields a valuable timber which is imported into Britain.

The **Japanese laurel** belongs to another genus of the family CORNACEAE, namely, *Aucuba*. The botanical name for this plant is *Aucuba japonica*. Its leaves are very large, lance-shaped and pointed, and they are usually mottled with yellow patches, though there is an all-green form, *A. japonica* var. *vera*.

The genus *Griselinia* comprises some New Zealand and South American species, some of which are cultivated in Britain. They are handsome evergreen shrubs, in some cases variegated.

42

ASH

(Oleaceae)

It seems a pity that this tree—the " Venus of the Forest ", so graceful of form, so elegant of foliage, should bring forth that foliage so very late in the season only to lose it again so very early. Yet such is the case, for the ash is about the last of our trees to clothe itself with foliage, and then, almost before autumn is upon us, leaf-fall sets in.

> Delaying as the tender ash delays
> To clothe herself, when all the woods are green.
>
> _The Princess_ : TENNYSON

> The tree, that showed no green till June,
> October bares ;
>
> _The Ash_ : WILFRID GIBSON

The favourite haunts of the ash are meadows and valleys where running water abounds and in the close proximity of farms. But that inveterate field-naturalist, the Rev. C. A. Johns, knew where to look for it, and we can do no better than follow him : " Far away, in some secluded valley, through which a mountain stream, prolific in miniature waterfalls, hurries or lingers,

> '— at its own sweet will,' "

now penned up between party-coloured rocks, and now undermining the deep alluvial soil, which, in furtherance of the end for which it bubbled forth from the earth, it brought with it, ages ago, from the hills—among straggling mosses and strange-looking liverworts, which have no names save in the books and memory of the Naturalist—here the Ash is in its home. You may find it at times, a handsome looking tree in the neighbourhood of farms, or in parks, and contributing greatly to the beauty of the landscape even in these localities. . . . This must be a tree that _enjoys_, in common with many of its brethren, the beauties of the haunts I have described, not simply living and flourishing, but actually delighting in the brilliant sparkling of the water, watching the ousel as he bathes in his rapid flight, gracefully sweeping its branches over the streams, climbing up the sides of the steep hill, or endeavouring to peep at what is passing in the world beyond."

The ash belongs to the large family OLEACEAE which is widely distributed over temperate and tropical regions.[1]

Ash is a member of the genus _Fraxinus_, a genus comprising about fifty species native to Europe (especially Mediterranean regions), eastern Asia and North America. The **common ash** (_F. excelsior_) is native to Britain and to most other parts of Europe. It has been known and recognised for many centuries. Cupid's bows, according to the Greeks, were made of ash, though this was later supplanted by cypress. The spears of Homer's heroes were also made of ash. Furthermore the tree figures largely in Teutonic and other mythologies. According to Dr.

---

[1] See _Flowers in Britain_, pp. 198-200

Winter.   Summer.   *Eric J. Hosking*

Ash Tree in Suffolk.

Brewer, in his *Dictionary of Phrase and Fable*, it was the *yggdrasil* of Scandinavian mythology.   Its roots ran in three directions : one to the Asagods in heaven, one to the Frost-giants, and the third to the underworld.   Under each root was a fountain of wonderful virtues.   In the tree, which dropped honey, sat an eagle, a squirrel and four stags.   At the root lay the serpent Nithhöggr gnawing it, while the squirrel Ratatöskr ran up and down to sow strife between the eagle at the top and the serpent at the root.

In the past, the most extraordinary medicinal virtues have been ascribed to the ash.   Some of these have been recorded by such authorities as Pliny, Dioscorides, and the much more recent John Evelyn and still later by Gilbert White.   Both Evelyn and White recorded stories of the belief, probably handed down from the pre-Christian Saxons, that children suffering from distemper, hernia, and other afflictions were cured of these maladies if they were made to strip and then pass through a cleft ash trunk.   Even today, some people will tell of the so-called ' shrew-ash ' around which many superstitions have been built in the past.   This phenomenon has also been discussed by Johns, Evelyn, Gilbert White and other authorities.   White describes how such an ash was made : " Into the body of the tree, a deep hole was bored with an auger, and a poor devoted shrew-mouse was thrust in alive, and plugged in, no doubt with several incantations, long since forgotten." If any person suffering from lameness and certain other maladies were stroked with a branch from such a shrew-ash he was cured, for the wretched animal, when alive, was believed to cause such troubles among man and other animals. The tree was also supposed to cure lame cattle.

The ash is also mentioned in the Bible :

> He heweth him down cedars, and taketh the cypress and the oak, which he strengtheneth for himself among the trees of the forest: he planteth an ash, and the rain doth nourish it.
>
> *Isaiah*, 44

But it is probable that the translation from the Hebrew is incorrect, for the ash never grew in those parts of Asia. It has been suggested that what was really indicated was some species of pine.

The ash has no connexion with Ash Wednesday—the first Wednesday in Lent. This is derived from the ancient Roman Catholic custom of sprinkling ashes on the heads of those condemned to do penance on that day.

The tree, which does not live for more than about two hundred years, thrives best in moist soils, though it is intolerant of stagnant marshy ground. It attains a height of anything from 50 to 80 feet, and the trunk persists well into the crown. The branches leave the trunk very near the vertical, but soon break out into graceful curves. The bark is of a pale grey colour, beautifully fissured on the main trunk (p. 329). It has been suggested that the common name is derived from the ashen-greyness of the bark or from the fact that the colour of the bark resembles that of wood-ashes ; but it is not likely that either of these suggestions is correct.

The winter twigs are unmistakable. They are of the characteristic ashen-grey colour, smooth of surface, and bear pronounced black buds at the ends of the twigs and laterally in opposite pairs (Plate 5). The stout twigs themselves have a flattened appearance. The sombre blackness of the buds is due to closely packed black hairs on the enveloping bud-scales.

> more black than ash buds in the front of March.
>
> TENNYSON

The very beautiful leaves are arranged in opposite pairs. Each leaf is compound, comprising a long leaf-stalk on which are inserted one terminal leaflet and three to eight pairs of lateral leaflets—lance-

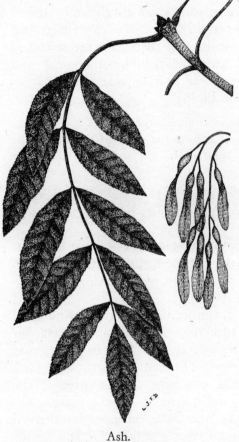

Ash.
Left, leaf; right, fruit.

shaped and having serrated margins (Plate 5). As already stated (p. 322), the leaves open out very late in the season and fall at varying times, but always very early in the autumn. But graceful and beautiful as the ash leaves are (in any event when in their prime), they are also a nuisance, for from the many apices of their leaflets drips the water which renders the soil beneath untenable for smaller plants; and this effect is intensified by the roots of the same tree, which grow very near the horizontal and therefore at the soil surface, which they drain of nutriment. Furthermore, ash leaves seldom make a grand exit in a blaze of autumnal colours, though sometimes they assume a pleasant yellow hue. The Rev. W. Gilpin gives a picturesque description of this habit: "Instead of contributing its tint, therefore, in the wane of the year, among the many-coloured offspring of the woods, it shrinks from the blast, drops its leaf, and in each scene where it predominates, leaves wide blanks of desolated boughs, amidst foliage yet fresh and verdant. Before its decay, we sometimes see its leaf tinged with yellow, well contrasted with the neighbouring greens. But this is one of Nature's casual beauties. Much oftener its leaf decays in a dark, muddy unpleasing tint. And yet sometimes, notwithstanding this early loss of foliage, we see the Ash, in a sheltered situation, when the rains have been abundant and the season mild, retain its green (a light pleasing green) when the Oak and the Elm in its neighbourhood have put on their autumnal attire." The time when the ash sheds its leaves varies among the individuals.

The Romans, and, indeed, the English of bygone days (especially the Elizabethans) used young ash leaves as fodder for cattle and deer. Even today, the leaves are used for this purpose in some rural districts. Moreover, in past days they, when dried, have been used for adulterating tea.

The reddish flowers, as one might expect in the circumstances, appear before the leaves, that is, during March and April. They are not conspicuous, but grow in dense racemes on the sides of the twigs (Plate 5). The flowers may be hermaphrodite or unisexual, but in any event they are inconspicuous because they have neither sepals nor petals and so are very simple indeed. (In this respect, the flowers are quite unlike those of other species of ash, p. 328.) Each hermaphrodite flower has two purple stamens and two carpels. A unisexual flower has either two carpels or two stamens, but not both. All three forms of flower may be borne on the same tree, whereas other trees may be either hermaphrodite, or entirely male or entirely female. Pollination takes place through the agency of the wind; the flowers of this species cannot attract insects since they are neither visually attractive nor do they produce any perfume.

The fruit is the characteristic samara, hanging in clusters popularly known as 'keys' (p. 326 and Plate 5). The samara is very similar to that of the maple (p. 311) except that it is single, whereas that of the maple is double. The extended wing, slightly twisted, is useful for dissemination by wind. This method of dispersal is a very effective one and explains why ash trees often appear in the most inaccessible places such as the crevices of high rocks. The ash seldom bears fruit until it is about forty years old. Sometimes, of course, one comes across an ash which never bears fruit at all because it produces no female flowers. Furthermore, it seems that in general the amount of fruit that an ash bears varies inversely as the luxuriance of its foliage. Among the ancients, ash fruit were prized as an article of diet. The seeds and samaras were pickled and served with salads. The ancients also ascribed medicinal virtues to these fruits.

Ash wood has for long been, and still is, of considerable economic importance. It is one of the very few woods which will burn brightly while still in the 'green' state, so it makes excellent fuel.

> Of all the trees in England,
> Her sweet three corners in,
> Only the Ash, the bonnie Ash
> Burns fierce while it is green.
> WALTER DE LA MARE

Y

The main value of ash wood lies in its firm but very elastic, and therefore pliable, character. For this reason it is used for making all sorts of agricultural implements and machinery; but for many purposes for which it was hitherto used it has now been supplanted by steel and other metals. Ash is still very often coppiced or pollarded in order to produce young staves which are capable of taking a great strain. These are used for all sorts of handles, for sports gear such as oars and hockey sticks, and also for those parts of vehicles which are continually subject to intermittent stress and strain. Unfortunately ash wood perishes if it is kept in continuous contact with the soil, so it is useless for poles and fences.

OTHER SPECIES AND VARIETIES OF ASH

The **manna ash** (F. *ornus*) is sometimes cultivated in Britain for ornamental purposes. It is native to Mediterranean Europe, where it is sometimes called the 'flowering ash'; for its flowers, unlike those of the common ash, have sepals and greenish-white petals. When growing in favourable situations and on very hot days, this species exudes a sweet sugary substance from its bark. This is called 'manna', and is used as a sweetmeat, especially in Mediterranean regions such as Sicily. Sometimes the exudation is expedited by making incisions in the bark, and the juice collected.

In the same regions of southern Europe there is the **small-leaved ash** (F. *parviflora*); then in the Himalayan regions grows the **large-flowered ash** (F. *floribunda*) which bears large white flowers. But neither of these species is to be seen in Britain. However, other exotic species of 'flowering ash' are sometimes cultivated in Britain, for example: F. *mariesii*, from northern China, having pure white flowers arranged in fragrant panicles; F. *californica* with extremely large bright yellow flowers; and F. *mexicana* with flowers of a deeper yellow hue.

One variety of the common ash, F. *excelsior* var. *heterophylla*, has simple leaves. This is not a very interesting tree; but it does grow wild in Britain and in other parts of Europe. Another variety, F. *excelsior* var. *pendula* is of weeping habit. It arose as a 'sport' from a tree growing at Wimpole in Cambridgeshire and has since been propagated from cuttings.

Among the score or so of American species of ash are several which yield very valuable timber; some of this is imported into Britain.

The Winchelsea Ash;
Girth 14 ft.

LR
3-7-33

Lonsdale Ragg

The Winchelsea Ash, Sussex.

43
THE ELDER FAMILY
(Caprifoliaceae)

The elder family, CAPRIFOLIACEAE, is mainly one of shrubs and trees; there are very few herbs in it. It is distributed far and wide throughout the world, though more commonly in the north temperate zone. Most of its members have soft wood (not of much economic value) and very broad pith. There are about a dozen genera, and these contain some very beautiful ornamental plants such as elder, guelder rose, wayfaring tree, snowball tree—all shrubs or small trees and the honeysuckle —a woody climber. All these are described in *Flowers in Britain* (pp. 204-206); the botany of those members which sometimes assume arboreal habit is here reproduced from the above-mentioned volume with additional topics of interest concerned with trees.

ELDER

Elder belongs to the genus *Sambucus*—a genus comprising about a score of species distributed very widely in north temperate regions, South America, Asia and Australia.

The **common elder** (*S. nigra*) is actually a very fast-growing tree, 10 to 20 feet high when growing in a wood; but it frequently assumes the habit of a shrub in hedges where it is so often seen. It thrives best on moist, well-drained soils.

This tree has been the subject of much traditional belief. In some parts it is said that the Cross of Calvary was made of elder wood. In other parts it is believed that Judas hanged himself on an elder tree (see also p. 191).

Fast by is the elder-tree on which Judas hanged himself.
JOHN DE MAUNDEVILLE

Judas he japed
With Jewish siller,
And sithen on an elder tree
Hanged himsel.
PIERS PLOWMAN

330

STRAWBERRY TREE

Buds

Flowers

Fruits

DOGWOOD

Buds

Fruits

Flowers

Buds

GUELDER ROSE

Fruits

Flowers

BLACKTHORN (SLOE)

Flowers

Fruits

Buds

Flower

Fruits

Buds

ROWAN

ELDER

Flowers

Bud

Fruits

PURGING BUCKTHORN

Fruits

Buds

Flowers

HAWTHORN

Flowers

Fruits

Buds

WAYFARING TREE

Fruits

Buds

Flowers

DOROTHY FITCHEW

PLATE 7

The bark of the elder is greyish-brown in colour and dotted with very pronounced lenticels. On the older branches the bark becomes corrugated and rough.

The leaves are borne in opposite pairs, two adjacent pairs being at right angles to each other. Each leaf is large and compound, with two to five pairs of lateral leaflets and a terminal one. Each leaflet is lance-shaped and serrated. There are no stipules. In having compound leaves, the elder differs from the rest of the family CAPRIFOLIACEAE (p. 333 and Plate 7).

The flowers are very small, but they are borne in dense inflorescences shaped like large irregular disks, and there are usually so many of them on one plant that it looks very handsome in June when it is in bloom (p. 333 and Plate 7).

Each inflorescence is composed of five main branches all of which bear their flowers at the same level, thus giving the disk-shaped effect.

The five sepals of the flower are united and display five teeth at the upper rim. There are five petals, which towards their bases are united to form a tube, but higher up are separate and spreading. The stamens are equal in number to the petals and alternate with them. The three carpels are united and have three stigmas joined immediately on top of the ovary, for there are no styles. The fruit is the familiar berry which contains three to six seeds. The berry is first green, then red and eventually deep purple (p. 333 and Plate 7). Elder berries are edible though neither palatable nor nourishing. A wine is sometimes made from them.

This plant, grown as a shrub, is useful as a screen for other more delicate shrubs. The old wood from an elder tree is used for making skewers and other small articles. The wood from younger twigs, hollowed out by the removing of the broad tissue of pith, is used for making various noisy toys. (The generic name is derived from *sambuca*, a 'musical instrument'.) The pith is used for microscope work, especially in botany.

For centuries, the medicinal virtues of elder have been recognised though frequently exaggerated, for some of them are more imaginary than real. The inner bark has been used as a cathartic. From the dried flowers an oil is extracted. The leaves emit an odour repugnant to insects ; that is why one frequently sees twigs of elder leaves tied to a horse's head, for it keeps irritating flies away.

The **dwarf elder** or **danewort** (*S. ebulus*) differs from the common elder in that it grows only two or three feet high, its leaves have stipules, the inflorescences have only three main branches, and the flowers are purplish in colour.

The **scarlet-berried elder** (*S. racemosa*) is a tree attaining a height of 15 to 20 feet. Frequently this species bears no fruit.

Among the species and varieties of elder cultivated for ornamental purposes are several varieties of the common elder. The **golden elder** (*S. nigra* var. *aurea*) is one of the most conspicuous yellow-leaved shrubs. The **parsley-leaved** or **cut-leaved elder** (*S. nigra* var. *laciniata*) has deeply cleft leaflets. The **round-leaved elder** (*S. nigra* var. *rotundifolia*) is rather rare. Its leaflets are almost circular. *S. nigra* var. *virescens* has white bark and its berries never turn to any colour from their original green.

WAYFARING TREE AND GUELDER ROSE

Two shrubs, often attaining the size and habits of trees, are the **wayfaring tree** and the **guelder rose**. Both are species of the genus *Viburnum*, a large genus represented mainly in Asia and North America. The wayfaring tree is *V. lantana* and the guelder rose, *V. opulus*.

Both these plants are inhabitants of woodlands, the guelder rose blooming during June and July and the wayfaring tree during May and June. The leaf of the guelder rose is five-lobed, whereas that of the wayfaring tree is simpler with a downy under-surface (Plate 7). A curious feature of the wayfaring tree is that the winter buds have no protective bud-scales.

The flowers of both these species are very like that of the elder and they are borne in similar inflorescences (Plate 7). In the case of the guelder rose, the outer flowers of the disk are much larger than the inner ones and they are neuter. In both, the fruits are berries—dark red in the case of the guelder rose, and purplish-black in the case of the wayfaring tree (Plate 7).

The origins of the common names of these two wild species of *Viburnum* are interesting. That of the guelder rose may be derived from *rose de Gueldre*, or Guelders, the Dutch province; but Sir J. E. Smith, in his *English Flora*, suggests that the name is a corruption of 'elder rose' which indicates that the plant is related to elder.

W. Howitt suggests an origin for the name 'wayfaring tree' which is possibly more romantic than true:

> Wayfaring Tree ! What ancient claim
> Hast thou to that right pleasant name ?

The Elder Family.
Above left, snowball tree; below left, foliage, fruit and flower of guelder rose;
above right, foliage, flowers and fruit of wayfaring tree; below right, foliage,
flowers and fruit of elder.
(The inflorescences of the last three have been drawn more opened out to
elucidate structure.)

> Was it that some faint pilgrim came
> Unhopedly to thee,
> In the brown desert's weary way,
> 'Midst thirst and toil's consuming sway,
> And there, as 'neath thy shade he lay,
> Blessed the Wayfaring Tree?

The Rev. C. A. Johns, in his *Forest Trees of Britain*, says that it " would
seem to owe its name to the soiled appearance of its leaves which,
wherever the tree is growing, gives one the notion of its having been
powdered with dust from the highway."

All members of this family so far mentioned, and many varieties,
are cultivated for their decorative effects. The varieties of elder have

already been mentioned. But *Viburnum* figures even more extensively among our shrubberies and sometimes also as solitary shrubs and trees. Perhaps the most popular cultivated species is *V. sterile*, the **snowball tree**. This plant is very closely related to the guelder rose, but its inflorescences are spherical and all the flowers are neuter (p. 333). There are also several varieties of this species.

Other species of *Viburnum* include the evergreen *V. burkwoodii* which bears sweetly scented white flowers tinged with pink; and *V. macrocephalum*, of Chinese origin, which produces enormous inflorescences. But then it should be no cause for wonder that the genus *Viburnum* has given us so many species and varieties with which to bedeck our gardens for the sake of their foaming flowers or their striking fruit and autumnal foliage. Most of them, however, are either shrubs or wall plants.

44

MISCELLANY

There are four exotic trees of local interest to town dwellers and those others who have access to cultivated parklands and gardens.

STRAWBERRY TREE
(*Ericaceae*)

The **strawberry tree** is a popular decorative plant in some parts of Britain; though, while it is a true tree in its native habitats, it frequently assumes nothing but the habit of a sturdy bush here. It is actually native to the Mediterranean regions of Europe and to southwest Ireland, especially in and around Killarney. · In those parts of Eire, this tree is an outstanding feature of the landscape, and along the shores of the Mediterranean it has thrived for centuries.

> Nunc viridi membra sub Arbuto
> Stratus, nunc ad aquae lene caput sacrae.
>
> HORACE

The strawberry tree belongs to the family ERICACEAE, to which also belong such well-known mountain and moorland plants as heath and heather (*Erica*)[1], and the ever-popular rhododendron (*Rhododendron*).[1]

[1] See *Flowers in Britain*, p. 189

Foliage, Flowers and Fruit of Strawberry Tree.

This tree is included in the genus *Arbutus* which is distributed widely through western Asia, southern Europe and North America. The strawberry tree is *A. unedo*. To the same genus belongs the North American **madrona laurel** or **madroño** (*A. menziesii*), a tree which attains a height of more than 120 feet and yields a useful timber. But the strawberry tree never reaches such a height—it is usually 20 to 30 feet in Britain, and perhaps 40 feet or more elsewhere. The trunk has a twisted appearance. The bark is of a reddish colour and is scaly in structure peeling off in thin sheets.

The leaves are evergreen and are therefore tough and leathery. They are oval in shape, about three inches long, and have finely serrated margins (Plate 7). The flowers are borne in drooping racemes, pink or white in colour, at the tips of some of the branches. Each flower is bell-shaped with joined petals—typical of the British herbaceous members of the family. The flowers bloom in September and are pollinated by insects. The bell of joined petals is deciduous and falls off after fertilisation has taken place.

Since it takes more than a year for the fertilised flowers to produce ripe fruits (which take the form of bright red berries covered with many fine, blunt spines), both flowers and fruits appear on the same tree at the same time, namely in early autumn (p. 335 and Plate 7). That is why this handsome evergreen is such a desirable plant for shrubberies and more open garden decoration. It thrives along the coastal regions of the south; but further inland and north it cannot withstand the sharp frosts.

The strawberry tree derives its common name from the very superficial resemblance of its fruit to the strawberry. The resemblance is certainly very superficial, for the strawberry (which is not a berry, but really a swollen receptacle covered with many small, stony fruits) is not spherical but it is palatable, whereas the fruit of the strawberry tree is spherical and, though edible, does not please the taste of most people. In fact, according to Pliny, this is signified in the specific name *unedo*, meaning 'one I eat', that is, seldom does one try the fruit a second time.

The wood of the strawberry tree is of very little economic importance, except, as in Eire, for the making of certain fancy articles.

Other species and varieties of *Arbutus* are sometimes grown in Britain for ornamental reasons. *A. andrachne* may be seen in and around London, in the form of an evergreen shrub. Then there is the variety, *A. unedo* var. *rubra* which bears rose-red flowers. This variety is small and is useful for conservatories and for indoor decoration in the form of a pot plant. Other varieties have double flowers.

PERSIMMON
(*Ebenaceae*)

The **persimmon** is not at all common in Britain, not even in British parks, though there is an example in Kensington Gardens, London, more than thirty feet high, and quite a number of specimens elsewhere. Perhaps the tree has not achieved popularity in Britain because it demands both a good soil and a sheltered position.

Persimmon belongs to the family EBENACEAE—a very important family from the commercial point of view, for it contains trees which yield valuable heavy timbers, such as **ebony** (*Diospyros ebenum*), **Calamander wood** (*D. quaesita*), **African ebony** (*Diospyros crassiflora*, etc.), **Macassar ebony** (*D. macassar*) and **Andaman marble** (*D. kuzii*).

Persimmon also belongs to the genus *Diospyros* (*D. virginiana*), and its wood, together with those of the other species mentioned, is imported into Britain.

The persimmon is very common in many parts of North America. There it attains a height of 80 feet or more, especially in the Mississippi area. The oval and pointed leaves are rather leathery with wavy though smooth margins. These are unisexual, male flowers having sixteen stamens, and hermaphrodite flowers having eight stamens.

The fruit takes the form of a succulent, orange-coloured berry about an inch and a half in diameter. This is edible though it has an extremely astringent flavour when green. When ripe, however, it is sweet. It is very popular in the southern States.

> Have you ever
> On your travels
> Through the queer, uncertain south,
> Had a 'simmon—
> Green persimmon—
> Make a sortie in your mouth ?

F. H. SWEET

There are other species of persimmon which produce edible fruits ; perhaps the most popular abroad is the **Chinese persimmon** or **date-plum** (*D. kaki*) which is often dried and used as a sweetmeat.

Though the Virginian persimmon was brought to Britain so far back as 1629 it has never been so well acclimatised as to bring forth ripe fruit satisfactorily.

PAULOWNIA
(*Scrophulariaceae*)

The handsome exotic *Paulownia imperialis*, which hails from Japan, may be seen growing in such places as Regent's Park, the Royal Botanic Gardens, Kew, and other London parks and commons and elsewhere ; though whether it will ever become firmly established in Britain as an ornamental tree is yet to be proved. It is not very likely.

Paulownia belongs to the snapdragon family (SCROPHULARIACEAE)[1] to which the foxglove also belongs ; in fact, the flowers of *Paulownia* resemble those of the foxglove, though the former are delicately perfumed and are borne in erect or pendulous panicles. They are purplish-violet in colour. Unfortunately, the flowers appear so early in the season that they are frequently caught by the frost.

[1] See *Flowers in Britain*, pp. 272 and 283

Even in Britain, however, *Paulownia* is fast-growing, and attains a height of 30 to 40 feet. It is deciduous, but when in leaf it makes a handsome spectacle, for its oval leaves are as much as ten inches long (sometimes they even exceed twice this length), which gives the whole tree a tropical appearance. The leaves are covered with woolly hairs.

Paulownia succeeds best in Continental towns which are not smoky : in Paris it is a very common ornamental tree.

The timber of *Paulownia* is exceedingly light in weight, and though seldom used for any commercial purpose in Britain, it is commonly used for cabinet-making in Japan. The tree also figures in Japanese heraldry, for the ' Order of the Paulownia Sun ' is the highest of the ' Rising Sun ' orders. This decoration has a motif of leaves and flowers of *Paulownia imperialis*.

CATALPA
(*Bignoniaceae*)

Catalpa is a genus of deciduous trees of considerable ornamental value which belongs to the tropical and sub-tropical family BIGNONI-ACEAE. The most common species to be seen in many parks and gardens in Britain is *Catalpa bignonioides*, sometimes called **Indian bean.**

Catalpa at Holland House, London.

Lonsdale Ragg

Many of these trees flourish in London and other towns. There is a very conspicuous group of them in the forecourt of the Houses of Parliament. There are also several other specimens, now famous, such as the large *Catalpa* at Finsbury Circus in the City of London. This is more than 30 feet high. The well-known *Catalpa* in Gray's Inn is supposed to have been planted by Francis Bacon ; but this is doubtful. *Catalpa* seems to flourish in smoky atmospheres.

Catalpa is native to North America, China and the West Indies, and trees from their native habitats yield a durable timber. Seldom is home-grown timber available for use. In Britain, *C. bignonioides* is a spreading, irregular tree with curving branches (p. 338). Even in winter it is easy to identify, for the winter twigs, though thick and robust, have very small winter buds, but very large, almost circular leaf-scars, each of which displays a pronounced circle of vein-scars. *Catalpa* is a useful shade tree to have on a lawn, for during the season it is thickly covered with very large, heart-shaped leaves. Their margins are not serrated.

Catalpa frequently blooms in Britain. The white flowers, streaked with yellow and purple, are long and tubular. They are particularly welcome, for they appear after most flowering trees have already bloomed.

There is a golden variety of this species, namely, *C. bignonioides* var. *aurea.* Some fine examples of it can be seen in some of our towns : again, London can boast many. Then there is another species sometimes seen in Britain, namely, *C. bungei.* This species presents greenish-yellow flowers spotted with brown. It comes from China, but is smaller than *C. bignonioides* and is altogether less attractive. *C. kaempferi* may also be seen. There is a handsome specimen of this form in Chelsea Physic Garden ; but in general this species is not so successful as *C. bignonioides.*

C. speciosa is a North American species which attains a height of 120 feet in its native country. It is not grown in Britain ; but the timber is imported, though in not very large quantities.

O dreamy, gloomy, friendly Trees,
I came along your narrow track
To bring my gifts unto your knees
And gifts did you give back ;
For when I brought this heart that burns——
These thoughts that bitterly repine—
And laid them here among the ferns
And the hum of boughs divine,
Ye, vastest breathers of the air,
Shook down with slow and mighty poise
Your coolness on the human care,
Your wonder on its toys,
Your greenness on the heart's despair
Your darkness on its noise.

H. TRENCH

What does he plant who plants a tree?
He plants the friend of sun and sky ;
He plants the flag of breezes free ;
The shaft of beauty, towering high ;
He plants a home to heaven anigh
For song and mother-croon of bird
In hushed and happy twilight heard—
The treble of heaven's harmony—
These things he plants who plants a tree.

H. C. BUNNER

In such green palaces the first kings reign'd,
Slept in their shades, and angels entertain'd ;
With such old counsellors they did advise,
And, by frequenting sacred groves, grew wise.

E. WALLER

The very leaves live for love and in his season every happy tree experiences love's power.

CLAUDIAN

A tree is a nobler object than a prince in his coronation robes

A. POPE

The groves were God's first temples

W. C. BRYANT

———

The lines in the illustration opposite are
taken from Spenser's *Faerie Queene*.

Much can they praise the trees so straight and hy,
The sayling Pine; the Cedar proud and tall;
The vine-propp Elme; the Poplar never dry;
The builder Oake, sole king of forrests all;
The Aspine good for staves; the Cypresse funerall;
The Laurell, meed of mightie Conquerours
And Poets sage; the Firre that weepeth still;
The Willow, worne of forlorne Paramours;
The Eugh, obedient to the benders will;
The Birch for shaftes; the Sallow for the mill;
The Mirrhe sweete-bleeding in the bitter wound;
The warlike Beech; the Ash for nothing ill;
The fruitfull Olive; and the Platane round;
The carver Holme; the Maple seeldom inward sound.

L.J.F.B.

1. TULIP-TREE
2. LIME
3. BLACKTHORN
4. DAMSON
5. CULTIVATED PLUM
6. ALMOND
7. GEAN
8. CULTIVATED
   CHERRY
9. CULTIVATED PEAR

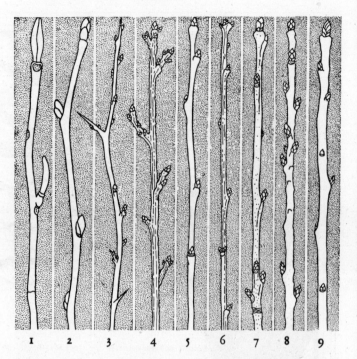

1   2   3   4   5   6   7   8   9

10. CULTIVATED APPLE
11. WHITE BEAM
12. WILD SERVICE
13. ROWAN
14. HAWTHORN
15. LABURNUM
16. FALSE ACACIA
17. PLANE

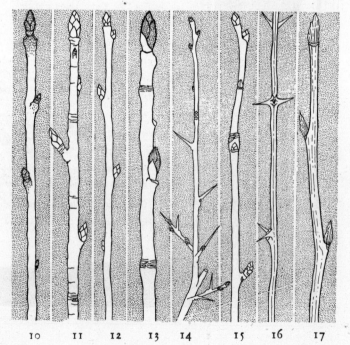

10   11   12   13   14   15   16   17

18. CRACK WILLOW
19. BLACK POPLAR
20. WHITE POPLAR
21. ASPEN
22. BIRCH
23. ALDER
24. HORNBEAM
25. HAZEL

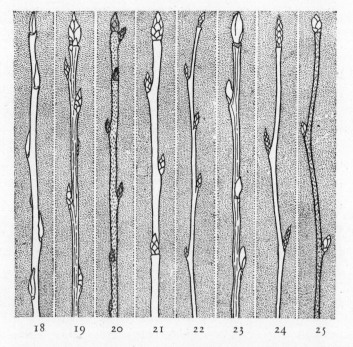

18   19   20   21   22   23   24   25

26. TURKEY OAK
27. ENGLISH OAK
28. SWEET CHESTNUT
29. BEECH
30. WYCH ELM
31. ENGLISH ELM
32. FIG
33. MULBERRY

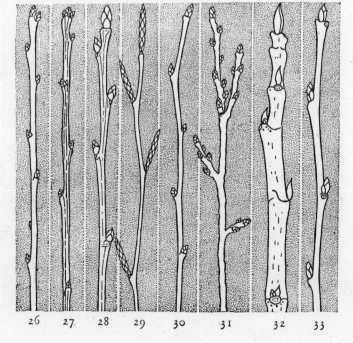

26   27   28   29   30   31   32   33

z

34. SPINDLE

35. PURGING BUCK-
    THORN

36. ALDER BUCK-
    THORN

37. TREE OF HEAVEN

38. HORSE-CHESTNUT

39. ENGLISH MAPLE

40. NORWAY MAPLE

41. GREAT MAPLE (or
    SYCAMORE)

42. WALNUT

43. DOGWOOD

44. ASH

45. ELDER

46. WAYFARING TREE

47. GUELDER ROSE

48. CATALPA

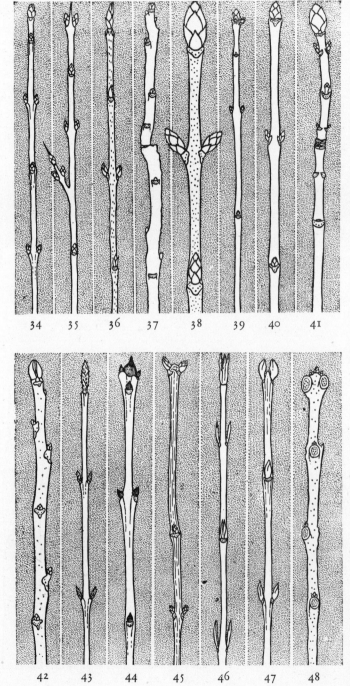

INDEX OF BOTANICAL NAMES

Abies, 84; A. alba, 85, 86; A. alba, *var.* compacta, 88; A. alba *var.* tortuosa, 88; A. amabilis, 88; A. balsamea, 87; A. brachyphylla, 87; A. cephalonica, 88; A. concolor, 87; A. firma, 87; A. forestii, 87; A. fraseri, 87; A. grandis, 87; A. magnifica, 88; A. nobilis, 88; A. nordmanniana, 88; A. numidica, 88; A. pectinata, 85, 86; A. pectinata *var.* compacta, 88; A. pectinata *var.* tortuosa, 88; A. pinsapo, 88; A. veitchii, 88; A. webbiana, 87

Abietaceae, 49, 59, 71, 79, 84, 89, 95, 120

Acer campestre, 309; A. japonicum *var.* aureum, 315; A. macrophyllum, 315; A. negundo, 314; A. palmatum, *var.* atropurpureus, 315; A. palmatum *var.* dissectum, 315; A. palmatum *var.* reticulatum, 315; A. platanoides, 314; A. pseudoplatanus, 312; A. rubrum, 315; A. saccharum, 315

Aceraceae, 309

Aesculus, 303; A. californica, 309; A. carnea, 306; 309; A. carnea *var.* briotii, 309; A. hippocastanum, 303, 309; A. indica, 309; A. ohioensis, 308; A. parviflora, 309; A. turbinata, 308, 309

Agathis, 55

Ailanthus glandulosa, 300; A. glandulosa *var.* pendula, 302; A. imberiflora, 302; A. punctata, 302

Alnus glutinosa, 239; A. glutinosa *var.* laciniata, 242; A. incana *var.* incisa, 242

Amelanchier, 184; A. canadensis, 184; A. vulgaris, 184

Anacardiaceae, 294

Anacardium occidentale, 294

Aquifoliaceae, 294

Araucaria, 55; A. araucana, 55; A. bidwillii, 58; A. brasiliana, 88; A. cunninghamii, 58; A. excelsa, 58

Araucariaceae, 49, 55

Arbutus andrachne, 336; A. menziesii, 335; A. unedo *var.* rubra, 336

Aucuba japonica, 143, 320, 322; A. japonica *var.* vera, 322

Bennettitales, 49

Betula, 232; B. alba, 232; B. alba *var.* youngii, 238; B. alba *var.* purpurea, 238; B. lutea, 238; B. nana, 238; B. papyrifera, 238; B. pendula, 232; B. pubescens, 232

Bignoniaceae, 238

Betulaceae, 231

Blastophaga, 293

Bombyx mori, 285, 302

Broussonetia papyrifera, 290

Bryophyta, 3

Buxaceae, 197

Buxus, 198; B. japonica *var.* aurea, 200; B. macowanii, 198; B. sempervirens, 198; B. sempervirens *var.* elegantissima, 200

Caprifoliaceae, 330

Carpinus, 242; C. betulus, 242; C. betulus *var.* pryamidalis, 240

Carya alba, 320; C. olivaeformis, 320; C. tomentosa, 320

Cassia, 189; C. acutifolia, 189; C. angustifolia, 189; C. fistula, 189; C. obovata, 189

Castanea, 45, 264; **C. dentata,** 267; C. sativa, 264

Catalpa bignonioides, 338 C. bignonioides *var.* aurea, 339; C. bungei, 339; C. kaempferi, 339; C. speciosa, 339

Cedrus, 71; C. atlantica, 72; C. atlantica *var.* glauca, 72; C. brevifolia, 72; C. deodara, 72, 78, 79; C. deodara, *var.* aurea, 72; C. deodara *var.* nana, 72; C. libani, 71, 72, 73, 75; C. libani *var.* nana pyramidata, 72

Cedrela odorata, 71

Celastraceae, 297

Celastrus, 298; C. scandens, 298

Celtis, 278

Cerasus vulgaris, 161

Cercis, 192; C. canadensis, 192; C. chinensis, 192; C. occidentalis, 192; C. reniformis, 192; C. siliquastrum, 192

Chamaecyparis lawsoniana, 71, 107

Chermes, 86, 88, 100

Cinnamomum camphora, 143; C. zeylanicum, 143

Coleophora, 83

Coniferales, 38, 49

Corchorus capsularis, 151

Cordaitales, 49

Cornaceae, 320

Cornus, 320; C. florida, 322; C. kousa, 322; C. mas, 322; C. sanguinea, 143, 320; C. sanguinea *var.* elegantissima, 322; C. sanguinea *var.* spathii, 322; C. stolonifera *var.* flaviramea, 322; C. suecica, 322

Corylaceae, 242

Coryllus, 247; C. avellana, 247; C. avellana *var.* aurea, 249; C. avellana *var.* purpurea, 249

Corylopsis, 195

Crataegus, 180; C. oxyacantha, 180; C. oxyacantha *var.* pendula, 184; C. oxyacantha *var.* praecox, 184; C. oxyacanthoides, 180

Cryptomeria, 126; C. japonica, 126; C. japonica *var.* alba variegata, 126; C. japonica *var.* elegans, 126

Cupressaceae, 49, 101, 106, 121, 122, 124, 126

Cupressus, 106, 147; C. funebris, 110; C. lusitanica, 110; C. macrocarpa, 110; 122; C. pisifera, 110; C. sempervirens, 109

Cycadales, 38, 49

Cycadofilicales, 49

Cydonia lagenaria, 173; C. vulgaris, 172

Cytisus adami, 188; C. purpureus, 188

Dasyscypha, 83

Diospyros crassiflora, 336; D. ebenum, 336; D. kaki, 337; D. kuzii, 337; D. macassar, 337; D. quaesita, 336; D. virgiana, 337

Distylum racemosum, 195

Ebenaceae, 336

Elaeagnaceae, 299

Erica, 334

Ericaceae, 334

Eucalyptus, 144

GENERAL INDEX

PRINTED IN GREAT BRITAIN BY ROBERT MACLEHOSE AND CO. LTD.
THE UNIVERSITY PRESS, GLASGOW